An Introduction to Logic Programming through Prolog

Prentice Hall International Series in Computer Science

C.A.R. Hoare, Series Editor

Series listing continues at back of bc

An Introduction to Logic Programming through Prolog

Michael Spivey

PRENTICE HALL
London New York Toronto Sydney Tokyo Singapore
Madrid Mexico City Munich

First published 1996 by
Prentice Hall Europe
Campus 400, Maylands Avenue
Hemel Hempstead
Hertfordshire, HP2 7EZ
A division of
Simon & Schuster International Group

Printed and bound in Great Britain by
Redwood Books, Trowbridge, Wiltshire

Library of Congress Cataloging-in-Publication Data

Spivey, J. M.
    An introduction to logic programming through Prolog / Michael
Spivey.
        p.   cm. -- (Prentice-Hall international series in computer
science)
    Includes bibliographical references and index.
    ISBN 0-13-536047-1 (pbk. : alk. paper)
    1. Logic programming.   2. Prolog (Computer program language)
I. Title.   II. Series.
QA76.63.S64   1996
005.13'3--dc20   95-52339
                                                               CIP

British Library Cataloguing-in Publication Data

A catalogue record for this book is available
from the British Library

ISBN 0-13-536047-1

---

1 2 3 4 5   00 99 98 97 96

Contents

Preface

As we approach the fiftieth anniversary of the first programmable computer, the twenty-fifth anniversary of the 'software crisis' is already long past, that expression first having been used at an international conference in 1968. Thus more than half of the history of computer science has been lived under the shadow of our inability to manage the complexity of the artifacts we have created. Under these circumstances, few would dare to suggest that the problems of our discipline have a single technological solution. It is certainly not the purpose of this book to suggest that logic programming, interesting and powerful though it may be, is a panacea for the problems programmers face today.

A more encouraging possibility is that we may be able to find theories and programming paradigms that link together different ways of understanding programs and computer systems. The purpose of this book is to explore to what extent logic programming provides such a theory. Based on predicate logic, it allows computing problems to be expressed in a completely 'declarative' way, without giving instructions for how the problem is to be solved. An execution mechanism, like the one embodied in implementations of Prolog, can then be used to search efficiently and systematically for a solution to the problem. For some problems, the simplest expression of the problem in logical terms also leads to an effective procedure for solving it when a simple execution mechanism is used. Other problems require either a more intelligent execution mechanism, or need to be recast in such a way that a simple execution mechanism can find solutions effectively. Through the medium of logic, we can separate the task of capturing the problem from the task of finding an effective way to solve it.

The implementation of Prolog provides an excellent example of the construction of a software system that satisfies a strong, mathematical specification. In the case of Prolog, this specification is the mathematical meaning that underlies the declarative interpretation of logic programs, and the relevant mathematical foundation is the model theory of Horn clause logic. The thread that links the first part of this book (which presents the mathematical logic behind Prolog) with the last part (which describes how Prolog can be implemented) is this: that the implementation of Prolog can be viewed as carrying out symbolic reasoning with logical formulas, and its correctness is expressed in the fact that it faithfully realizes the inference rule of resolution, which is itself sound with respect to the declarative meaning of programs. The soundness of the resolution rule is established in the first part of the book, and its (almost) faithful implementation in Prolog is explained informally in the last part, but in a way that reflects the structure of a formal development by stepwise (data) refinement.

Another attractive feature of logic programming is the rich web of links it has with other topics in computer science. These are some of the links that are explored in this book:

- Relational databases, stripped of their inessentials, provide operations on relations that are closely linked to ways of combining relations in logic programming. We touch on these links in Chapter 2.
- Mathematical logic, important in formal methods of software development and in artificial intelligence, is also the foundation of logic programming. Studying logic programming is a good introduction to mathematical logic, because the logic behind logic programming is simple, and allows results like the soundness and completeness of inference systems to be proved in the simplest possible setting. In these books, these results are established for the Horn clause logic of Prolog in Chapters 5 to 7.
- Automated theorem proving is increasingly used in the verification of hardware and software systems. It is closely related to logic programming, both because they share some of the same foundations, and because logic programming is a useful vehicle for implementing theorem provers. Some simple applications of logic programming to theorem proving are explored in Chapter 11.
- Type systems for modern programming languages like ML are expressed as systems of inference rules that are in effect logic programs. Compilers for these languages infer types for the expressions in a program by using the same techniques that we shall use to implement Prolog in Chapters 15 to 18.

In a wider sense, every computer system implements a kind of logic. By providing input data, we give the system information about some part of the world. The computer derives some other information which it presents as its output. If the input data is accurate, and the rules we have built into the computer system are sound, then the output data will describe a valid conclusion. Logic programming depends explicitly on this view of computer systems by allowing both the program and its input and output data to be expressed as sentences in formal logic.

Oriel College, Oxford   J. M. S.
January, 1996

Using this book

The chapters of this book can be grouped into four parts, each developing different themes from the theory, application and implementation of logic programming. Chapters 1 to 3 introduce the ideas of logic programming; writing programs by defining relations, combining relations to define new ones, recursion in data and programs. The exposition here is mainly by example, and many topics are touched upon that are explored fully in later parts of the book.

Chapters 4 to 8 develop the 'logical' theme by presenting the semantics of logic programs and developing the inference system of SLD–resolution that is the logical basis of Prolog implementations. This is the most mathematical part of the book, and develops in miniature the standard theory of mathematical logic, including proofs that various inference systems for Horn clause logic are sound and complete.

Chapters 9 to 13 present more practical topics, from the formulation of graph-searching problems so that they can be solved by Prolog's simple search strategy, to applications of logic programming in parsing, algebraic simplification and simulating hardware circuits.

The final part of the book, in Chapters 14 to 18, picks up where the second part left off. It explains how SLD–resolution can be implemented efficiently by machine, using the conventional technology of Prolog implementation. These chapters describe the functioning of an actual interpreter for a Prolog subset, and the complete source code for this interpreter is included as Appendix C of this book. The presentation in this part of the book is based on stepwise refinement of data representations. The account begins with a simple implementation of depth-first search that uses abstract data types like sequences, terms and substitutions with corresponding abstract operations. Later chapters explain how these abstract data types can be implemented using the concrete data types provided by a machine.

Getting a copy of picoProlog

A distribution kit is available that contains the Pascal source code of the pico-Prolog interpreter, code for all the example programs from the book, the 'ppp' macro processor that is needed to pre-process the picoProlog source and C source code for a Pascal–to–C translator that can be used to compile it via C. The kit is ready-to-build for Sun and Linux machines, and can be ported easily to MS–DOS using either Turbo Pascal directly, or Turbo C and the Pascal–to–C translator.

You can obtain the kit by anonymous FTP from `ftp.comlab.ox.ac.uk` in the directory `/pub/packages/picoProlog`. Teachers adopting the book who have no access to FTP may obtain the distribution kit on floppy disk from the publisher.

Chapter 1

Introduction

What kind of thing is a computer program?

One answer is that a program is a collection of instructions for carrying out some computing task. This is the answer that would have been given by the first computer programmers, who had to describe in complete detail both how data was stored in the memory of their computers and the sequence of data movements and arithmetic operations needed to compute the solutions to problems. This made programming tedious and error-prone, and so limited the ambition of most programmers to fairly simple numerical problems. Luckily, computers were small in those days too.

The same answer – that a program is a collection of instructions – is the basis for the high-level languages like Fortran and Algol 60 that were invented to ease the programming task; the successors of these languages, including Pascal, C and Ada, are still with us today. These languages allowed programmers to assign symbolic names to storage locations and write algebraic expressions instead of explicit sequences of movements and operations. Programmers no longer needed to concern themselves with the exact layout of data in memory, or with the exact sequence of operations needed to evaluate an algebraic expression, but could leave these details to be filled in by a compiler.

Despite all these benefits, programs in these languages are still made up of commands that work by changing values stored in memory locations. Programs are understood in terms of what happens when a computer obeys the commands. For this reason, programming languages such as these are often described as *imperative*, by analogy with the grammatical mood used to give commands in natural language.

Another answer to the question 'What kind of thing is a program?' stems from languages like Lisp and – of special interest in this book – like Prolog. The distinguishing feature of these *declarative* programming languages, at least in their pure forms, is that programs are made up not of commands to be executed, but of definitions and statements about the problem to be solved. Grammatically, they are in the declarative mood, used for ordinary statements in natural language. Unlike the commands in imperative programs, they can be understood in a way that is independent of the mechanism that executes the program. Declarative programs contain no explicit instructions to be followed by the computer that executes them. Instead, the job of the computer is to manipulate the information contained in the program so as to derive the solution to a given problem.

In logic programming, a program consists of a collection of statements expressed as formulas in symbolic logic. There are rules of inference from logic that allow a new formula to be derived from old ones, with the guarantee that if the old formulas are true, so is the new one. Because these rules of inference can be expressed in purely symbolic terms, applying them is the kind of symbol-manipulation that can be carried out by a computer. This is what happens when a computer executes a logic program: it uses the rules of inference to derive new formulas from the ones given in the program, until it finds one that expresses the solution to the problem that has been posed. If the formulas in the program are true, then so are the formulas that the machine derives from them, and the answers it gives will be correct. To ensure that the program gives correct answers, the programmer checks that the program contains only true statements, and that it contains enough of them to allow solutions to be derived for all the problems that are of interest. The programmer may also be concerned to ensure that the derivations the machine must carry out are fairly short, so that the machine can find answers quickly, and this may affect the form in which definitions are made and properties stated in the program. Nevertheless, each formula can be understood in isolation as a true statement about the problem to be solved.

This kind of declarative programming allows the programmer to disregard the precise sequence of actions that takes place when a program is executed, to a much greater extent than is made possible even with high-level imperative programming languages. In checking that the program gives correct answers, for example, the programmer need only check that each logic formula in the program makes a true statement about the problem, and need not worry about its relationship with other parts of the program. This stands in stark contrast with imperative programming, where the correctness of a command like '$x := x + 1$' depends crucially on its place in the whole program, including interactions with other commands that use x, some of them millions of lines away.

1.1   Introducing logic programming

The contrast between imperative and declarative programming can be illustrated by looking at two solutions to a small programming problem, one using the conventional approach of Pascal, and the other using the approach of logic programming. The problem is to provide a program that will help an architect in designing motel suites. The client has already decided that each suite will have two rooms, a lounge and a bedroom, and its floor plan will be something like

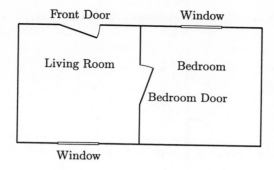

Figure 1.1: *Floor plan of motel suite*

Figure 1.1. The program must determine the directions in which the doors and windows may face, following these guidelines:

1. The lounge window should be opposite the front door to create a feeling of space.
2. The bedroom door should be in one of the walls at right angles to the front door to provide a little privacy.
3. The bedroom window should be in one of the walls adjacent to the bedroom door.
4. The bedroom window should face East to catch the morning light.

In Pascal, directions might be represented by elements of an enumerated type, like this:

> **type** *direction* = (*north, south, east, west*);

Guidelines (1) and (2) constrain the design of the lounge. They can be expressed in Pascal by writing a Boolean-valued function *lounge* that takes as arguments proposed directions for the two doors and the lounge window, and checks whether the guidelines are satisfied (see Figure 1.2). Names like *fd* and *bw* stand for 'front door' and 'bedroom window', and the two Boolean functions *opposite* and *adjacent* have the obvious meanings.

Guidelines (3) and (4) concern the design of the bedroom, and they are expressed by the function *bedroom* that checks the directions for the bedroom door and window. The functions *lounge* and *bedroom* are combined in the *suite* function that checks a set of choices for the whole motel suite.

Defining these functions seems to capture the essence of the problem, but the Pascal program is not complete until we have shown how they are to be used in a search for valid designs. For a simple problem like this one, and exhaustive

```
function lounge(fd, lw, bd: direction): boolean;
begin
    lounge := opposite(fd, lw) ∧ adjacent(fd, bd)
end;

function bedroom(bd, bw: direction): boolean;
begin
    bedroom := adjacent(bd, bw) ∧ (bw = east)
end;

function suite(fd, lw, bd, bw: direction): boolean;
begin
    suite := lounge(fd, lw, bd) ∧ bedroom(bd, bw)
end;
```

Figure 1.2: *Pascal functions for checking motel suite designs*

```
for fd := north to west do
    for lw := north to west do
        for bd := north to west do
            for bw := north to west do
                if suite(fd, lw, bd, bw) then
                    print(fd, lw, bd, bw)
```

Figure 1.3: *Exhaustive search*

search like the one shown in Figure 1.3 will do the job: it tries every combination of four directions, printing out the combinations for which the *suite* function returns *true*. Except for a few details (such as the procedure *print* for printing out the answers) this completes the imperative solution.

How can the problem be solved using logic programming? Like the Pascal solution, the heart of the program is a definition of the properties that describe valid designs. Instead of the Boolean functions of the Pascal program, it uses a notation more suited to symbolic calculation. In this notation, the definition of *lounge* looks like this:

```
lounge(FD, BD, LW) :−
    opposite(FD, LW), adjacent(FD, BD).
```

In this definition, the symbol ':−' is to be read as 'if'; think of it as looking a little like the leftward-pointing arrow '⇐' that is sometimes used in ordinary logic. The comma that separates the formulas *opposite*(FD, LW) and *adjacent*(FD, BD) is to be read as 'and'. Names like *lounge* stand for relations that hold between objects, and names like *FD* are variables that stand for any object. So the whole definition means 'Directions *FD*, *BD* and *LW* together form a valid design for the lounge if *FD* is opposite to *LW*, and *FD* is adjacent to *BD*'. As in the Pascal program, we assume that the relations *opposite* and *adjacent* have already been defined.

In the same notation, here is a definition of the relation *bedroom* that describes valid designs for the bedroom:

$$bedroom(BD, BW) :- adjacent(BD, BW), BW = east.$$

Here the name '*east*' stands for a constant direction. This definition reads 'Directions *BD* and *BW* form a valid design for the bedroom if *BD* is adjacent to *BW*, and *BW* is the direction *east*'.

The *lounge* and *bedroom* relations are combined in the following definition, describing what constitutes a valid design for the whole suite:

$$suite(FD, LW, BD, BW) :-$$
$$lounge(FD, LW, BD), bedroom(BD, BW).$$

The final ingredient in the logic program is a statement of exactly what problem is to be solved: i.e., that the program must find groups of four directions that satisfy the *suite* relation. This is expressed by writing a *goal* or *question* like this:

$$\# :- suite(FD, LW, BD, BW).$$

The symbol # is just a conventional sign, used so that goals have the same superficial form as other formulas in the program, with one atomic formula on the left of the ':−' sign and a list of atomic formulas on the right. It might be pronounced 'success', so that the goal means 'Success is achieved if direction *FD*, *LW*, *BD* and *BW* together form a valid design for the motel suite'.

Unlike the Pascal program, the logic program contains no explicit instructions for finding a solution to the problem, and there is nothing that corresponds to the nested **for**–loops that search through all possible combinations of directions. In fact, it may seem fanciful to call what we have written a program at all, since it does not seem to describe a computational *process*; but this absence of explicit instructions is one of the attractions of a declarative style of programming. It turns out that there are powerful, general strategies for finding solutions to problems that have been expressed as logic programs. Each implementation of logic programming includes such a strategy as a central component – for example, many implementations of the logic programming language Prolog use a strategy known as 'SLD–resolution with depth-first search'. Whilst this strategy is not the most powerful one, it is relatively easy to implement efficiently.

Having written a logic program, what can we do with it? One possibility is to use the statements in the program to prove that certain relationships must hold.

For example, suppose the facts

> *opposite*(*east*, *west*)   and   *adjacent*(*east*, *south*)

are known. Putting $FD = east$, $BD = south$ and $LW = west$ into the definition of *lounge* gives the formula

> *lounge*(*east*, *south*, *west*) :−
>   *opposite*(*east*, *west*), *adjacent*(*east*, *south*).

This formula is obtained by substituting *east* for every occurrence of FD in the definition of *lounge*, *south* for every occurrence of BD, and so on.

The symbol ':−' means 'if' and the comma means 'and'. Also, the two conditions on the right of the ':−' sign in the new formula are both known to be true. So the conclusion on the left must be true as well:

> *lounge*(*east*, *south*, *west*).

This formula says that there is a valid design for the lounge in which the front door faces East, the bedroom door faces South, and the lounge window faces West. We have reached this conclusion by very simple steps: substituting constants for variables, and checking that two formulas are identical. These are operations that (as we shall see in more detail later) can easily be carried out by machine.

Carrying on, we might substitute $BD = south$ and $BW = east$ into the definition of the *bedroom* relation to obtain the formula

> *bedroom*(*south*, *east*) :− *adjacent*(*south*, *east*), *east* = *east*.

Again this formula has known facts on the right-hand side of the ':−' sign, so whatever is on the left-hand side must be true also: we may deduce the conclusion

> *bedroom*(*south*, *east*).

As a final step, we might take an instance of the definition of *suite*, again obtained by substituting constants for variables:

> *suite*(*east*, *west*, *south*, *east*) :−
>   *lounge*(*east*, *west*, *south*), *bedroom*(*south*, *east*).

Again, the same constant has been substituted for every occurrence of each variable. By good fortune, the two conditions that appear on the right-hand side are exactly the same as the two facts we derived earlier. So we may conclude that the formula

> *suite*(*east*, *west*, *south*, *east*)

is true: in other words, that a valid design for the motel suite can have the front door facing East, the lounge window facing West, the bedroom door facing South, and the bedroom window facing East. In fact, this design is the one shown in Figure 1.1, if we take North to be towards the left of the picture.

In this sequence of logical steps, we worked 'forwards' from known facts to desired conclusions, and we were able to prove that a certain set of choices constituted a valid design for the motel suite. Such reasoning is of less use in *finding* a valid design, rather than just checking that a proposed design is valid. For that purpose, a different pattern of reasoning is more appropriate, one that works 'backwards' from problems we would like to solve towards the known facts that are the ingredients of a solution. This method is used by Prolog as its way of solving problems that call for the values of variables to be found.

Let us see how we might go about solving the motel design problem by hand, using this 'backwards' method in essentially the same way as is used automatically by Prolog. We wish to derive a conclusion of the form

$suite(FD, LW, BD, BW)$.

How might we do this? Plainly, we must use the definition of the *suite* relation, and this definition says that we must find a way of satisfying both the following conditions:

$lounge(FD, LW, BD)$ and $bedroom(BD, BW)$,

with the variable BD taking the same value in both.

Leaving the second of these sub-problems aside for a moment, we concentrate on the first one. To derive a conclusion like this, we plainly need to use the definition of *lounge*, which it says that to derive a conclusion $lounge(FD, LW, BD)$, we must satisfy both of these conditions:

$opposite(FD, LW)$ and $adjacent(FD, BD)$,

with FD taking the same value in both.

We have now decomposed the problem into relations like *opposite* and *adjacent* that we know how to deal with. But the condition $opposite(FD, LW)$ can be satisfied in many ways. For example, we might try putting $FD = north$ and $LW = south$ (as in Figure 1.1, but this time with North at the top of the picture). We also need to satisfy the second condition, that is, $adjacent(FD, BD)$, where we are supposing for the moment that $FD = north$. There are two ways to do this, so we first try putting $BD = east$, following Figure 1.1 again.

This completes a tentative solution to the *lounge* part of the problem, and we can turn to the *bedroom* sub-problem we put aside earlier. By now, we have chosen to put $BD = east$, so the problem we have to solve is $bedroom(east, BW)$, or (expanding the definition of *bedroom*),

$$adjacent(east, BW) \quad \text{and} \quad BW = east$$

We can solve the first of these in two ways, by putting $BW = north$ or $BW = south$, but neither of these leads to a solution of the second part, since it is not true that $north = east$ or $south = east$. A dead end!

What has gone wrong is that we made arbitrary choices in solving the *lounge* part of the problem, and these choices have turned out not to allow us to complete the solution of the *bedroom* part. What we should do now is to go back and change those choices, hoping that choosing differently will lead to more success in completing the solution. This process of systematically exploring choices is an automatic part of the execution of logic programs, and need not be an explicit part of the logic program itself, unlike the nested **for**–loops of the Pascal program.

A sensible way to proceed is to revise the latest choice we made, leaving earlier choices alone until we have explored all other possibilities for later ones. This 'backtracking' scheme is the one followed by Prolog. We first try revising our choice of *east* as the value of BD, but unfortunately this does not help: we chose $BD = east$ to solve the problem $adjacent(north, BD)$, and the only other possibility is to put $BD = west$, but this does not lead to a solution of the *bedroom* part of the problem either. Eventually, we hit on the idea of setting $FD = east$ and $LW = west$ as our solution to the sub-problem $opposite(FD, LW)$, then taking $BD = south$ so that $adjacent(FD, BD)$ is true, and taking $BW = east$ to establish $adjacent(BD, BW)$, finally checking that the requirement $BW = east$ is satisfied (it is!). These choices solve all the sub-problems, so we have found a design that satisfies all the guidelines; in fact, the design is the same one we checked earlier.

We have discovered a solution to the motel design problem by trying different possibilities in sequence, and that is what Prolog does when it is implemented on ordinary, sequential computers. However, there is nothing in the program that would prevent us from exploring several sets of choices concurrently, perhaps by giving them to several assistants, or by using several processors in parallel to do the same thing by machine. This potential for such a transparent exploitation of parallelism is another attractive feature of declarative programming.

The problem of designing a motel suite has several solutions: another one has $FD = east$, $LW = west$, $BD = south$, $BW = east$. It is quite natural for logic programs to return several answers to the same question (and also natural for them to return no answers at all, if the problem posed is in fact insoluble). We call this feature of a program *non-determinism*. If a program is non-deterministic, Prolog's systematic search prints all the answers to a goal in the order they are discovered. There is a sense in which our Pascal program also produces all the answers, but only because the program prints the answers in an explicit sequence. With the logic program, the treatment of multiple answers is natural and implicit.

Some real-time programs also exhibit a kind of non-determinism that is caused by haphazard timing of events. This is different from the non-determinism of logic programming and much less useful. With these real-time programs, it is chance (or the inner workings of the machine) that decides which answer is produced, and the user must be prepared to accept any of the possible answers. With a logic program, it is the environment of a program that decides which answer is accepted, so that the user can ask for a list of all the answers from a program and pick the one that is wanted, or can use the program as part of a larger program that applies further constraints to the solutions. For example, here is a goal that asks for a suite design satisfying the additional constraint that the front door should face West:

$$\# :- suite(FD, LW, BD, BW), FD = west.$$

The Prolog strategy (which always solves multiple subgoals by working from left to right) would answer this question by generating all the solutions to the original design problem, then rejecting the ones that did not satisfy the additional requirement $FD = west$.

The logic programs we shall study in this book are usually made up of logical formulas that look like this:

$$P :- Q_1, Q_2, \ldots, Q_n,$$

with P and the Q_i being *literals* or *atomic formulas* like $bedroom(BD, BW)$. We call these formulas *Horn clauses*, and we read them as asserting that if all the Q_i are true, then P is true also. Horn clauses are more restrictive than the formulas of full predicate logic. For instance, predicate logic allows the connectives 'and' (which we write with a comma) and 'implies' (which is equivalent to our ':−') to be combined in any way we choose, not just in the fixed pattern demanded by the syntax of Horn clauses. It also provides other connectives such as 'or' and 'not' that are not allowed in Horn clauses at all. Full predicate logic provides the quantifiers 'for all' and 'there exists' that are only partially reflected in the way we use variables in Horn clauses.

Despite these restrictions, Horn clauses are of special interest because many computing problems can be expressed in Horn clause form, and it is possible to build efficient mechanized theorem provers for theories that are expressed as Horn clauses – and that is just what a Prolog implementation is, or should be.

A special case of Horn clauses occurs if we allow $n = 0$ in the formula above, so that there are no Q_i on the right-hand side, like this:

$$P :- .$$

We read this formula as stating simply that P is true. This makes sense, because there are no formulas Q_i that must be true for the clause to assert the P is true also. Clauses like this, with no conditions on the right-hand side, are called *unit clauses* or simply *facts*.

A list of facts can be used to define a relation by listing all instances of it. For example, the *opposite* and *adjacent* relations might be defined in this way:

> *opposite*(*north, south*) :− .
> *opposite*(*south, north*) :− .
> *opposite*(*east, west*) :− .
> *opposite*(*west, east*) :− .
>
> *adjacent*(*north, east*) :− .
> *adjacent*(*north, west*) :− .
> *adjacent*(*south, east*) :− .
> *adjacent*(*south, west*) :− .
> *adjacent*(*east, north*) :− .
> *adjacent*(*east, south*) :− .
> *adjacent*(*west, north*) :− .
> *adjacent*(*west, south*) :− .

As we shall see, this means that logic programs can be used like relational databases.

Summary

- A logic program consists of a series of assertions written in the language of formal logic.
- Results are derived from logic programs by symbolic reasoning.
- Logic programming systems solve goals by systematically searching for a way to derive the answer from the program.

Exercises

1.1   A deluxe motel suite has two bedrooms, but must otherwise obey the design rules listed in this chapter. Show how to modify the design program for use in designing luxury suites. How many solutions to the problem are there? How many can reasonably be built?

Practical exercise

This exercise illustrates the use of picoProlog to solve the motel design problem discussed in Section 1.1. The Preface explains how to get a copy of picoProlog. Alternatively, Appendix B explains how to do the practical exercises in the book using an ordinary Prolog system in place of picoProlog.

```
/* motel.pp */

suite(FD, LW, BD, BW) :-
    lounge(FD, LW, BD),
    bedroom(BD, BW).

lounge(FD, LW, BD) :-
    opposite(FD, LW),
    adjacent(FD, BD).

bedroom(BD, BW) :-
    adjacent(BD, BW),
    BW = east.

opposite(north, south) :- .
opposite(south, north) :- .
opposite(east, west) :- .
opposite(west, east) :- .

adjacent(north, east) :- .
adjacent(north, west) :- .
adjacent(south, east) :- .
adjacent(south, west) :- .
adjacent(east, north) :- .
adjacent(east, south) :- .
adjacent(west, north) :- .
adjacent(west, south) :- .
```

Figure 1.4: *The file* motel.pp

Included with the picoProlog system is the file motel.pp shown in Figure 1.4. This contains the clauses of the motel design program, written using the conventions that picoProlog expects. Names of variables like *FD* are written in upper case, and both names of relations (like *suite*) and names of constants (like *east*) are written in lower case. Each clause in the program ends with a full stop. Comments are enclosed in the markers /* and */.

To start the picoProlog system and load this file of clauses, you should use the command

$ *pprolog motel.pp*

at the operating system prompt. (In this and the following instructions, you should type what appears in *italic* type.) PicoProlog prints a welcome message, then reads the clauses from the file `motel.pp` and stores them internally, before printing its usual prompt:

```
Welcome to picoProlog
Loading motel.pp

# :-
```

PicoProlog is now waiting for you to type a goal to be solved. Let us ask it to solve the motel design problem:

```
# :- suite(FD, LW, BD, BW).
```

Do not forget to include the final full stop, or picoProlog will just sit there and wait for it. All being well, picoProlog will find a solution to the problem, and display it like this:

```
FD = east
LW = west
BD = north
BW = east ?
```

PicoProlog now waits for your response. You can choose either to accept this solution by typing a full stop (followed by a carriage return), or ask picoProlog to find another solution, by typing just a carriage return. In the latter case, another solution is displayed just like the first:

```
FD = east
LW = west
BD = south
BW = east ?
```

By continuing to reply with just a carriage return, you can get picoProlog to produce all the solutions one after another. After it has shown the last solution, it finally answers 'no', meaning that no (more) solutions could be found, and returns to the '`#` `:-`' prompt. At any point in the stream of answers, you can type a full stop. PicoProlog then answers '**yes**', meaning that an answer was found and accepted, and immediately returns to its prompt.

You can end the session with picoProlog by typing the end-of-file character (usually Control–Z or Control–D) at the prompt.

Chapter 2

Programming with relations

Logic programming works by defining relations between data items. In this chapter, we look at some of the techniques that can be used to define new relations in terms of existing ones. Drawing on database techniques, we examine various ways of combining relations to derive the answers to questions.

The simplest way to define a relation is to give an explicit list of facts; that is, to define the relation by a table. Figure 2.1 is a list of facts defining a relation $uses(PERSON, PROGRAM, MACHINE)$ that holds between certain people and the software products and machines they use. This example looks more like a database than a program, and we can use it like a database by formulating queries about it as logical goals. For example, the goal

$$\# :- \; uses(mike, X, sun).$$

asks 'What software products does Mike use on the Sun?'. The goal can be answered by searching the table for facts that match it; the first argument of $uses$ takes the value $mike$, and the third takes the value sun, but the second argument may be anything. There are two solutions: one with $X = compiler$ and one with $X = editor$.

Relational database systems have the ability to answer questions by combining information from more than one relation, and we can mimic this in logic programming too. For example, Figure 2.2 defines a relation $needs(PROGRAM, MEMORY)$ that relates programs to the amount of memory (in kilobytes) needed to run them. With this information, we can answer a question like 'What are the memory requirements of the programs people run on the Mac?' by defining a new relation:

$$answer(PROGRAM, MEMORY) :-$$
$$uses(PERSON, PROGRAM, mac),$$
$$needs(PROGRAM, MEMORY).$$

uses(*mike, compiler, sun*) :− .
uses(*mike, compiler, pc*) :− .
uses(*mike, compiler, mac*) :− .
uses(*mike, editor, sun*) :− .
uses(*mike, editor, pc*) :− .
uses(*mike, diary, pc*) :− .
uses(*anna, editor, mac*) :− .
uses(*anna, spreadsheet, mac*) :− .
uses(*jane, database, pc*) :− .
uses(*jane, compiler, pc*) :− .
uses(*jane, editor, pc*) :− .

Figure 2.1: *The uses relation*

needs(*compiler*, 128) :− .
needs(*editor*, 512) :− .
needs(*diary*, 64) :− .
needs(*spreadsheet*, 640) :− .
needs(*database*, 8192) :− .

Figure 2.2: *The needs relation*

With this definition, the goal # :− *answer*(X, Y) has answers in which X is a program used on the Mac and Y is the amount of memory it needs. In database terms, the *answer* relation is called a *view*. It is a relation that is not stored explicitly in the database, but computed in order to answer a query.

Relational databases provide a number of operations on relations that can be used to solve many data-processing problems. These operations can all be represented in logic programming, and they provide a useful classification of the ways relations can be combined. It is the emphasis on relation-level (rather than record-level) operations that give relational databases their name and their claimed advantages over other kinds of database.

The operation of *selection* means restricting a relation with an extra condition, as in the query 'What are the memory requirements of programs that need more than 256K?', which is answered by the view

answer(*PROGRAM, MEMORY*) :−
    needs(*PROGRAM, MEMORY*), *MEMORY* > 256.

We assume here that the ordering relation > on numbers is defined elsewhere.

Selection with an extra condition that is an equation $X = c$, where c is a constant, can also be achieved by substituting c for X in the rest of the query.

For example, we can understand the question 'How much memory does the editor need?' as asking 'What are the memory requirements of the program that is the editor?', and answer it with the view

> $answer(PROGRAM, MEMORY)$:−
> $needs(PROGRAM, MEMORY), PROGRAM = editor$

This is a direct example of selection, with the extra condition $PROGRAM = editor$. We can achieve the same effect by substituting *editor* for $PROGRAM$ and deleting the equation:

> $answer(editor, MEMORY)$:−
> $needs(editor, MEMORY)$.

This definition makes it more obvious that all the records that are in the *answer* relation have *editor* as their $PROGRAM$ component.

Another database operation, *projection*, involves removing some of the arguments of a relation (that is, some of the columns in the table of the relation). It can be achieved by defining a view that has fewer arguments than the relation it uses. For example, the question 'What programs does each person use?' can be answered by the view

> $answer(PERSON, PROGRAM)$:−
> $uses(PERSON, PROGRAM, MACHINE)$.

Here the third argument, $MACHINE$, of the *uses* relation has been omitted from the *answer* relation.

The *uses* relation contains the clause

> $uses(mike, compiler, sun)$:− .

and this definition of *answer* lets us derive from it the conclusion

> $answer(mike, compiler)$:− .

that records the fact that Mike uses the compiler, without specifying the machine. The same conclusion can be derived from any clause in the *uses* relation that mentions Mike and the compiler, whatever machine is involved.

It is often natural to combine projection and selection. For example, the question 'What programs need more than 256K of memory?' is answered by the view

> $answer(PROGRAM)$:−
> $needs(PROGRAM, MEMORY), MEMORY > 256$.

This query selects those records from the *needs* relation with a *MEMORY* field larger than 256, then projects the result on just the *PROGRAM* field. The actual memory requirement has been omitted from the arguments of the *answer* relation, so the answer contains just the program names.

A better view for answering the question 'How much memory does the editor need?' is this one:

> *answer*(*MEMORY*) :−
>   *needs*(*editor*, *MEMORY*).

where the constant *editor* has been omitted from the arguments of the *answer* relation. Again, this view combines selection and projection, by first selecting records that satisfy the condition *PROGRAM* = *editor*, then projecting on the *MEMORY* field.

The operation of *relational join* combines two relations by matching the values of one or more fields. An example is provided by the all-embracing question 'What people use what programs on what machines, and how much memory do they need?'. This question is answered by the view

> *answer*(*PERSON*, *PROGRAM*, *MACHINE*, *MEMORY*) :−
>   *uses*(*PERSON*, *PROGRAM*, *MACHINE*),
>   *needs*(*PROGRAM*, *MEMORY*).

This is the relational join of the *uses* and *needs* relations on the *PROGRAM* field, so called because *PROGRAM* is the only field that occurs in both relations. The answer is a list of values for all four variables. It contains the same information as the two separate relations *uses* and *needs*, but is rather repetitious because each program is associated with the same memory requirement each time it appears.

Again, relational join can be combined in a natural way with projection and selection. For example, the following view answers the question 'What are the memory requirements of programs Anna uses on the Mac?':

> *answer*(*PROGRAM*, *MEMORY*) :−
>   *uses*(*anna*, *PROGRAM*, *mac*),
>   *needs*(*PROGRAM*, *MEMORY*).

This view combines relational join with selection of the records that satisfy the conditions *PERSON* = *anna* and *MACHINE* = *mac*, followed by projection on the *PROGRAM* and *MEMORY* fields.

It is possible to join a relation with itself on some of its fields. This operation is useful in answering questions like 'Which programs are used by two different people on the same machine?'. To answer this question, we first make a join of the *uses* relation with itself on the *PROGRAM* and *MACHINE* fields, making a relation *answer1* (*PERSON*$_1$, *PERSON*$_2$, *PROGRAM*, *MACHINE*) that is true if *PERSON*$_1$ and *PERSON*$_2$ both use *PROGRAM* on *MACHINE*:

> *answer1* (*PERSON*$_1$, *PERSON*$_2$, *PROGRAM*, *MACHINE*) :−
>   *uses*(*PERSON*$_1$, *PROGRAM*, *MACHINE*),
>   *uses*(*PERSON*$_2$, *PROGRAM*, *MACHINE*).

This relation includes the case that *PERSON*$_1$ and *PERSON*$_2$ are in fact the same person, so we select the records in which they are different, and finally project on the *PROGRAM* field:

> *answer*(*PROGRAM*) :−
>   *answer1* (*PERSON*$_1$, *PERSON*$_2$, *PROGRAM*, *MACHINE*),
>   *PERSON*$_1$ ≠ *PERSON*$_2$.

The definition of the sub-view *answer1* could be merged with this to give a single clause defining *answer*.

The relational operations of *intersection*, *union* and *difference* correspond to conjunction, disjunction and negation in logic. Intersection can be used to answer questions like 'What programs do both Anna and Jane use?' by combining two sub-views with the ',' operator (which is read as 'and'), like this:

> *answer*(*PROGRAM*) :−
>   *answer1* (*PROGRAM*),
>   *answer2* (*PROGRAM*).
>
> *answer1* (*PROGRAM*) :− *uses*(*anna*, *PROGRAM*, *MACHINE*).
>
> *answer2* (*PROGRAM*) :− *uses*(*jane*, *PROGRAM*, *MACHINE*).

Here, the *answer* view is the intersection of the two views *answer1* and *answer2*, which are themselves obtained by selection and projection. Intersection is the same as the special case of relational join in which a pair of relations have identical fields, and the join is on all of them.

The *answer* view for our last query can actually be defined by a single clause, like this:

> *answer*(*PROGRAM*) :−
>   *uses*(*anna*, *PROGRAM*, *MACHINE*$_1$),
>   *uses*(*jane*, *PROGRAM*, *MACHINE*$_2$).

The variable *MACHINE* has been renamed here as *MACHINE*$_1$ in one literal and *MACHINE*$_2$ in the other, so that the answers will include programs that are used

by both Anna and Jane but on different machines. Without this renaming, the
results would be different. The view computed by the definition

> *answer*(*PROGRAM*) :−
>   *uses*(*anna*, *PROGRAM*, *MACHINE*),
>   *uses*(*jane*, *PROGRAM*, *MACHINE*).

answers instead the question 'What programs do both Anna and Jane use *on the
same machine?*'. This view is obtained by joining the *uses* relation with itself on
the *PROGRAM* and *MACHINE* fields, then selecting and projecting.

The operation of relational union corresponds to 'or' in logic. Our Horn clause
notation has no symbol for 'or', but we can achieve the same effect by using more
than one clause in the definition of a relation. For example, the question 'What
programs are used by either Anna or Jane?' is answered by the view

> *answer*(*program*) :− *answer1*(*PROGRAM*).
> *answer*(*program*) :− *answer2*(*PROGRAM*).

where *answer1* and *answer2* are as before. If a program P is used by Anna – so
that it satisfies *answer1*(P) – then we can derive the conclusion *answer*(P) using
the first clause in the definition of *answer*. Similarly, if P satisfies *answer2*(P),
then the second clause allows us to derive the conclusion *answer*(P).

The final operation of relational algebra is difference of relations, and this can
be achieved by a combination of conjunction and negation. For example, the
question 'What programs are used by Anna but not by Jane?' can be expressed
in the view

> *answer*(*PROGRAM*) :−
>   *answer1*(*PROGRAM*), **not** *answer2*(*PROGRAM*).

The **not** operator is missing from our Horn clause notation, but a restricted
version, powerful enough for database applications, can be implemented using
the technique of *negation as failure* that is explained in Chapter 8. Briefly,
to prove **not** P, negation as failure requires that we attempt to prove P instead. If we cannot prove P, then we conclude that **not** P is true; conversely,
if we do succeed in proving P, then **not** P is false. This is a valid form of
reasoning, provided that P contains no unknown variables, and we can ensure
that this is so in the example by arranging that the literal *answer1*(P) is solved
first.

There are several important differences between the view of relational databases presented here and the database systems that are used in practice. We have
been identifying the fields of relations by their position in the list of arguments,
and that becomes tedious to get right when the database contains more than
two or three relations with two or three fields each. Real databases have better

naming schemes for fields, and associate types with the fields to prevent mistakes and allow more economical storage. Real databases can maintain indexes for their relations that allow joins and selections to be computed in a reasonable time, even when there are thousands or millions of records in the relations. They are carefully designed to make fast and economical use of disk storage.

On the other hand, logic programming is more general than relational databases in many ways. Logic programs can define relations partly by plain facts and partly by clauses that have variables and bodies that express constraints on the values of the variables. The data in logic programs is not restricted to be atomic, as with databases, and (as we shall see in the next chapter) relations over recursive data structures can themselves be given recursive definitions. These things have no analogues in relational databases.

Summary

- Relational databases work by combining relations (tables of data) using operations that work on whole relations, rather than individual records.
- Queries about a database are answered by defining views, new relations that are derived using the relational operators.
- The tables of relational databases can be expressed in logic programming by relations that are defined as lists of facts.
- Each of these relational operators can be expressed in logic programming by combining existing relations in the definition of a new one.

Exercises

2.1   The staff of an office run a coffee club, and they have set up a database containing the following relations:

- *manager*(*NAME*), which is true if *NAME* is a manager.
- *bill*(*NAME*, *NUMBER*, *AMOUNT*), which is true if *NAME* has been sent a bill numbered *NUMBER* for *AMOUNT*.
- *paid*(*NUMBER*, *AMOUNT*, *DATE*), which is true if a payment of *AMOUNT* was made on *DATE* for the bill numbered *NUMBER*.

Define views that answer the following questions:

a. Which managers have been sent a bill for less than ten pounds?
b. Who has been sent more than one bill?
c. Who has made a payment that is less than the amount of their bill?
d. Who has received a bill and either not paid it at all, or not paid it before February 1st?

In each case, explain how the query can be expressed in terms of the six operations of relational algebra. Use as a condition for selection the relation *before*(*A*, *B*) that holds if date *A* is before date *B*, and use the constant *feb1* to name February 1st.

Practical exercise

You might like to try running database queries like the ones discussed in this chapter, or running your solutions to the exercises. To help with this, picoProlog comes with a file **database.pp** that contains (in picoProlog form) the tables of people and programs from Figures 2.1 and 2.2. It also contains the definition of a relation *greater*(*X*, *Y*) that holds if *X* is a larger integer than *Y*.

Chapter 3

Recursive structures

In Chapter 1, we looked at a very simple programming problem that could be solved by trying a finite set of choices drawn from only four possible directions. Realistic programming problems are usually more complex than this. They involve data that has more internal structure than the simple directions used in the motel suite example, and they lead to programs that are able to produce answers that are more complex than a simple list of facts. How can we represent this complex data in the notation of logic? And how can we build programs that are capable of more than a fixed, finite collection of choices?

The answers to both these questions are the same: we use *recursion* to build data that has a nested structure and programs that relate answers to complex problems with answers to their structural parts. We shall look at the data first, using as an example one of the most useful recursive data structures, sequences or lists.

3.1 Lists

Suppose we want to build a program that gives street directions between places in a city that has a rectangular array of streets, as many American cities do. The directions can be represented by finite sequences of moves, so that the sequence

   North, East, South, South

would mean 'Go one block North, then one block East and finally two blocks South'. Any sequence of moves can be represented by a *list*, constructed according to the following rules:

1. There is an empty list, which we write *nil*.
2. If x is an item and A is a list, then there is a list that consists of the item

X followed by all the items in the list *A*. We write this list as *X*:*A*.

3. Nothing is a list except according to rules (1) and (2).

For example, the sequence of four moves is represented by the list

$$north:(east:(south:(south:nil))).$$

We can check that this expression really is a list by reasoning like this:

nil is a list because of rule (1).
So *south*:*nil* is a list because of rule (2).
So *south*:(*south*:*nil*) is a list because of rule (2).

and so on. To stop the notation from becoming cumbersome, we adopt the convention that the ':' symbol *associates to the right*, so that *X*:*Y*:*A* means the same as *X*:(*Y*:*A*), and our list of moves can be written without parentheses as

$$north:east:south:south:nil.$$

Notice that any list is built up by starting with *nil* and repeatedly using the ':' operation to add further elements, so any properly-constructed list must end in *nil*. It is tempting at first to save writing and omit the ':*nil*' from the end of expressions for lists, but the expression *north*:*east*:*south*:*south* does not mean the same thing as *north*:*east*:*south*:*south*:*nil* – it is not a proper list because it ends in *south* instead of *nil*. Including an explicit *nil* at the end of every list means that we do not have to treat as a special case the *singleton* lists that contain just one element. Instead, they are exactly the lists like *east*:*nil* that are made by using the ':' operation just once.

If we know how to get from *X* to *Y* in our city, and we know how to get from *Y* to *Z*, then we know one way of getting from *X* to *Z*: just go via *Y*. This is probably not the best way of getting from *X* to *Z*, but it is better than nothing. The list of one-block moves that we would follow in going from *X* to *Z* consists of all the moves for getting from *X* to *Y*, followed by all the moves for getting from *Y* to *Z*.

Let us try to define a relation *append*(*A*, *B*, *C*) that is true of three lists *A*, *B* and *C* exactly if *C* is the list that contains all the elements of *A* followed by all the elements of *B*. As a first approximation, we might think of defining it by a long list of facts like this:

$$append(nil, nil, nil) :- .$$
$$append(nil, X:nil, X:nil) :- .$$
$$append(nil, X:Y:nil, X:Y:nil) :- .$$

$$\vdots$$

append(P:*nil*, *nil*, P:*nil*) :− .
append(P:*nil*, X:*nil*, P:X:*nil*) :− .
append(P:*nil*, X:Y:*nil*, P:X:Y:*nil*) :− .

    ⋮

append(P:Q:*nil*, *nil*, P:Q:*nil*) :− .
append(P:Q:*nil*, X:*nil*, P:Q:X:*nil*) :− .

    ⋮

This collection of facts could be arranged in a two-dimensional array, in which each row corresponds to one possible length for the first argument A, and each column corresponds to one length for the second argument B. Each element of the array is a fact that can be used to solve *append* problems for exactly one combination of lengths for the arguments: for example, the fact

    append(P:*nil*, X:Y:*nil*, P:X:Y:*nil*) :− .

can be used to solve any problem in which a list 1 and a list of length 2 are to be joined. Plainly, any true instance of *append* appears somewhere in the array, but it would be much more useful to summarize the contents of this infinite array in a finite description that could be written out in full and used as a program for appending lists. What we are looking for is a *finite* collection of clauses from which all the facts in the array could be derived.

    Actually, even the infinite array takes a big step in cutting down the size of the problem, because it uses variables like P, Q, X, Y in place of constants. Instances like

    append(*north*:*east*:*nil*, *south*:*south*:*nil*, *north*:*east*:*south*:*south*:*nil*)

can be obtained by substituting constants for the variables that appear in a fact from the array.

    A second simplifying step is to notice that whatever appears as the second argument of *append* also appears as a sub-expression of the third argument, like this:

    append(P:Q:*nil*, X:Y:*nil*, P:Q:(X:Y:*nil*)) :− .

In this formula, I have put in a pair of parentheses that could have been omitted according to our convention about ':'. We can reduce the two-dimensional array of facts into a one-dimensional (but still infinite) array by summarizing each row of the two-dimensional array as a single fact. Each of these facts uses a variable for the second argument of *append*, and that variable can stand for any list:

    append(*nil*, B, B) :− .

$append(Z{:}nil, B, Z{:}B) :- .$
$append(Y{:}Z{:}nil, B, Y{:}Z{:}B) :- .$
$append(X{:}Y{:}Z{:}nil, B, X{:}Y{:}Z{:}B) :- .$

$\vdots$

Again, every true example of the *append* relation is an instance of a fact from this list. Just choose the fact according to the number of items in the first argument of *append*, then fill in the second argument with a list of the right length.

There is still some pattern in this new list of facts, and it can be used to summarize it further. If line i of the list is

$append(A, B, C) :- .$

then line $i + 1$ differs from it by adding a new element in front of both A and C, like this:

$append(X{:}A, B, X{:}C) :- .$

We can make this into a Horn clause:

$append(X{:}A, B, X{:}C) :- append(A, B, C).$

If we take this clause together with the very first fact in the list (the one about *nil*), then we obtain a finite definition of *append*:

$append(nil, B, B) :- .$ (app.1)
$append(X{:}A, B, X{:}C) :- append(A, B, C).$ (app.2)

This is the definition that is often used in logic programming.

There is an appealing similarity between this pair of clauses that define *append* and the three rules for building lists that began this chapter. The first rule for building lists says the *nil* is a list, and the clause (app.1) tells us what happens when the list *nil* is appended with another list. The second rule for building lists says that we can build a list $X{:}A$ if we already have a list A, and the clause (app.2) tells us what happens when a list of this form is appended with another list, provided we already know what happens with the list A itself. The third rule for building lists does not correspond to anything in the program for *append*, but to a principle that will apply whenever we use the program to solve problems:

No lists A, B and C satisfy the relation $append(A, B, C)$ unless they can be proved to do so using clauses (app.1) and (app.2).

This principle is an example of the *closed world assumption*. It is important because it guarantees that the only solutions to *append* problems are the ones

that are generated by the program, so that if a question about *append* has any
answers, they will be found by using the program.

3.2 Deriving facts about *append*

In Chapter 1, we found that the *suite* program could be used in two ways. The
simpler way was to derive from it the fact that a certain, known design was
correct. In a similar way, the *append* program can be used by deriving from it
the fact that certain lists satisfy the *append* relation. Later, we shall see how the
append program can be used to solve problems in which the lists involved are not
known in advance.

Let us first use the *append* program to derive a particular fact, say

$$append(1{:}2{:}nil, 3{:}4{:}nil, 1{:}2{:}3{:}4{:}nil).$$

I am using lists of numbers instead of lists of directions to save space. To derive
this fact, we will take certain instances of the clauses (app.1) and (app.2) –
obtained by substituting constants for the variables that appear in those clauses
– then appeal to the meaning of the ':–' sign to derive what is on the left from
what is on the right. It may not be obvious what clauses we should use, and
what constants should be substituted for variables, but if we cannot guess how
to do the derivation, we can at least check that the processes of substitution and
matching are carried out properly as the derivation proceeds.

We begin with an instance of (app.1), obtained by substituting 3:4:*nil* for the
variable B:

$$append(nil, 3{:}4{:}nil, 3{:}4{:}nil). \tag{1}$$

Now we take an instance of (app.2), substituting 2 for X, *nil* for A and 3:4:*nil*
for both B and C:

$$append(2{:}nil, 3{:}4{:}nil, 2{:}3{:}4{:}nil) :- append(nil, 3{:}4{:}nil, 3{:}4{:}nil). \tag{2}$$

This formula has the form $P :- Q$, and the formula (1) is exactly identical to
the right-hand side Q. So we can deduce that the left-hand side P is true:

$$append(2{:}nil, 3{:}4{:}nil, 2{:}3{:}4{:}nil). \tag{3}$$

Next, we take another instance of (app.2), this time substituting different constants for the variables:

$$append(1{:}2{:}nil, 3{:}4{:}nil, 1{:}2{:}3{:}4{:}nil) :- append(2{:}nil, 2{:}4{:}nil, 2{:}3{:}4{:}nil). \tag{4}$$

The right-hand side of this formula exactly matches the fact (3), so again we can derive the left-hand side as a conclusion:

$$append(1{:}2{:}nil, 3{:}4{:}nil, 1{:}2{:}3{:}4{:}nil). \tag{5}$$

And this is exactly the conclusion we were aiming for.

At first, it might seem that the second clause in the definition of *append* is useless, because it has *append* on the right-hand side as well as the left – so surely it cannot be a good definition. The derivation we have just looked at shows that this is not so, because (app.2) lets us derive more complicated *append* facts from simpler ones, so it lets us build up facts about complex lists in the same way that the lists themselves are built up with the ':' operation.

The approach of working from known facts towards a desired conclusion is fine for use *by hand* in proving *append* facts that are already known. But now that there is an infinite space of possibilities to explore, it is not reasonable to expect a *machine* to have the insight required to see what instances of which clauses should be used. This is all the more so when the problem is to answer a goal like

$$\# :- append(3{:}1{:}nil, 2{:}4{:}nil, W).$$

that contains variables. This goal asks for a W that is the result of appending the lists $3{:}1{:}nil$ and $2{:}4{:}nil$. Instead of blindly guessing a suitable list W and then constructing the proof that it is right, the machine running the *append* program finds the correct answer W and the proof that it is right simultaneously. Let us follow the Prolog method for solving this problem, working backwards as we did with the program for designing motel suites.

First, it is obvious that clause (app.1) cannot be used directly to solve this goal. Why not? Because (app.1) can only establish *append* facts where the first argument is *nil*, and here the first argument, $3{:}1{:}nil$, is not the same as *nil*. If the problem can be solved at all, it must be solved by using clause (app.2). Let us compare the goal in hand with the left-hand side or *head* of (app.2):

$$\# :- append(\, 3{:}1{:}nil, \; 2{:}4{:}nil, \; W \,).$$
$$append(X{:} \;\; A, \quad\quad B, \quad X{:}C) :- append(A, B, C).$$

If we are to use (app.2) to answer the goal, then these two formulas must match exactly, and this can only happen if the parts connected by lines match; that is, if $X = 3$, $A = 1{:}nil$, $B = 2{:}4{:}nil$ and $W = 3{:}C$. These substitutions are the minimum that must be done to make the goal and the head of (app.2) identical. If we apply them to the right-hand side or *body* of (app.2), we obtain the new goal

$$\# :- append(1{:}nil, 2{:}4{:}nil, C).$$

If only we can find an answer to this new goal, we can obtain an answer to the original goal by putting $W = 3{:}C$. To derive this answer, we take whatever derivation leads to an answer to the new goal, and add one extra step, using (app.2) and applying the substitution we have just discovered to make the formulas match.

So now we try to solve the goal

$$\# :- \ append(1{:}nil, 2{:}4{:}nil, C).$$

Again (app.1) is no help, because the first argument of *append* is not *nil*. So we try (app.2) again, changing the names of variables to prevent confusion:

$$\# :- \ append(\ 1 :nil, 2{:}4{:}nil, \quad C \quad).$$
$$append(X'{:}\ A', \quad B', \quad X'{:}C') :- \ append(A', B', C').$$

Again, the goal and the head of (app.2) can be made the same, this time by setting $X' = 1$, $A' = nil$, $B' = 2{:}4{:}nil$ and $C = 1{:}C'$. Filling in these values in the body of (app.2) gives the new goal

$$\# :- \ append(nil, 2{:}4{:}nil, C').$$

So our original goal can be answered (with $C = 1{:}C'$ and so $W = 3{:}1{:}C'$) provided we can answer this simpler goal.

But the new goal can be solved directly using (app.1). We rename the variable B of (app.1) as B'' to avoid confusion, and compare the goal with the head of (app.1):

$$\# :- \ append(nil, 2{:}4{:}nil, C').$$
$$append(nil, \quad B'', \quad B'') :- \ .$$

The two match, provided we take $C' = B'' = 2{:}4{:}nil$, and the new goal is the *empty goal*

$$\# :- \ .$$

There is no more work to do, and we need only assemble the parts of the answer that were discovered at each step to recover an answer to the original goal:

$$W = 3{:}C = 3{:}1{:}C' = 3{:}1{:}2{:}4{:}nil.$$

This may seem like an enormous effort just to append two lists, but the only operations we have used – matching goals against the heads of clauses, and performing substitutions to generate new goals – are both easy to mechanize efficiently, and it is this that makes logic programming practical.

Now let us consider a slightly different goal:

$$\# :-\ append(U, V, 1{:}2{:}3{:}nil).$$

This asks for a pair of lists U and V that when appended give the list $1{:}2{:}3{:}nil$. If we compare this goal with the heads of clauses (app.1) and (app.2), we find that both of them match. Using (app.1) looks like this:

$$\# :-\ append(\ U,\ V, 1{:}2{:}3{:}nil).$$
$$append(nil, B,\quad B\quad) :-\ .$$

The match can be made with $U = nil$ and $V = B = 1{:}2{:}3{:}nil$, and the new goal is empty, indicating a direct answer to the original goal: $U = nil$, $V = 1{:}2{:}3{:}nil$.

Alternatively, we may use (app.2) like this:

$$\# :-\ append(\ U,\ V, 1{:}2{:}3{:}nil).$$
$$append(X{:}A, B, X{:}\quad C\quad) :-\ append(A, B, C).$$

The matching substitutions are $X = 1$, $U = X{:}A = 1{:}A$, $V = B$ and $C = 2{:}3{:}nil$. The new goal is

$$\# :-\ append(A, B, 2{:}3{:}nil).$$

One way to answer this new goal is to use (app.1), giving the immediate answer $A = nil$, $B = 2{:}3{:}nil$, and so leading to a second answer to the original goal: $U = 1{:}nil$, $V = 2{:}3{:}nil$. Another way to answer the new goal is to use (app.2) first; this generates a third goal, and so on. In all, the original goal has four solutions:

$$U = nil,\qquad V = 1{:}2{:}3{:}nil;$$
$$U = 1{:}nil,\qquad V = 2{:}3{:}nil;$$
$$U = 1{:}2{:}nil,\qquad V = 3{:}nil;$$
$$U = 1{:}2{:}3{:}nil,\qquad V = nil.$$

Like the multiple solutions to the problem of designing a motel suite, these can all be found by exploring systematically the choices that can be made. A Prolog system will find all four solutions and present them one after another.

The process (called *unification*) of matching the head of a clause with a goal to be solved is the key to execution of logic programs. Unlike the pattern-matching used in some functional programming languages, it involves information flow in both directions: from the goal to the clause that is being used to solve it, and from the clause back to the goal. For example, in the last application of (app.2) shown above, the matching tells us that the variable U in the goal should take the value $1:A$, and the variable C in the clause should take the value $2:3:nil$.

A special feature of logic programs illustrated by this example is that they are 'bi-directional'; there is no need to select in advance a fixed set of inputs and a fixed set of outputs for a program. We can supply values for any combination of the three arguments of *append* and have the machine compute values for the others. We have looked at an example where we supplied the first two arguments, and left the machine to compute the (unique) value of the third argument that made the *append* relation true, and another example where we supplied the third argument, and the machine would give a list of different possibilities for the other two arguments.

Because of the generality of the unification process, we can place constraints on the values that are found by using the same variable more than once in the goal. For example, the goal

$$\# :- append(X, X, 1{:}2{:}3{:}1{:}2{:}3{:}nil).$$

asks for a list that, when appended with itself, gives the list $1:2:3:1:2:3:nil$. A Prolog system will succeed in solving this goal, finding the solution $X = 1:2:3:nil$. In effect, it does so by generating pairs of lists that append to give $1:2:3:1:2:3:nil$, and selecting from the seven such pairs of lists the one pair in which both lists are the same.

It is even possible to supply none of the arguments of the *append* relation, as in the goal

$$\# :- append(X, Y, Z).$$

This produces an infinite list of answers like this:

$$X = nil, \qquad Z = Y;$$
$$X = A{:}nil, \qquad Z = A{:}Y;$$
$$X = A{:}B{:}nil, \qquad Z = A{:}B{:}Y;$$
$$\vdots \qquad\qquad \vdots$$

In other words, this is exactly the list of facts about *append* that we summarized in the recursive definition.

3.3 More relations on lists

Recursion provides us with a way to define other useful relations on lists. One example is the relation $list(A)$ that is true exactly when A is a list constructed according to our three rules. This relation can be defined by expressing two of the three rules as Horn clauses:

$$list(nil) :- .$$ (list.1)
$$list(X{:}A) :- list(A).$$ (list.2)

The first of these clauses says that *nil* satisfies the relation *list*, and the second says that if A satisfies *list*, so does $X{:}A$. From the two clauses, we can deduce that various objects are lists. For example, the fact that $1{:}2{:}nil$ is a list can be deduced as follows: $list(nil)$ is true because of (list.1); so by applying (list.2) with $X = 2$ and $A = nil$, we may deduce $list(2{:}nil)$. Applying (list.2) again, this time with $X = 1$ and $A = 2{:}nil$, we deduce $list(1{:}2{:}nil)$.

The third rule about lists is implicit in the program. Just as with the *append* relation, we say an object A satisfies the relation $list(A)$ only if it can be proved to do so from the definition of *list*. Any object that is not a proper list, perhaps because it does not end in *nil*, cannot be proved from the definition to satisfy the *list* relation.

We can think of the two clauses (list.1) and (list.2) as a *specification* of a relation *list*, and ask what relations satisfy that specification. Certainly, the relation we had in mind, the one that is true of proper lists and false of everything else, satisfies the specification. But so do many other relations, for example the one that is true of proper lists and also lists that end in 3 instead of *nil*. Even the relation that is true of every object satisfies the specification. The relation we intended to define by writing the clauses (list.1) and (list.2) is the *least* or *smallest* relation that satisfies the specification. It is an important fact about logic programs, which we shall prove in Chapter 5, that a program written as a set of Horn clauses always has such a 'least model'.

For now, we content ourselves with defining some other useful relations on lists. Here is the definition of a relation $member(X, A)$ that is true if X is a member of the list A:

$$member(X, X{:}A) :- .$$
$$member(Y, X{:}A) :- member(Y, A).$$

The first clause says that X is a member of the list $X{:}A$, and the second says that Y is a member of $X{:}A$ if it is a member of A. Neither of these clauses applies to the empty list, because the empty list has no members. It is quite permissible to write definitions that have no clause that applies to certain input values, and the result is to define a relation that does not hold for these values.

We can use the *member* relation to test for membership. For example, the goal $\# :- member(2, 1{:}2{:}3{:}nil)$ receives the answer 'yes', and the goal $\# :- member(5, 1{:}2{:}3{:}nil)$ receives the answer 'no'. It can also be used to *generate* the members of a list, so that the goal $\# :- member(X, 1{:}2{:}3{:}nil)$ receives the three answers $X = 1$, $X = 2$ and $X = 3$.

To apply this idea, let us define *dominates*(X, A) as the relation that is true when X is greater than or equal to (*geq*) every member of the list A:

dominates(X, nil) :− .
dominates($X, Y{:}A$) :− *geq*(X, Y), *dominates*(X, A).

Any number dominates the empty list, and a number X dominates the list $Y{:}A$ if it is greater than or equal to Y and dominates the list A. Now we can define the relation *maximum*(X, A) that that is true if X is the maximum of the list A:

maximum(X, A) :− *member*(X, A), *dominates*(X, A).

This definition simply says that the maximum of a list A is a member of A that is greater than or equal to every member of A. A goal like

:− *maximum*($X, 3{:}1{:}4{:}2{:}nil$).

is executed by solving the two immediate subgoals *member*($X, 3{:}1{:}4{:}2{:}nil$) and *dominates*($X, 3{:}1{:}4{:}2{:}nil$). The Prolog strategy is to generate solutions to the first *member* subgoal one after another, then test each one to see if it makes the *dominates* subgoal true.

Another, more efficient, definition of *maximum* uses recursion directly. We first define a relation *max1*(X, Y, A) that is true if X is the maximum number among Y and the members of list A:

max1(X, X, nil) :− .
max1($X, Y, Z{:}A$) :− *geq*(Y, Z), *max1*(X, Y, A).
max1($X, Y, Z{:}A$) :− *less*(Y, X), *max1*(X, Z, A).

In terms of *max1*, we can write a new definition of *maximum*:

maximum($X, Y{:}A$) :− *max1*(X, Y, A).

This definition is more efficient as a program, because the maximum of a list is found in a single pass through the list, rather than the multiple passes needed by our earlier program.

We defined *member* directly by recursion, but there is another definition that uses the *append* relation instead:

member(X, A) :− *append*($U, X{:}V, A$).

This definition says that X is a member of A if there are lists U and V such that appending U and $X{:}V$ gives the list A. With this definition, a goal like # :− *member*($2, 3{:}1{:}2{:}4{:}nil$) is executed by searching for a solution to the subgoal

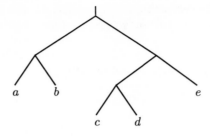

Figure 3.1: *A binary tree*

append(U, 2:V, 3:1:2:4:*nil*). By trying both clauses for *append* and backtracking, Prolog is able to find a solution where $U = 3$:1:*nil* and $V = 4$:*nil*.

3.4   Binary trees

Lists, represented with *nil* and the ':' operator, are the simplest and most useful recursive data type, but logic programming also allows more general data structures. As an example, we consider here the type of *binary trees* with labels at the leaves, defined by the following rules:

1. If X is any object, then *tip*(X) is a binary tree.
2. If L and R are binary trees, then so is *fork*(L, R).
3. Nothing is a tree except according to rules (1) and (2).

For example, the binary tree shown in Figure 3.1 is represented by the term

> *fork*(*fork*(*tip*(a), *tip*(b)),
>   *fork*(*fork*(*tip*(c), *tip*(d)), *tip*(e)))

These rules for forming trees have the same recursive character as the rules for forming lists, and we can define relations on trees by recursion just as we used recursion to define relations on lists.

We can use recursion to define a relation *flatten*(T, A) between a tree T and a list A that is true when A contains in order all the tips from T, so that if T is the tree of Figure 3.1 then *flatten*(T, a:b:c:d:*nil*) is true.

> *flatten*(*tip*(X), X:*nil*) :– .

> *flatten*(*fork*(L, R), C) :–
>   *flatten*(L, A), *flatten*(R, B), *append*(A, B, C).

The first clause says that *tip*(X) flattens to give the list containing just X; the second says that a tree *fork*(L, R) flattens to give a list C that is obtained by flattening L and R separately and joining the results with *append*.

This definition of *flatten* can be used to find the flattened form of a given binary tree, and it gives one list as the answer for each tree. Also, because of the direction-less character of logic programming, it can be used to find trees that flatten to a given list. Each list is the flattening of several trees, and backtracking returns these trees one after another.

Summary

- Complex information can be modelled by data that has a nested structure.
- Relations over these data structures can be defined using recursion.
- Prolog solves goals by matching them with clauses from the program and generating subgoals. If the goal uses a recursive relation, these subgoals may use a simpler instance of the same relation.

Exercises

3.1   What is the result of executing the following goal?

$\# :- maximum(X, nil).$

3.2   What solutions would a Prolog system display for the goal

$\# :- maximum(X, 3{:}1{:}3{:}2{:}nil).$

using the two definitions of *maximum* from the text? Why?

3.3   Use recursion or definition in terms of *append* or other relations to define the following relations on lists:

a. *prefix*(A, B) if list A is a prefix of list B.
   Example: *prefix*(1:2:*nil*, 1:2:3:4:*nil*).
b. *suffix*(A, B) if list A is a suffix of list B.
   Example: *suffix*(3:4:*nil*, 1:2:3:4:*nil*).
c. *segment*(A, B) if list A is a contiguous segment of list B.
   Example: *segment*(2:3:*nil*, 1:2:3:4:*nil*).
d. *sublist*(A, B) if list A is a sub-list (not necessarily contiguous) of list B.
   Example: *sublist*(1:3:*nil*, 1:2:3:4:*nil*).
e. *delete*(A, X, B) if list B is the result of deleting a single occurrence of X from list A. Example: *delete*(3:1:4:2:*nil*, 4, 3:1:2:*nil*).

    f. *perm*(A, B) if list A is a permutation of list B.
      Example: *perm*(4:1:2:3:*nil*, 3:1:4:2:*nil*).

3.4   Define a relation *last*(A, X) that is true if A is a non-empty list, and X is its last element. Write definitions (a) using direct recursion, and (b) in terms of *append*. What are the solutions of the goal # :− *last*(A, 3), where A is a variable?

3.5   How many answers does picoProlog display for the goal

$$\# :- maximum(X, 3:1:3:2:nil)$$

using each of the definitions of *maximum* given in the text? Why is this?

3.6   When it is used as a Prolog program, the definition of *flatten*(T, A) in the text works well if it is given the tree T and asked to find its flattened form A, or if it is given both T and A and asked to check that the relation holds. It works less well, however, if given the list A and asked to find corresponding trees T. Why is this? How can the problem be solved?

Chapter 4

The meaning of logic programs

We have seen how the simple logic of Horn clauses can be used to write computer programs, and how symbolic reasoning can be used by hand or by computer as a way of executing programs written in this way. The answers that are output by a logic program are statements that can be derived from the program by steps of symbolic derivation. In this chapter, we begin a closer look at logic programs by giving precise rules for the syntax of a program, and more importantly, explaining what a logic program means as a logical theory.

That programs have such a logical meaning at all is an aspect of the declarative nature of logic programming. It is important because it allows us to understand logic programs in a way that is independent of what happens when they are executed. To ensure that the answers output by a logic program are correct, the programmer need only ensure that the clauses of the program, when interpreted according to their logical meaning, are true of the problem to be solved. It is the responsibility of whoever implements a logic programming language to ensure that its rules of reasoning are *sound*, that is, they deliver true conclusions whenever they are applied to true premises.

The programmer also needs to ensure that the program is capable of giving answers to enough different questions to be useful. The empty program (containing no clauses at all) certainly gives no incorrect answers, because it gives no answers at all, but it is not a very interesting program. For this purpose, the programmer needs to be sure that the clauses of the program contain all relevant information about the problem, and also that the rules of reasoning used by the implementation are *complete*, that is, any conclusion which follows from the program can in fact be derived from it by the symbolic rules.

Defining a logical meaning for logic programs helps us to understand what information is expressed by clauses and programs. It also gives a reliable criterion for judging whether the rules of reasoning embodied by a particular implementation of logic programming are sound and complete. So the logical semantics given in this chapter are the beginning of two parallel stories. One story tells how programming problems can be expressed in the logic of Horn clauses. We have already begun to tell this story in the first few chapters of this book, and we will return to it later.

The other story tells how particular rules of reasoning (hopefully sound and complete) can be embodied in an implementation of logic programming and used to execute programs and solve goals. This story is told in the next few chapters, where we shall find that a single rule of reasoning called *SLD–resolution* is the basis for an effective, sound and complete procedure for solving goals. The story is concluded in the last part of the book, where the implementation of SLD–resolution in picoProlog is described.

The first section of this chapter contains a summary of the syntax of the simplest kind of logic programs, without certain extensions that we shall add later. In the main part of the chapter, we define the logical meaning of programs written in this simple language. This prepares the way for the next chapter, which formalizes the rules of reasoning we have been using informally, and contains a proof that they are sound and complete.

4.1   Syntax

A typical program is the one that defines the *flatten* relation:

$$flatten(tip(X), X{:}nil) :- \ .$$

$$flatten(fork(U, V), A) :-$$
$$\quad flatten(U, B), flatten(V, C), append(B, C, A).$$

Three kinds of name are used in this clause:

- *flatten* and *append* are *relation symbols* that name a relation between data objects such as trees or lists. In Prolog, relation symbols can have any name that begins with a lower-case letter. In this book, they are shown in lower-case italics *like this*. Each relation symbol has a fixed number of arguments (two for *flatten*, three for *append*); this number is called the *arity* of the symbol.
- *fork* and *tip* are *function symbols* that construct data objects (in this case, trees). In Prolog and in this book, function symbols have names that could also be used for relation symbols, but they can be distinguished by the fact that relation symbols are always outermost in a formula like *flatten*(*fork*(U, V), A), and function symbols are used only in writing the arguments of the formula.
- X, U, V, A, etc., are *variables*. In Prolog, variables can be given any name that starts with an upper-case letter. In this book, they are shown in small capitals LIKE THIS.

For convenience, some relation and function symbols, such as the list constructor ':' and the equality sign '=' are written as infix operators, so we can write

$$X = 1{:}2{:}3{:}4{:}nil$$

instead of something like

$$equal(X, cons(1, cons(2, cons(3, cons(4, nil))))).$$

These infix symbols are just a matter of syntactic convenience, and we could manage without them by using an ordinary symbol instead, with only the disadvantage that our programs would be more difficult to read. Consequently, when we discuss the meaning of logic programs and the mechanisms by which they are executed, we can ignore the existence of infix symbols except in examples. Most Prolog systems allow the programmer to introduce new infix symbols, but picoProlog provides only a fixed collection, and new ones could be added only by modifying picoProlog itself.

Both relation symbols and function symbols have a fixed arity or number of arguments, and this number can be zero. Relation symbols with no arguments are rather uninteresting, because they are the same as *propositional variables* like 'it is raining', or 'I am wet'. We can write a clause that expresses the statement 'If it is raining, then I'll get wet':

$$wet :- raining.$$

But programs built from clauses like this are not able to achieve any very useful calculations.

On the other hand, function symbols with no arguments play a vital part in most programs, because they are the same as *constants* such as the empty list *nil*, or atomic data items like *editor* and *mac* in the database example of Chapter 2. Constants are the basis on which we can build up more complex terms by applying function symbols such as ':' or *fork*.

In terms of this classification of the symbols they contain, we can summarize the syntax of logic programs as follows:

- A *program* is a set of clauses. From a logical point of view, the order in which these clauses are written has no importance.
- A *clause* is a formula

$$P :- Q_1, \ldots, Q_n.$$

P is a literal called the *head* of the clause, and $Q_1, \ldots, Q_n$ are literals that together form the *body* of the clause. In the case $n = 0$, there are no literals in the body; such a clause is written $P :- .$

- A *literal* or *atom* is a formula

$$p(t_1, \ldots, t_k)$$

  where p is a relation symbol of arity k and t_1, ..., t_k are k terms. In the case $k = 0$, the literal is written simply as p.

  For the present, the terms 'atom' and 'literal' are synonymous. In Chapter 8, however, we shall introduce *negated* literals **not** P, where P is an atom of the form $p(t_1, \ldots, t_k)$.

- A *term* is either a variable like X or $PERSON$, or it is a *compound term*

$$f(t_1, \ldots, t_k)$$

  where f is a function symbol of arity k, and t_1, ..., t_k are k smaller terms. A function symbol with no arguments is a constant, written simply as f.

In this summary, the words in italics are the ones we shall use to refer to parts of programs. In discussing logic programming in general (rather than writing logic programs themselves), we use a few extra notational conventions. Upper-case letters such as C, P and Q refer to clauses and atoms, the letters t and u are used for terms, and p and q are relation symbols.

Prolog does not require relation or function symbols to be declared, and unlike picoProlog, most Prolog systems do not enforce our convention that they should have a fixed arity, but it will be simpler for us to stick to this convention. We shall talk about the *alphabet* of a program, meaning the sets of relation and function symbols used in the program, together with their arities. In the *flatten* program, there are two relation symbols: *append* of arity 3, and *flatten* of arity 2. There are four function symbols: ':' of arity 2, *nil* of arity 0, *tip* of arity 1 and *fork* of arity 2. We can write down the alphabet of this program using the following notation, in which a semicolon separates the relation symbols from the function symbols:

$$\{append/3, flatten/2; :/2, nil/0, tip/1, fork/2\}.$$

More generally, we shall say 'f/k is a function symbol' as a short way of including the information that f has arity k. We shall assume that the alphabet of every program contains at least one constant symbol, because this allows us to avoid a number of annoying difficulties with the theory. If a program does not contain constant symbols already, we can always add one to its alphabet.

We say a program T is *well-formed* with respect to an alphabet L if all the relation and function symbols used in T are drawn from L and used with the correct arity. If L is an alphabet, we write $Term(L)$ for the set of terms that are well-formed with respect to L. We write $GrTerm(L)$ for the set of well-formed *ground terms* with respect to L, that is, the set of well-formed terms that contains no variables. Analogously, we write $GrLit(L)$ for the set of well-formed *ground literals* with respect to L.

4.2 Truth tables

The clauses of a logic program may contain complex terms with function symbols and variables, and if we are to explain the meaning of logic programs, we must give a meaning to them. We leave that for later, and begin by explaining the meaning of the very simple logic programs that contain only relation symbols with no arguments. Such relation symbols are like the propositional variables of Boolean algebra, and we can explain the meaning of these programs using the familiar method of truth tables.

For example, here is a clause the we could read as saying 'I'll get wet if it's raining':

$$wet :- raining. \tag{1}$$

There are two relation symbols, *wet* and *raining* in this clause, so there are four possible assignments of the truth values *true* and *false* to them. Each row of this truth table shows one truth assignment and the resulting truth value of the clause:

wet	*raining*	(1)
T	T	T
T	F	T
F	T	F
F	F	T

A clause like (1) is considered true unless the right-hand side is true but the left-hand side is false, something that happens in only one row of the truth table.

If we know that clause (1) is true, and also that the clause

$$miserable :- wet. \tag{2}$$

is true (meaning 'I'll be miserable if I get wet'), then we expect that the clause

$$miserable :- raining. \tag{3}$$

to be true as well, with the informal meaning 'I'll be miserable if it's raining'. We can use a truth table to check that this is a valid inference. The table has eight rows, one for each assignment of truth values to the three symbols *miserable*, *wet* and *raining*. Each row shows the truth values taken by the clauses (1), (2) and (3).

miserable	wet	raining	(1)	(2)	(3)	
T	T	T	T	T	T	*
T	T	F	T	T	T	*
T	F	T	F	T	T	
T	F	F	T	T	T	*
F	T	T	T	F	F	
F	T	F	T	F	T	
F	F	T	F	T	F	
F	F	F	T	T	T	*

If clause (3) really does follow logically from clauses (1) and (2), then it should be true in each row of the truth table where both (1) and (2) are true. These rows are marked with * in the truth table, and they all do contain a T for clause (3) as well as clauses (1) and (2); we may conclude that clause (3) does follow from clauses (1) and (2).

We can use truth tables to assign a 'meaning' to clauses as follows: we say that the meaning of a clause is the set of rows in a truth table where the clause is given the value T. This definition lets us judge whether a claimed conclusion follows from stated premises. We check that every row that makes all the premises true also makes the conclusion true. If so, then the conclusion really is a logical consequence of the premises.

This way of assigning meanings to clauses is also attractive because it assigns the same meaning to clauses that are evidently equivalent from a logical point of view. For example, the two clauses

miserable :− *wet, cold.*

and

miserable :− *cold, wet.*

both express the idea 'I'll be miserable if it's cold and I get wet'. They have the same mathematical meaning, because they are true in the same rows of a truth table – in fact in all rows except the one where *wet* and *cold* are true but *miserable* is false.

As a way of checking that one propositional formula follows from others, the method of truth tables has the advantage that it can be carried out in a completely routine way. A disadvantage is that truth tables become very large unless the number of different propositional variables is very small, and it then becomes more attractive to justify conclusions by symbolic reasoning than by the exhaustive testing implied by truth tables. Even so, we can still use the idea of a truth table as our criterion for judging whether a method of symbolic reasoning is sound and complete.

Methods that replace exhaustive testing by symbolic reasoning become even more attractive when we extend the picture to include clauses that contain variables and function symbols. Analogues of truth tables exist in this broader setting, and we shall use them as a criterion of truth against which symbolic methods can be judged. However, these analogues of truth tables are no longer based on finite arrays of T's and F's, but on infinite mathematical sets and functions. The table has an infinite number of 'rows', so it is no longer possible to check them all one by one.

4.3 Adding functions and variables

Truth tables work well enough for simple programs that contains only relation symbols with no arguments, but something more is needed when relations can have arguments that contain variables and function symbols. In place of rows in a truth table, we will use *interpretations* that assign a truth value to each member of the (perhaps infinite) set of literals that can be formed from the alphabet of the program. If the relation symbols have no arguments, then the set of ground literals is finite; they are just the relation signs themselves. In that case, an interpretation is much the same as a row in the truth table, giving a truth value (T or F) for each relation symbol.

More generally, we define an interpretation M over an alphabet L to be a set $M \subseteq GrLit(L)$ of ground literals formed from L. The idea is that the members of M are the literals that are true, and all the others are false. If L contains relation and function symbols that take arguments, then $GrLit(L)$ is infinite, because we can form infinitely many terms like nil, $0{:}nil$, $0{:}0{:}nil$, etc. The set of interpretations is infinite too, because the set of all subsets of an infinite set is also infinite.

Each row of a truth table shows the truth values taken by some premises and a conclusion when the literals take certain truth values. These truth values for the formulas are calculated from the truth values for the literals by following rules connected with the meaning of the logical operators. Following the analogy, we now give rules that determine, for each interpretation, the truth value of a clause with function symbols and variables.

We deal first with ground clauses, which may contain function symbols but contain no variables. If M is an interpretation, we say the ground clause

$$P :- Q_1, \ldots, Q_n.$$

is true in M exactly if either $P \in M$, or $Q_i \notin M$ for some i. This agrees with the rule we used earlier with truth tables: a clause is considered true unless all the literals in the body are true, but the head of the clause is false. We translate 'P is true' by $P \in M$, because M contains exactly the ground literals that are considered true under the interpretation.

Now for clauses that contain variables: we say a clause C is true in an interpretation M exactly if every *ground instance* of C is true in M. A ground instance of a clause C with variables is any clause that can be obtained from C by systematically substituting ground terms for the variables of C. By 'systematically', we intend that the same ground term should be substituted for each variable wherever it appears. We shall be more precise about this when we introduce the concept of a formal substitution in Section 4.4.

Finally, we say that a program T is true in an interpretation M if each clause of the program, considered separately, is true in M. In this case, we also say that M is a *model* of T, and write $\models_M T$. Similarly, we write $\models_M C$ if an individual clause C is true in M. The meaning of a program T is the set of all models of T, that is, the set of all interpretations M such that $\models_M T$.

If the clauses of T contain variables, it may be that the same variable appears in several different clauses. We define the meaning of a program by treating the clauses separately, allowing ground terms to be substituted for variables in each clause independently of the others. Because of this, the value of a variable in one clause is not related to its values in other clauses. On the other hand, we required the same ground term to be substituted for a variable wherever it occurs inside a single clause; this makes sure that within a clause, each variable refers to a single value.

We say that a clause C *follows from* a program T (or that T entails C) if C is true in every model of T. This is just like the criterion for entailment we used with truth tables, because it is equivalent to saying that every interpretation (row of the truth table) that makes all the clauses of T true also makes C true.

This way of giving meaning to logic programs says nothing about what happens when a program runs. This makes it a little unsatisfying for us as programmers, because we want to know what the computer *does* when we present it with a program. On the other hand, this is exactly what we should expect for a declarative programming language: programs have a meaning that is independent of the way the programming language is implemented. Later, when we come to describe the mechanisms by which logic programs are executed, we will have a strong expectation about what the mechanisms should achieve, because executing a program should produce all and only the conclusions that are entailed by the program.

4.4   Substitutions

In describing what it means for a clause to be true in an interpretation, we used the idea of systematically substituting ground terms for variables. We now make this idea more precise by introducing formally the idea of a substitution and the operation of applying a substitution to a term or clause to obtain an instance of it.

A *substitution* $s: Var \rightarrow Term(L)$ is a function from variables to terms. It associates a term with each variable, and when we 'systematically' substitute terms for variables according to s, it is the term $s(x)$ that we substitute for each occurrence of a variable x. We shall use the notation $\{x_1 \leftarrow t_1, \ldots, x_n \leftarrow t_n\}$ for the substitution that maps each of the variables x_i to the corresponding term t_i (for $1 \leq i \leq n$), and maps all other variables to themselves.

The *instance* of a term t under a substitution s is the term $t[s]$ defined as follows: if t is a variable x, then $t[s] = s(x)$. If f is a function symbol of arity k, and $t = f(t_1, \ldots, t_k)$, then

$$t[s] = f(t_1[s], \ldots, t_k[s]).$$

This last equation tells us how to form $t[s]$ for a compound term t from the arguments of t: we recursively apply the same substitution s to each of them, then build the results into a new compound term that also has f as its function symbol. Because the arguments of the original term are smaller than the term itself, this equation lets us work out the instance under s of any term t. The recursion stops with variable symbols (to which the first part of the definition applies) and constants (which are unchanged by substitution). As a slight abuse of notation, we write $t[x \leftarrow u]$ as an abbreviation for $t[\{x \leftarrow u\}]$, saving a pair of braces.

We shall also use the notation $P[s]$ for the instance of a literal P under the substitution s: if $P = p(t_1, \ldots, t_k)$ then

$$P[s] = p(t_1[s], \ldots, t_k[s]).$$

Also, we write $C[s]$ for the instance of a clause C under s: if C is the clause

$$P :- Q_1, \ldots, Q_n,$$

then $C[s]$ is the clause

$$P[s] :- Q_1[s], \ldots, Q_n[s].$$

A *ground substitution* is simply a substitution g such that $g(x)$ is a ground term for every variable x. Plainly, if g is a ground substitution, then $t[g]$ is a ground term for every term t.

The main reason for introducing the idea of a substitution explicitly is that substitutions themselves have helpful algebraic properties. For example, if r and s are substitutions, then there is another substitution $r \triangleright s$ called the *composition* of r and s, such that $t[r \triangleright s] = t[r][s]$ for all terms t. We can define the substitution $r \triangleright s$ by giving its action on variables: it is the substitution u such that

$$u(x) = r(x)[s]$$

for all variables x. That is, to compute $u(x)$, we first apply r to x, then take the instance under s of the resulting term. We need to *prove* that this substitution has the properties we desire, and this we do in the proposition below.

There is also an identity substitution I such that $t[I] = t$ for all terms t. It is defined by $I(x) = x$ for all variables x. Again, we must prove that I has the desired properties.

PROPOSITION
Let t be a term, and let r, s and w be substitutions.

1. $t[r \triangleright s] = t[r][s]$.
2. $t[I] = t$.
3. Composition is associative: $(r \triangleright s) \triangleright w = r \triangleright (s \triangleright w)$.
4. The identity substitution I is a unit element for composition: $I \triangleright s = s = s \triangleright I$.

Proof: For part (1), we use induction on the structure of the term t; that is, if $P(t)$ is the property we wish to prove for all terms t, we first prove $P(x)$ for all variables x, then prove for every function symbol f of arity k that $P(f(t_1, \ldots, t_k))$ is implied by the induction hypotheses $P(t_1), \ldots, P(t_k)$. Since every term is built up from variables by using a finite number of function symbols, it follows that $P(t)$ holds for all terms t.

Applying this idea to the specific problem in hand, we see that

$$x[r \triangleright s] = r(x)[s] = x[r][s]$$

for any variable x. Also, if f is a function symbol of arity k, and $t_1, \ldots, t_n$ are such that $t_i[r \triangleright s] = t_i[r][s]$ for each i, then

$$\begin{aligned}
f(t_1, \ldots, t_k)[r \triangleright s] &= f(t_1[r \triangleright s], \ldots, t_k[r \triangleright s]) \\
&= f(t_1[r][s], \ldots, t_k[r][s]) \\
&= f(t_1[r], \ldots, t_k[r])[s] \\
&= f(t_1, \ldots, t_k)[r][s].
\end{aligned}$$

This completes the proof of part (1). We leave part (2) as an exercise. The proof requires another structural induction on t.

For parts (3) and (4), we are required to prove the equality of various substitutions. For this, we use the fact that two substitutions are equal if they agree on every variable. If x is any variable, then

$$x[(r \triangleright s) \triangleright w] = x[r \triangleright s][w] = x[r][s][w] = x[r][s \triangleright w] = x[r \triangleright (s \triangleright w)].$$

Also, $x[I \triangleright s] = x[I][s] = x[s] = x[s][I] = x[I \triangleright s]$. $\square$

The concept of a substitution allows us to be more precise about the meaning of logic programs, and specifically the ground instances of a clause C that we used in defining what it means for C to be true in a certain interpretation; they are simply the instances $C[g]$ where g is a ground substitution. Substitutions will also let us formulate a set of rules of reasoning by which valid conclusions can be derived from programs; that is the subject of the next chapter.

A particularly simple kind of substitution is one that acts as a permutation on the set of variables. We call such a substitution s a *renaming*. Its defining properties are that $s(V)$ is a variable for each V, and if $V_1 \neq V_2$ then $s(V_1) \neq s(V_2)$. If clauses C and C' are such that $C' = C[s]$ for some renaming s, we say that C' is a *variant* of C. Because each renaming s has an inverse s' such that $s \triangleright s' = s' \triangleright s = I$, it follows that if C' is a variant of C then also C is a variant of C'. Variants are important in executing and reasoning with logic programs, because replacing clauses from a program by variants of them allows us to avoid confusion between the variables used in one application of a clause from those used in another application.

Summary

- Logic programs are made up of Horn clauses that contain relation, function and variable symbols.
- Programs can be given a meaning as logical theories. This meaning is independent of any execution mechanism.
- Inference rules and execution mechanisms for logic programs can be assessed by comparing their effect with the logical meaning of the program.

Exercises

4.1 Show using a truth table that the conclusion

$$valuable \mathrel{:-} metal, yellow, heavy. \tag{1}$$

follows from the two premisses

$$valuable \mathrel{:-} gold, heavy. \tag{2}$$

and

$$gold \mathrel{:-} metal, yellow. \tag{3}$$

4.2 At first, we defined $\models_M C$ first for C a ground clause. Later, we extended the definition to allow C to be any clause. Show that the two definitions are consistent, that is, if C is a ground clause then $\models_M C$ (in the earlier sense) if and only if $\models_M C[g]$ for all ground substitutions g. What part is played in the proof by our assumption that L contains at least one constant?

4.3   Prove by structural induction that if the variable X does not appear in the term t then $t[X \leftarrow u] = t$.

4.4   Complete the proof that $t[I] = t$ for every term t.

4.5   Prove that if X and Y are distinct variables, and X does not appear in w, then

$$t[X \leftarrow u][Y \leftarrow w] = t[Y \leftarrow w][X \leftarrow u[Y \leftarrow w]].$$

Chapter 5

Inference rules

Our way of giving meaning to logic programs fixes precisely what it means for a clause to be entailed by a program – and so what it means for an answer to a goal to be correct – but it does not give us any practical way of checking whether this is so for a particular program and a particular clause. In this chapter, we begin to develop formal inference rules that allow conclusions to be derived from programs in a way that can be checked by symbolic calculation. For each rule, we prove as a theorem that any clause that can be derived according to the rule is in fact entailed by the program – in other words, that the rule is sound.

5.1 Substitution and ground resolution

The first inference rule is the following *rule of substitution*, which we have in fact been using since Chapter 1:

From a clause C, derive the instance $C[s]$, where s is any substitution.

The soundness of this rule follows from the following proposition:

PROPOSITION
Let C be a clause, M be an interpretation and s be a substitution. If $\models_M C$ then $\models_M C[s]$.

Proof: If $\models_M C$, it follows by the definition of $\models_M$ that $\models_M C[g]$ for any ground substitution g. If h is a ground substitution, then $s \triangleright h$ is also a ground substitution, since $(s \triangleright h)(x) = s(x)[h]$ is a ground term for each variable x. Putting $g = s \triangleright h$, we deduce that $\models_M C[s \triangleright h]$. But $C[s][h] = C[s \triangleright h]$, so $\models_M C[s][h]$. Since this is true for any ground substitution h, it follows that $\models_M C[s]$. $\qquad\square$

COROLLARY

For any program T, clause C and substitution s, if $T \models C$ then $T \models C[s]$.

Proof: Let M be any model of T. Then $\models_M C$, and so by the proposition $\models_M C[s]$ also. Therefore $T \models C[s]$. □

The substitution rule allows us to derive instances of a clause by 'filling in' the values of variables, one of the key steps in the kind of derivation we carried out in Chapter 1. The other key step is to combine two clauses that have a matching literal, to derive a new clause. We consider first the special case used there, in which both the clauses are ground. It is called the *rule of ground resolution*:

From two ground clauses

$$P :- Q_1, \ldots, Q_j, \ldots, Q_n$$

and

$$Q :- R_1, \ldots, R_m$$

such that $Q = Q_j$, derive the clause

$$P :- Q_1, \ldots, Q_{j-1}, R_1, \ldots, R_m, Q_{j+1}, \ldots, Q_n$$

obtained by taking a copy of the first clause and replacing Q_j with the body of the second clause.

We call the clause that is derived in this rule the *ground resolvent* of the first two clauses on Q_j. The soundness of the rule follows from the following proposition:

PROPOSITION

Let the three ground clauses above be C_1, C_2 and C_3, and let M be an interpretation. If $\models_M C_1$ and $\models_M C_2$ then $\models_M C_3$.

Proof: Using the definition of $\models_M$, we can distinguish various (not mutually exclusive) cases:

1. P is true in M. In this case, C_3 is automatically true in M.
2. One of the Q_i for $i \neq j$ is false in M. Again C_3 is true in M, because it contains Q_i in its body.
3. One of the R_i is false in M. Again the body of C_3 contains R_i, so C_3 is true in M.

Because C_1 is true in M, either P is true in M (case 1), or one of the Q_i is false in M. In the latter case, either $i \neq j$ (case 2), or $Q = Q_j$ is false in M. In that case, the truth of C_2 implies that one of the R_i is also false in M (case 3).   □

Combining the rule of substitution (using a ground substitution) with the rule of ground resolution allows us to derive new ground clauses from a program. Both rules say that if certain clauses are entailed by a program, then so is another clause. We can build up elaborate derivations by using the output from one application of a rule as input to another rule, so deriving more and more elaborate conclusions from a program. Such a derivation can be set out as a list, in which each item is justified by naming the rule that can be used to derive it from preceding items.

EXAMPLE
The following program defines a relation $reverse(A, B)$ that holds between two lists A and B if the members of B are those of A in reverse order:

$reverse(nil, nil) :- $.   (rev.1)
$reverse(X{:}A, C) :- reverse(A, B), append(B, X{:}nil, C).$ (rev.2)

$append(nil, B, B) :- $.   (app.1)
$append(X{:}A, B, X{:}C) :- append(A, B, C).$ (app.2)

From this program, we can derive the fact

$reverse(1{:}2{:}nil, 2{:}1{:}nil) :- $.

by the derivation shown in Figure 5.1. In a derivation like this, each line is obtained either by applying the rule of substitution (subst) to a program clause, or by applying the rule of ground resolution (GR) to preceding lines in the derivation. Since each line depends only on program clauses or lines that have been derived before it, we can be sure that each line (including the last) is entailed by the program, and thus that the program entails the final conclusion.   □

Although derivations are traditionally presented as linear lists, the structure of a derivation can be shown more clearly as a tree, as in Figure 5.2, where each numbered node refers to a line in the derivation of Figure 5.1. At the leaves of the tree are clauses derived from those in the program by the substitution rule. All the clauses at interior nodes are derived from their two children by a step of ground resolution. This example shows how the rules of substitution and ground resolution can be used to derive answers to goals of the form $\# :- P$ that consist of a single literal P. We simply look for a way to derive a ground clause $P[g] :- $ where $P[g]$ is a ground instance of P.

  Although it works, this procedure is inconvenient for manual use and inefficient for machine implementation, because we are forced to guess the substitutions that

1. $reverse(1{:}2{:}nil, 2{:}1{:}nil) :-$ $reverse(2{:}nil, 2{:}nil), append(2{:}nil, 1{:}nil, 2{:}1{:}nil).$	(rev.2), subst
2. $append(2{:}nil, 1{:}nil, 2{:}1{:}nil) :- append(nil, 1{:}nil, 1{:}nil).$	(app.2), subst
3. $reverse(1{:}2{:}nil, 2{:}1{:}nil) :-$ $reverse(2{:}nil, 2{:}nil), append(nil, 1{:}nil, 1{:}nil).$	1, 2, GR
4. $reverse(2{:}nil, 2{:}nil) :-$ $reverse(nil, nil), append(nil, 2{:}nil, 2{:}nil).$	(rev.2), subst
5. $reverse(nil, nil) :- .$	(rev.1)
6. $reverse(2{:}nil, 2{:}nil) :- append(nil, 2{:}nil, 2{:}nil).$	4, 5, GR
7. $append(nil, 2{:}nil, 2{:}nil) :- .$	(app.1), subst
8. $reverse(2{:}nil, 2{:}nil) :- .$	6, 7, GR
9. $reverse(1{:}2{:}nil, 2{:}1{:}nil) :- append(nil, 1{:}nil, 1{:}nil).$	3, 8, GR
10. $append(nil, 1{:}nil, 1{:}nil) :- .$	(app.1), subst
11. $reverse(1{:}2{:}nil, 2{:}1{:}nil) :- .$	9, 10, GR

Figure 5.1: *Derivation of a* reverse *fact*

are needed to make the derivation fit together properly. For example, in writing down the first line of the example, the author was forced to guess that the reverse of $1{:}2{:}nil$ would be $2{:}1{:}nil$, and a machine might not have the insight to make that guess correctly. A wrong guess would have been revealed only later in the derivation, when the literals in the body of the clause would fail to match the heads of other clauses.

To solve this problem, we need to use a different inference rule that combines features of the rules of substitution and ground resolution, allowing decisions about what to substitute for variables to be delayed until information is available that allows the decision to be made correctly. We shall study this *rule of general resolution* in the next chapter. First, however, we look at ways of using our present inference rules to solve a wider class of problems.

5.2 Refutation

The goal

$$\# :- append(1{:}2{:}nil, 3{:}4{:}nil, A), append(A, 5{:}6{:}nil, B).$$

asks for the lists $1{:}2{:}nil$ and $3{:}4{:}nil$ to be concatenated, and the result to be concatenated with $5{:}6{:}nil$ to give the final answer B. We can use a trick to extend our method of substitution and ground resolution to cope with goals like this that contain more than one literal.

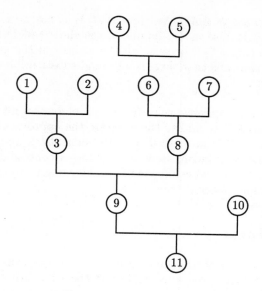

Figure 5.2: *Tree structure of the* reverse *derivation*

The trick is to give a special meaning to the symbol # that we have been using to write goals. We add # to the alphabet of the program as a relation symbol #/0 with no arguments, and add the goal to the program as an extra clause. Then we try to use substitution and ground resolution to derive the empty clause # :− from this *augmented program*. If we succeed, then we conclude that there are values of the variables in the original goal that make all its literals true. As we shall see, it is possible to find out from the derivation of # :− what these values are.

Why does this method work? The precise claim is this: we start with a program T with alphabet L, and a list of literals $P_1, \ldots, P_n$. We add the clause

$$\# :- P_1, \ldots, P_n. \tag{$*$}$$

to T to get an augmented program T' over $L' = L \cup \{\#/0\}$, and claim the following:

PROPOSITION
If $T' \models (\# :-)$ then for each model M of T, there is a ground substitution g such that $\models_M P_i[g]$ for each i.

Proof: Let M be a model of T. Then M is an interpretation over L, but we can use it as an interpretation over L' also. It makes # act like the propositional constant *false*, because $\# \notin M$. We know that M is not a model of T', because $T' \models (\# :-)$ and $\#$ is false in M. So one of the clauses of T' is false in M, and it can only be the clause $(*)$, because all the clauses of the original program T are true in M. This means that there is a ground substitution g that makes $P_i[g]$ true in M for each i. □

This trick changes our inference rules from a proof system into a *refutation* system, because the trick is to add to the program the opposite of the fact we want to prove (since $\# :- P$ is in effect $P \Rightarrow$ *false* or **not** P), and to show that the resulting set of clauses is inconsistent by deriving a contradiction. This refutes the assumption that the goal is allowing false, allowing us to conclude that some choice of substitution makes it true.

5.3 Completeness

We have seen how substitution and ground resolution can be used to derive consequences from logic programs, and that the rules are sound, so that the only consequences that can be derived are ones that really do follow from the program. A natural question is whether every valid consequence of the program can be derived in this way. The answer is 'yes', as the following theorem states:

THEOREM [Completeness of substitution and ground resolution]
Let T be a program with alphabet L, and let P be a ground literal over L. If $T \models P$, then the clause $P :-$ can be derived from T by substitution and ground resolution.

Proof: We prove the theorem by constructing a special model M_0 of T, called the *least model* of T, in which a ground literal R is true exactly if $R :-$ is derivable from T using substitution and ground resolution. If P is true in all models of T, then it is true in this special model M_0, and we can conclude that $P :-$ is derivable from T. So let $M_0 = \{ R \mid R :-$ is derivable from $T \}$. We must show that M_0 really is a model of T. Let $C = (Q :- R_1, \ldots, R_n)$ be a clause of T, and let g be a ground substitution. We must show that $\models_{M_0} C[g]$, i.e., that if $\models_{M_0} R_i[g]$ for each i then also $\models_{M_0} Q[g]$. Since C is a clause of T, we can use the substitution rule to derive the clause

$$C[g] = (Q[g] :- R_1[g], \ldots, R_n[g]).$$

If $\models_{M_0} R_i[g]$ for each i, then (by the definition of M_0) all the clauses $R_i[g] :-$ are derivable, so we can also derive $Q[g] :-$ from these and $C[g]$ by n steps of ground resolution. Thus $\models_{M_0} Q[g]$, and we may conclude that $\models_{M_0} C$. Since this is true for each clause C of T, we conclude that M_0 is a model of T. This completes the proof. □

The least model M_0 constructed in the proof is actually more interesting than the theorem itself. The ground literals that are true in M_0 are those that are derivable from the program T. The closed world assumption of Chapter 3 states that these literals are the ones that are actually true: thus the closed world assumption is equivalent to saying that the least model of the program faithfully represents the relations that the program is intended to describe. This is a safe assumption, because the soundness of our inference rules guarantees that the ground literals that are true in M_0 are also true in every other model of the program. The closed world assumption will become important in Chapter 8, where we shall assume that any ground literal that is not true in M_0 is in fact false.

The theorem establishes the *ground-literal completeness* of substitution and ground resolution – in the sense that any ground literal that follows from a program can be derived from it using these rules. We shall also be interested in two other kinds of completeness for systems of inference rules:

- *refutation completeness*: that if every model of T contains values that satisfy $P_1, \ldots, P_n$, then the empty goal can be derived from the augmented program $T' = T \cup \{\# :- P_1, \ldots, P_n\}$. This follows immediately from ground-literal completeness, because the symbol $\#$ is a ground literal.
- *answer completeness*: that any correct answer to a goal can be extracted from a refutation. We shall explore this in Section 7.4.

In the next chapter, we shall abandon ground resolution in favour of the computationally more attractive rule of general resolution, but the work we have put into the analysis of ground resolution will not be wasted, because results about ground resolution can often be extended to cover general resolution too.

Summary

- Inference rules are syntactic rules that allow conclusions to be derived from a program.
- An inference rule is *sound* if it allows only valid conclusions to be derived from valid premisses.
- A system of inference rules is *complete* if it allows any valid conclusion to be derived.
- The rules of substitution and ground resolution are sound and complete.

Exercises

5.1 Show that the following *rule of commutation* is sound: from the clause $P :- Q_1, Q_2$ derive the clause $P :- Q_2, Q_1$. [More generally, if π is a permutation of $\{1, \ldots, n\}$, then from $P :- Q_1, \ldots, Q_n$ one may derive $P :- Q_{\pi(1)}, \ldots, Q_{\pi(n)}$.]

5.2 Prove the soundness of the following *rule of factoring*: if s is a substitution such that $Q_1[s] = Q_2[s]$, then from the clause $P :- Q_1, Q_2$ derive the clause $P :- Q_1[s]$. [More generally, if $Q_i[s] = Q_j[s]$, then from the clause

$$P :- Q_1, \ldots, Q_i, \ldots, Q_j, \ldots, Q_n.$$

one may derive the clause

$$P[s] :- Q_1[s], \ldots, Q_i[s], \ldots, Q_{j-1}[s], Q_{j+1}[s], \ldots, Q_n. \,]$$

5.3 Prove the soundness of the following *rule of direct resolution*: from clauses $P :- Q_1, \ldots, Q_n$ and $Q :- R_1, \ldots, R_m$ (not necessarily ground) with $Q = Q_j$, derive the clause

$$P :- Q_1, \ldots, Q_{j-1}, R_1, \ldots, R_m, Q_{j+1}, \ldots, Q_n.$$

Chapter 6

Unification and resolution

The inference rules of substitution and ground resolution allow us to derive consequences from programs, and the completeness theorem of Section 5.3 shows that any valid consequence can be derived using the rules. But these particular rules are rather inconvenient, because all the substitutions of ground terms for variables must be done in advance, at the leaves of the proof tree, and the information needed to determine what substitutions are appropriate only becomes available when we look at internal nodes, where clauses are combined by steps of ground resolution.

In a step of ground resolution, the head of one clause is matched with a literal in the body of another clause, and a new clause is made from them. For ground clauses, the matching is simple: two literals match if they are identical. Our aim now is to generalize the resolution rule so that it works on non-ground clauses. In a resolution step, two literals P and Q will match if they have a common instance, i.e., if there is a substitution s such that $P[s]$ and $Q[s]$ are identical. The new clause that results from the resolution step will have its variables filled in by applying the substitution s. For example, the two literals

$$append(1{:}2{:}nil, 3{:}4{:}nil, W) \quad \text{and} \quad append(X{:}A, B, X{:}C)$$

have a common instance $append(1{:}2{:}nil, 3{:}4{:}nil, 1{:}C)$ that is obtained by applying the substitution

$$\{X \leftarrow 1, A \leftarrow 2{:}nil, B \leftarrow 3{:}4{:}nil, W \leftarrow 1{:}C\}$$

to both literals. We shall use this fact to justify an inference step that begins with the goal

$$\# :- append(1{:}2{:}nil, 3{:}4{:}nil, W).$$

and the program clause

$$append(X:A, B, X:C) :- append(A, B, C).$$

and from them derives the new goal

$$\# :- append(2:nil, 3:4:nil, C).$$

This new goal is obtained by applying the matching substitution to the body of the program clause.

This style of reasoning has a marked advantage, because the values to be substituted for the variables in the goal and program clause can be discovered as part of the matching process between the literals involved in the resolution step, rather than being chosen in advance. The result of the step still contains a variable C, and its value can be chosen according to the needs of subsequent steps, without affecting the validity of the present one.

Unfortunately, the two literals that matched have many other common instances, such as these:

$$append(1:2:nil, 3:4:nil, 1:2:3:4:nil),$$
$$append(1:2:nil, 3:4:nil, 1:3:V).$$

We therefore face the problem of choosing which of the many common instances to use in the resolution step. Choosing the last of the common instances shown leads to a dead end, because it results in the new goal

$$\# :- append(2:nil, 3:4:nil, 3:V).$$

and that goal has no answer. What has happened here is that a value has been chosen for the variable C before the information was available to determine what that value should be. An impulsive guess has been made at the value of C, and that guess turns out to be wrong.

Luckily, there is a best choice of a common instance, in the sense that any other common instance of the two literals can be obtained from it by applying a further substitution. Later resolution steps may actually make further substitutions, and using this 'best' choice of substitution in the present step does not restrict their freedom to do so. In our example, the best choice of substitution is the first one we tried. In general, the best choice can be found by a pattern-matching algorithm called *unification*.

6.1 Unification

If t and u are two terms, we say a substitution s is a *unifier* of t and u if $t[s] = u[s]$. The terms t and u may have many unifiers, but we shall prove that if they have any unifiers at all, then they have a *most general unifier* (m.g.u.). This is a unifier r of t and u with the additional property that every other unifier s can be written as $s = r \triangleright w$ for some substitution w.

THEOREM [Unification]
If two terms t and u have any unifiers at all, then they have a most general unifier.

Proof: The proof of this theorem is constructive, in the sense that it does not consist merely of evidence that a most general unifier exists, but (at least implicitly) contains an algorithm for computing one. We shall need this algorithm later as part of the implementation of picoProlog, so we make the algorithm explicit as the program shown in Figure 6.1. The proof of the theorem is the proof that this program works.

The program is written using data structures such as terms, substitutions, and sequences, that are not directly provided by a programming language like Pascal. For now, it will be enough to prove that this abstract version of the algorithm works, and leave until later the details of how these data structures can be implemented. The inputs to the program are two terms t and u, and the outputs are a Boolean value ok that indicates whether the terms have any unifiers, and if they do, a most general unifier r. As the program is executed, the internal variable S holds a sequence of pairs of terms that are waiting to be matched with each other.

The sequence S is used rather like a stack. Sometimes a number of new pairs of terms are 'pushed' onto it by the command

$$S := \langle (p_1, q_1), \dots, (p_k, q_k) \rangle ^\frown S$$

(in which the notation $\langle \dots \rangle$ denotes a sequence with the elements listed, and the $^\frown$ operator is concatenation of sequences). Sometimes the first pair in S is 'popped' by the commands

$$(p, q) := head(S); S := tail(S).$$

The command

$$S := S[x \leftarrow q]$$

has the effect of replacing each pair (y, z) in S by the pair $(y[x \leftarrow q], z[x \leftarrow q])$, in which q has been substituted for x throughout. In the rest of the proof, we

```
function Unify(t, u: term; var r: substitution): boolean;
  var S: sequence of (term × term);
        ok: boolean;
        p, q: term;
begin
  S := ⟨(t, u)⟩; r := I; ok := true;
  while ok ∧ (S ≠ ⟨⟩) do begin
    (p, q) := head(S); S := tail(S);
    if (p is f(p₁, ..., pₖ)) ∧ (q is g(q₁, ..., qₘ)) then begin
      if f = g then
        S := ⟨(p₁, q₁), ..., (pₖ, qₖ)⟩ ⌢ S
      else
        ok := false
    end
    else if (p is a variable X) ∧ (p ≠ q) then begin
      if (X occurs in q) then
        ok := false
      else begin
        r := r ▷ {X ← q};
        S := S[X ← q]
      end
    end
    else if (q is a variable X) ∧ (p ≠ q) then begin
      if (X occurs in p) then
        ok := false
      else begin
        r := r ▷ {X ← p};
        S := S[X ← p]
      end
    end
    else
      { t is a variable and t = u: do nothing }
  end;
  Unify := ok
end;
```

Figure 6.1: *Unification algorithm*

say a substitution k *unifies* S if $y[k] = z[k]$ for every pair of terms (y, z) in S.

We are now ready to state the invariant that relate the values of the program variables to the original terms t and u. The idea is that ok is false only if t and u have no unifier, and if ok is true then any unifier w of t and u can be written $w = r ▷ k$ for some substitution k that unifies S. So r represents the part of a unifier for t and u that has been discovered so far, and S represents the parts of t and u that remain to be matched. More formally stated, the invariant consists of the following two statements:

- If t and u have a unifier, then ok is true.
- If ok is true, then $t[w] = u[w]$ for any substitution w if and only if there is a substitution k such that $w = r \triangleright k$ and k unifies S.

We must first show that the invariant is true initially. The initialization sets S to the sequence $\langle (t, u) \rangle$ that contains just the pair (t, u), and r to the identity substitution I, and ok to *true*. In this state, the invariant is true, because a substitution k unifies S exactly if k unifies t and u, and so we can write

$$w = I \triangleright w = r \triangleright k,$$

where $k = w$ unifies S.

The main part of the program is repeated until either ok is false, or the stack S is empty. Let S_0 be the value taken by S at the start of an execution of the loop body. The program removes a pair (p, q) from S, then performs one of the following actions:

Case 1: If $p = f(p_1, \ldots, p_k)$ and $q = g(q_1, \ldots, q_m)$ for some function symbols f/k and g/m, then the action depends on whether $f = g$:

- If $f \neq g$, then p and q have no unifier, so there is no substitution that unifies S_0. The invariant lets us deduce that t and u have no unifier either, so ok can be set to *false*.
- If $f = g$ (and so $k = m$), then the program adds the k pairs (p_1, q_1), $\ldots$, (p_k, q_k) to S. Any substitution that unifies p and q also unifies these k pairs of terms, and vice versa, so the invariant is maintained.

Case 2: If $p = x$ is a variable and $p \neq q$, the action depends on whether the variable x occurs in q.

- If so, then p and q have no unifier: for any substitution s, the term $q[s]$ will contain $p[s]$ as a proper sub-term, so cannot be equal to it. The flag ok can be made false.
- If x does not occur in q, the program sets r to $r \triangleright \{x \leftarrow q\}$ and sets S to $S[x \leftarrow q]$, the result of applying the substitution $\{x \leftarrow q\}$ to every pair in S. For any substitution w, the invariant tells us that if w unifies t and u, then w factors as $w = r \triangleright k$, where k unifies S_0. In particular, k unifies p and q. It follows that $\{x \leftarrow q\} \triangleright k = k$, since

$$k(x) = p[k] = q[k] = x[x \leftarrow q][k] = (\{x \leftarrow k\} \triangleright k)(x),$$

and for any variable Y different from X,

$$k(Y) = Y[k] = Y[X \leftarrow q][k] = (\{X \leftarrow q\} \triangleright k)(Y).$$

So

$$w = r \triangleright k = r \triangleright (\{X \leftarrow q\} \triangleright k) = (r \triangleright \{X \leftarrow q\}) \triangleright k,$$

and w factors through $r \triangleright \{X \leftarrow q\}$ just as it did through r. Also, k unifies $S[X \leftarrow q]$, since for any (y, z) in S,

$$(y[X \leftarrow q])[k] = y[\{X \leftarrow q\} \triangleright k] = y[k],$$

similarly $(z[X \leftarrow q])[k] = z[k]$, and $y[k] = z[k]$ because k unifies S_0.

Conversely, if k unifies $S[X \leftarrow q]$ then $\{X \leftarrow q\} \triangleright k$ unifies S_0, and so by the invariant $(r \triangleright \{X \leftarrow q\}) \triangleright k$ unifies t and u.

Case 3: If q is a variable and $p \neq q$ then the situation is symmetrical with Case 2.

Case 4: If $p = q = X$ is a variable, then the program leaves S equal to $tail(S_0)$. This maintains the invariant, because any substitution unifies S exactly if it unifies S_0.

If the program terminates, either ok is false, or S is empty. If ok is false, the first part of the invariant tells us that t and u have no unifiers. On the other hand, if ok is true and S is empty, then every substitution k unifies S. The second part of the invariant then tells us (taking $k = I$) that the substitution $r = r \triangleright I$ is a unifier of t and u. Also, if w is any other unifier of t and u, then w factors as $w = r \triangleright k$ for some substitution k. In short, if the program terminates, then it does so in a state where ok is true exactly if t and u have a unifier, and if so, r is a most general unifier of t and u.

Our final task is to prove that the program *does* terminate, whatever the values of t and u. Notice that case 2 (and by symmetry case 3), if they do not lead to immediate termination, reduce by 1 the number of distinct variables that occur in S, because $p = X$ occurs in S_0, but X does not occur in q, and so does not occur in $S[X \leftarrow q]$. Also, cases 1 and 4 leave the number of distinct variables unchanged, but reduce by 2 the total number of function and symbols in elements of S. Since the number of symbols in t and u is finite, these steps can only be executed a finite number of times before S becomes empty.   □

As we have explained it, the unification theorem applies to pairs of *terms*. Literals, however, have the same form as terms, differing only in that the outermost symbol is a relation instead of a function. An analogous result applies to literals, and the same algorithm can be used to compute most general unifiers for them.

EXAMPLE

Let us apply the unification algorithm to the literals $append(w, w, 1{:}2{:}1{:}2{:}nil)$ and $append(x{:}A, B, x{:}C)$. The algorithm begins with

$$S = \langle (append(w, w, 1{:}2{:}1{:}2{:}nil), append(x{:}A, B, x{:}C)) \rangle$$
$$r = I.$$

In the first iteration, it compares the two input literals and finds they are both constructed with $append/3$. So Case 1 applies, and the new state is

$$S = \langle (w, x{:}A), (w, B), (1{:}2{:}1{:}2{:}nil, x{:}C) \rangle$$
$$r = I.$$

The next iteration involves comparing w with $x{:}A$; here Case 2 applies. Because w does not occur in $x{:}A$, the new component $\{w \leftarrow x{:}A\}$ is added to r and applied to the rest of S, giving

$$S = \langle (x{:}A, B), (1{:}2{:}1{:}2{:}nil, x{:}C) \rangle$$
$$r = \{w \leftarrow x{:}A\}.$$

Next, the algorithm compares $x{:}A$ and B. Here Case 3 applies, and the new state is

$$S = \langle (1{:}2{:}1{:}2{:}nil, x{:}C) \rangle$$
$$r = \{w \leftarrow x{:}A, B \leftarrow x{:}A\}.$$

In the next iteration, both p and q are constructed with $:/2$, so Case 1 applies, and the new state is

$$S = \langle (1, x), (2{:}1{:}2{:}nil, C) \rangle$$
$$r = \{w \leftarrow x{:}A, B \leftarrow x{:}A\}.$$

Now the algorithm compares the terms 1 and x. Case 3 applies, and the new value of r is obtained by *composing* the new component $\{x \leftarrow 1\}$ with the previous value. The new value is

$$r = \{w \leftarrow x{:}A, B \leftarrow x{:}A\} \triangleright \{x \leftarrow 1\}$$
$$= \{w \leftarrow 1{:}A, B \leftarrow 1{:}A, x \leftarrow 1\}.$$

Because the substitutions are composed, the value of x has been substituted into the values recorded for w and B. The new state is

$$S = \langle (2{:}1{:}2{:}nil, C) \rangle$$
$$r = \{w \leftarrow 1{:}A, B \leftarrow 1{:}A, x \leftarrow 1\}.$$

A final application of Case 3 gives the state

$$S = \langle \rangle$$
$$r = \{W \leftarrow 1{:}A, B \leftarrow 1{:}A, X \leftarrow 1, C \leftarrow 2{:}1{:}2{:}nil\},$$

in which S is empty. At this point, the algorithm terminates with *ok* true, and the final value of r is a most general unifier of t and u.   □

The values taken by S at various stages in the example illustrates the subtlety of the argument that the algorithm terminates. The number of pairs in S grows and shrinks, but each step involving a variable eliminates that variable from S, and each other step reduces the total size of the terms in S. The very first step increases the size of S from 1 to 3 pairs, but makes the total size of the terms smaller by eliminating two occurrences of the *append* symbol.

6.2   Resolution

The inference rule of *resolution* generalizes and combines into one the two rules of substitution and of ground resolution. Unlike ground resolution, it works on clauses that may contain variables and produces a result that may also contain variables. Here is the statement of the rule of resolution:

From the two clauses

$$P :- Q_1, \ldots, Q_j, \ldots, Q_n.$$

and

$$Q :- R_1, \ldots, R_m.$$

where there exists a substitution s such that $Q[s] = Q_j[s]$, derive the clause

$$(P :- Q_1, \ldots, Q_{j-1}, R_1, \ldots, R_m, Q_{j+1}, \ldots, Q_n)[s].$$

We call this clause the *resolvent* of the two clauses on Q_j under the substitution s. It is obtained by replacing the literal Q_j in the body of the first clause by the whole body of the second clause, then applying the substitution s to the whole clause. We immediately state and prove the soundness of this rule:

PROPOSITION
Let M be an interpretation, and let the three clauses above be C_1, C_2 and C' respectively. If $\models_M C_1$ and $\models_M C_2$ then $\models_M C'$.

Proof: Let g be any ground substitution; we shall show that $\models_M C'[g]$. Since $\models_M C_1$ and $\models_M C_2$, it follows by the substitution rule that $\models_M C_1[s \triangleright g]$ and $\models_M C_2[s \triangleright g]$. Also, $Q[s \triangleright g] = Q[s][g] = Q_j[s][g] = Q_j[s \triangleright g]$, and $C'[g]$ is the ground resolvent of $C_1[s \triangleright g]$ and $C_2[s \triangleright g]$ on the literal $Q_j[s \triangleright g]$. Thus by the ground resolution rule, $\models_M C'[g]$. Since this is true for any ground substitution g, it follows that $\models_M C'$. □

As before, soundness of the resolution rule follows immediately from this proposition. In applying the resolution rule, it is natural to choose the substitution s to be a most general unifier of Q_j and Q. In this case, we call the resulting clause *the* resolvent of C_1 with C_2 on Q_j. As we shall show in the next section, these are the only resolvents we need to consider when searching for a derivation.

EXAMPLE

Here is the *reverse* program from Chapter 5:

$$reverse(nil, nil) :- . \qquad \text{(rev.1)}$$
$$reverse(X{:}A, C) :- reverse(A, B), append(B, X{:}nil, C). \qquad \text{(rev.2)}$$

$$append(nil, B, B) :- . \qquad \text{(app.1)}$$
$$append(X{:}A, B, X{:}C) :- append(A, B, C). \qquad \text{(app.2)}$$

From this program, we can use resolution to derive the conclusion

$$reverse(X_1{:}X_2{:}nil, X_2{:}X_1{:}nil) :- .$$

in which X_1 and X_2 are *variables*. This conclusion covers as a special case the conclusion $reverse(1{:}2{:}nil, 2{:}1{:}nil) :-$ that we derived from the same program by substitution and ground resolution. In fact, as we shall see later, we can take any derivation that uses ground resolution and produce a derivation that has the same 'shape', but uses general resolution instead, with a conclusion that covers the original conclusion as a special case.

Our derivation begins with variants of (rev.1) and (rev.2):

1. $reverse(X_1{:}A_1, C_1) :-$ (rev.2)
   $reverse(A_1, B_1), append(B_1, X_1{:}nil, C_1).$
2. $append(X_2{:}A_2, B_2, X_2{:}C_2) :-$ (app.2)
   $append(A_2, B_2, C_2).$

The head of (2) unifies with the *append* literal in the body of (1). The unifying substitution is $\{B_1 \leftarrow X_2{:}A_2, B_2 \leftarrow X_1{:}nil, C_1 \leftarrow X_2{:}C_2\}$ and the resolvent is

3. $reverse(X_1{:}A_1, X_2{:}C_2) :-$ 1, 2, R
   $reverse(A_1, X_2{:}A_2), append(A_2, X_1{:}nil, C2).$

Now we take a fresh variant of (rev.2) and a variant of (rev.1):

4. $reverse(X_4{:}A_4, C_4)$:−
   $reverse(A_4, B_4), append(B_4, X_4{:}nil, C_4).$ (rev.2)

5. $reverse(nil, nil)$:− .   (rev.1)

The head of (5) unifies with the *reverse* literal in the body of (4). The matching substitution is $\{A_4 \leftarrow nil, B_4 \leftarrow nil\}$, and the resolvent is

6. $reverse(X_4{:}nil, C_4)$:− $append(nil, X_4{:}nil, C_4).$ 4, 5, R

Now we take a variant of (app.1):

7. $append(nil, B_7, B_7)$:− .   (app.1)

and resolve it with (6). The matching substitution is $\{B_7 \leftarrow X_4{:}nil, C_4 \leftarrow X_4{:}nil\}$, and the resolvent is

8. $reverse(X_4{:}nil, X_4{:}nil)$:− .   6, 7, R

Now we can form a resolvent between (3) and (8), deriving

9. $reverse(X_1{:}X_2{:}nil, X_2{:}C_2)$:− $append(nil, X_1{:}nil, C_2).$ 3, 8, R

Finally, we resolve (9) with another variant of (app.1):

10. $append(nil, B_{10}, B_{10})$:− .   (app.1)

We obtain the final result

11. $reverse(X_1{:}X_2{:}nil, X_2{:}X_1{:}nil)$:− .   9, 10, R

To a human eye, this derivation seems more complicated than the original proof by ground resolution, because each step involves unifying two literals that may both contain variables. But the crucial difference between this style of derivation and one using ground resolution is that unification can be done by a systematic algorithm, and there is now no need to use insight in guessing what terms should be substituted for variables to make the proof work.

6.3 Derivation trees and the lifting lemma

Our aim in this section is to show that derivations by ground resolution can be 'lifted' to make derivations by general resolution. This provides a way of showing that general resolution is complete, because every consequence of a program can be derived by ground resolution, and this derivation can be lifted to use general resolution. In fact, the result is even more useful than this suggests, because lifting a derivation preserves its tree structure. This comes in useful later, when we become interested in the shapes of derivation trees that must be considered in the search for answers to a goal. Then, as now, we shall be able to work mostly with ground resolution, and, as a final step, lift our results to the general case.

We begin with a more precise definition of derivation trees.

DEFINITION

The set of *derivation trees* for a program T, and the *outcome* of each derivation tree are defined as follows:

1. If C is an instance of a clause of T, then $leaf(C)$ is a derivation tree with outcome C.
2. If D_1 and D_2 are derivation trees with outcomes C_1 and C_2, and C is a resolvent of C_1 with C_2, then $resolve(C, D_1, D_2)$ is also a derivation tree with outcome C.

□

Derivation trees are usually drawn like the tree in Figure 5.2, since the flow of logical implication then goes down the page in a natural way. The root, labelled with the final outcome, is at the bottom, and at the top are leaves, each labelled with an instance of a program clause. Derivations by substitution and ground resolution are a special case of derivation trees, in which the leaves are labelled with ground instances of clauses from T, and all the *resolve* nodes correspond to steps of ground resolution. Another special case occurs when the leaves are labelled with *variants* of program clauses rather than more specific instances, and each resolution step uses the most general unifier of the two literals involved: we call such a derivation tree *strict*.

The recursive definition of derivation trees gives a method of proving general results about them: we can argue by structural induction on derivations. This is quite different from an argument by structural induction on the clause that is the outcome of the derivation. In one case, we are examining the reason why the outcome is a clause, and in the other, we are examining the reason why it is entailed by the program. This method of proof is used to establish our most important result about derivation trees, the *lifting lemma*.

LEMMA [Lifting lemma]

Let T be a program and D be a derivation tree for T. Then there is a strict derivation tree D' for T such that

1. D' has the same shape as D, in the sense that either D and D' are both leaves, or they are both constructed by *resolve*, and in that case, the two immediate sub-trees of D' have the same shape as those of D.

2. Each sub-tree of D has an outcome that is an instance of the outcome of the corresponding sub-tree of D'.

Proof: We argue by induction on the structure of D. If D is a leaf $leaf(C[s])$, where C is a program clause and s is a substitution, then we may take D' to be $leaf(C')$, where C' is any variant of C.

If D has the form $resolve(C, D_1, D_2)$, and the lifting lemma is true of D_1 and D_2, then let D'_1 and D'_2 be strict versions of D_1 and D_2. We may suppose that no variable appears in both D'_1 and D'_2, since we can choose variants of program clauses to make this so. Let

$$C_1 = (P :- Q_1, \ldots, Q_j, \ldots, Q_n)$$
$$C_2 = (Q :- R_1, \ldots, R_m)$$

be the outcomes of D'_1 and D'_2. By hypothesis, there is a substitution s such that $C_1[s]$ and $C_2[s]$ are the outcomes of D_1 and D_2 respectively. The clause C is obtained from $C_1[s]$ and $C_2[s]$ by a step of resolution. Suppose it is resolution on the literal $Q_j[s]$ under the substitution s', so $Q[s \triangleright s'] = Q_j[s \triangleright s']$, and

$$C = (P :- Q_1, \ldots, R_1, \ldots, R_m, \ldots, Q_n)[s \triangleright s'].$$

Since Q and Q_j have a common instance, they have a most general unifier r, and $s \triangleright s'$ factors through r, say $s \triangleright s' = r \triangleright k$. Let C' be the resolvent of C_1 and C_2 on Q_j under r, and let $D' = resolve(C', D'_1, D'_2)$. Then D' has the same shape as D, its outcome C' is obtained by a resolution step under a most general unifier, and $C = C'[k]$ is an instance of C'. This completes the proof.   □

6.4   Completeness of resolution

The lifting lemma leads immediately to completeness results for general resolution. An example of such a result is the *refutation completeness* of resolution, that if a goal G can be solved by a program T, then there is a refutation of $T \cup \{G\}$ by resolution.

THEOREM [Refutation completeness of resolution]
Let T be a program and G a goal such that $T \cup \{G\} \models \#$. Then there is a strict derivation tree for $T \cup \{G\}$ with outcome $\# :-$.

Proof: By completeness of ground resolution, there is a derivation tree D for $T \cup \{G\}$ with outcome $\# :-$. By the lifting lemma, we can find a strict derivation tree D' (of the same shape) for $T \cup \{G\}$ whose outcome has $\# :-$ as an instance. But the clause $\# :-$ is an instance of no clause but itself, so D' is the required strict derivation tree.   □

Summary

- If two terms have a common instance, then they have a most general common instance, obtained by applying their most general unifier to either of them.
- The existence of most general unifiers allows the rules of substitution and ground resolution to be replaced by a single rule of resolution.
- Any derivation that can be carried out using substitution and ground resolution can be mimicked using the rule of resolution.
- Any goal that has a solution for a given program can be solved by refutation using the rule of resolution.

Exercises

6.1   What (if any) are the most general unifiers of the following pairs of terms?

a. $f(X, Y)$ and $f(g(Y), h(Z))$.
b. $f(X, X)$ and $f(Y, g(Y))$.
c. $p(X, g(X), h(Y))$ and $p(g(Y), z, h(a))$.

6.2   Suppose terms t, u and v are such that t and u have a unifier, and u and v have a unifier. Prove or disprove the statement that t and v necessarily have a unifier.

6.3   Let u_1, u_2, w_1, w_2 be terms. Consider the compound terms $t_1 = f(u_1, w_1)$ and $t_2 = f(u_2, w_2)$, and suppose that u_1 and u_2 have a m.g.u. r and $w_1[r]$ and $w_2[r]$ have a m.g.u. s. Show the $r \triangleright s$ is most general unifier of t_1 and t_2.

6.4   The concept of most general unifier can be extended to sets of terms (instead of just pairs): we say r is a unifier of a set S if $t_1[r] = t_2[r]$ for all terms $t_1, t_2 \in S$, and say r is a most general unifier (m.g.u.) of S if any other unifier s factors as $s = r \triangleright k$ for some substitution k.

If r is a m.g.u. of t_1 and t_2, and s is a m.g.u. of $t_1[r]$ and $t_3[r]$, prove that $r \triangleright s$ is a m.g.u. of the set $\{t_1, t_2, t_3\}$. Prove also that if this set has any unifiers, then it has a most general unifier that can be obtained in this way.

6.5   [Hard]

a. Let a relation $\preceq$ on terms be defined so that $t \preceq u$ if and only if $t[s] = u$ for some substitution s. Prove that $\preceq$ is reflexive and transitive, and find an example that shows it is not anti-symmetric.
b. Let $\phi\colon Term \times Term \to Var$ be a function that assigns a distinct variable to each pair of terms, and define a binary operation $\sqcap$ on terms as follows: if

f is a function symbol of arity k, then

$$f(t_1, \ldots, t_k) \sqcap f(u_1, \ldots, u_k) = f(t_1 \sqcap u_1, \ldots, t_k \sqcap u_k),$$

and for all other pairs of terms t and u, $t \sqcap u = \phi(t, u)$. Prove that $t \sqcap u$ is a greatest lower bound of t and u under $\sqcap$.

c. Explain how unification can be used to find a least upper bound for two terms t and u where one exists.

Chapter 7

SLD–resolution and answer substitutions

Resolution is a better candidate for machine implementation than ground resolution, but it still suffers from some drawbacks. One is that there are several ways that resolution might be used to produce a refutation of a goal. We might try using clauses from the program directly on the goal, matching the clause head with literals in the goal, and deriving a new goal, or we might try using resolution to combine program clauses with each other, making new clauses that can be used on the goal.

This choice of methods makes it appear that a machine searching for a refutation must explore a large and complex search space, sometimes carrying out resolution steps that do not involve the current goal at all. But luckily this complexity is an illusion, because (as we shall show in this chapter) every refutation can be recast in a 'straight-line' form, where every resolution step involves a clause taken directly from the program and the goal that was produced in the previous step. Derivation trees in straight-line form consist of a long, thin spine, with the original goal at the top and the empty goal at the bottom. All the nodes that are not on the spine are leaves, labelled with variants of program clauses. This means that the machine can search for a refutation in a systematic way by starting with the goal and repeatedly choosing a program clause to resolve with it. There is still some choice here – and in fact it is this remaining element of choice that makes logic programs non-deterministic – but the choice is severely restricted.

Another apparent source of complexity in searching for a refutation is that a goal may have several literals, and we may choose to solve them in any order. Even with straight-line derivations, we might choose to work on any one of the goal literals in the first resolution step, and subsequently we may choose from both the other literals of the original goal and the new literals introduced by previous resolution steps. It appears that, in order to succeed in finding a refutation, we might have to consider the literals in a particular order, and even perhaps interleave steps in the solution of one literal with the solution of other ones. Again, this complexity is only apparent, because every straight-line refutation can be rearranged until the literals are solved in a predetermined order. To keep the discussion simple, we shall consider only the strict left-to-right order that is used by Prolog, but in fact the same argument shows that any choice of order is permissible.

It is important to cut down the search space of derivations that a machine must examine, because this makes execution of logic programs more efficient. If we can show that every goal that has a refutation at all has one in a certain restricted form, then we can build an execution mechanism that considers only refutations in that restricted form. Also, if the form of refutations is restricted, it may be possible to use more efficient data structures to represent derivations inside the implementation. The Prolog approach, in which derivations have a straight-line form and literals are considered in a fixed order, is known as *SLD–resolution*. It allows a particularly simple and efficient form of search, and allows derivations to be represented by a simple stack-like data structure similar to the one used in implementing other programming languages.

The first part of this chapter treats SLD–resolution in more detail, showing that resolution remains complete when we adopt the restrictions of straight-line form and a fixed order of solving literals. The second part discusses a method for extracting an *answer substitution* from a refutation, so that solving a goal does not yield just a simple 'yes' or 'no', but also specific values of variables that make the literals of the goal true if possible. Answer substitutions extracted by this method are what Prolog displays when it has succeeded in solving a goal. We shall prove that the answers extracted from refutations are correct, and that every correct answer can be obtained in this way.

7.1   Linear resolution

DEFINITION
We say a derivation tree for an augmented program $T \cup \{G\}$ is *linear* if either it is a leaf, or it is of the form $fork(C, D_1, D_2)$, where D_1 is linear and D_2 is a leaf.   □

A linear tree looks like Figure 7.1. The clauses C_i are (instances of) program clauses, and the clauses C_i' are derived by a resolution step that has a program clause as its right-hand input. Obviously, the head of C_{i+1}' is an instance of the head of C_i', so if a linear derivation is actually a refutation, then all the clauses C_i' along the spine are goals, C_0 is an instance of the original goal G, and C_n' is the empty goal.

We are now going to show how any refutation that uses *ground resolution* can be recast in linear form. We shall then use the lifting lemma to argue that refutations using general resolution can also be put into linear form. The proof depends on making moves that begin with a derivation that is not linear and end with one that is a little bit more linear. Any non-linear derivation has at least

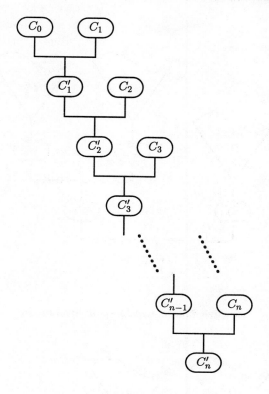

Figure 7.1: *Linear derivation tree*

one *fork* node that is not on the spine, as shown in Figure 7.2. The spine of the derivation tree runs through C_1 and C_5, and C_4 is a *fork* node that is not on the spine. The wavy-topped triangles labelled D_1, D_2 and D_3 may be any derivations that have outcomes C_1, C_2 and C_3 respectively.

If Figure 7.2 represents a valid derivation, then so does Figure 7.3. This derivation contains the same clauses C_1, C_2 and C_3 and has the same outcome C_5, but it has a different clause C_4 inside. Suppose the clauses in the tree of Figure 7.2 are as follows:

$$C_1 = (P :- Q_1, \ldots, Q_j, \ldots, Q_n)$$
$$C_2 = (Q :- R_1, \ldots, R_k, \ldots, R_m)$$
$$C_3 = (R :- S_1, \ldots, S_p),$$

with C_4 obtained from C_2 and C_3 by resolving on $R = R_k$:

$$C_4 = (Q :- R_1, \ldots, R_{k-1}, S_1, \ldots, S_p, R_{k+1}, \ldots, R_m),$$

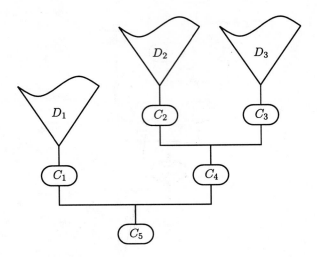

Figure 7.2: *A non-linear derivation tree*

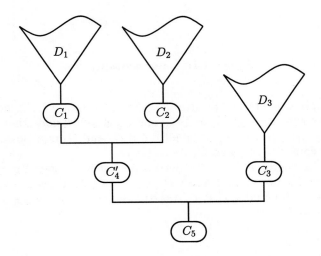

Figure 7.3: *Derivation tree after reshaping*

and C_5 obtained from C_1 and C_4 by resolving on $Q = Q_j$:

$$C_5 = (P :\!-Q_1, \ldots, Q_{j-1}, R_1, \ldots, R_{k-1},$$
$$S_1, \ldots, S_p, R_{k+1}, \ldots, R_m, Q_{j+1}, \ldots, Q_n).$$

Remember that we are using ground resolution.

In the new tree, C'_4 is obtained by resolving the clauses C_1 and C_2 on $Q = Q_j$:

$$C'_4 = (P :\!- Q_1, \ldots, Q_{j-1}, R_1, \ldots, R_k, \ldots, R_m, Q_{j+1}, \ldots, Q_n),$$

then C_5 is obtained by resolving C'_4 with C_3 on $R = R_k$, with the same result as before. Thus Figure 7.3 shows a valid derivation.

A move like this is possible whenever a tree contains a *fork* node that is not on the spine, and it reduces by one the number of such nodes. So by making a sequence of moves, we can reduce any derivation tree to linear form. More formally, the move is the basis for an argument that every clause that can be derived from the augmented program by ground resolution can also be obtained by linear ground resolution The argument is by mathematical induction on the number of off-spine *fork* nodes.

The refutation completeness theorem for ground resolution tells us that any goal that is false in every model of a program has a refutation from the program by ground resolution. Combining this with the result we have just proved tells us that such a goal also has a linear ground refutation. Actually, we are more interested in general resolution than in ground resolution, so we now apply the lifting lemma. If $T \cup \{G\} \models \#$ then (by refutation completeness of ground resolution) there is a derivation by ground resolution of $\# :-$ from $T \cup \{G\}$. As we have just argued, this derivation may be put into linear form. Finally, we apply the lifting lemma: there is a strict derivation tree with the same shape as this linear ground derivation (so it is also linear), such that each clause in the ground derivation is an instance of the corresponding clause in the strict derivation. In particular, the outcome $\# :-$ of the ground derivation is an instance of the outcome of the strict derivation. But this goal is an instance of nothing except itself, so the strict derivation is also a refutation of $T \cup \{G\}$.

7.2 SLD–resolution

At each step in constructing a linear refutation, we must choose which literal in the goal to match with program clauses. We now show that this choice does not matter, in the sense that if there is a refutation that takes the literals in any order, then there is one that takes them in left-to-right order. In other words, linear resolution remains refutation complete if we further restrict it to operate on goal literals from left to right. We call a refutation that obeys this further restriction an *SLD–refutation*. (SLD stands for 'Selected-literal Linear resolution

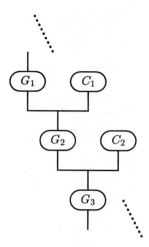

Figure 7.4: *A fragment of a linear tree*

for Definite clauses', and 'definite clauses' are just Horn clauses under another name.)

Again, we use an argument based on a move that replaces a bad fragment of derivation tree with a better one, and again we work with ground resolution first and then appeal to the lifting lemma, but the argument is a little more subtle this time. The move begins with a fragment of a linear tree as shown in Figure 7.4; G_1, G_2 and G_3 are goals, and C_1 and C_2 are instances of program clauses. Let us suppose that the resolution step that derives G_2 from G_1 and C_1 does *not* use the first literal of G_1, but that the resolution step that derives G_3 from G_2 and C_2 *does* use the first literal of G_2. Let the original goal and clauses be

$$G_1 = (\# :- P_1, P_2, \ldots, P_k, \ldots, P_n)$$
$$C_1 = (P :- Q_1, \ldots, Q_m)$$
$$C_2 = (P' :- R_1, \ldots, R_p).$$

Let G_2 be obtained from G_1 and C_1 by resolving on $P = P_k$ where $k > 1$:

$$G_2 = (\# :- P_1, P_2, \ldots, P_{k-1}, Q_1, \ldots, Q_m, P_{k+1}, \ldots, P_n).$$

Because $k > 1$, the first literal in G_2 is identical with that in G_1. Let G_3 be obtained by resolving with C_3 on this literal $P' = P_1$:

$$G_3 = (\# :- R_1, \ldots, R_p, P_2, \ldots, P_{k-1}, Q_1, \ldots, Q_m, P_{k+1}, \ldots, P_n).$$

Our move exchanges the two resolution steps, so that now the first step resolves G_1 with C_3 on $P' = P_1$ to obtain the goal

$$G'_2 = (\# :- R_1, \ldots, R_p, P_2, \ldots, P_k, \ldots, P_n).$$

Then the second step resolves this with C_2 on $P = P_k$ to obtain the same outcome G_3 as before.

What does a move like this achieve? It moves the 'good' resolution step closer to the top of the derivation tree, and pushes the 'bad' step further down. Suppose we have a linear refutation of $T \cup \{G\}$ that does not obey left-to-right order. Let G be the goal $\# :- P_1, P_2, \ldots, P_m$. At the top of the derivation tree is G, and at the bottom is the empty goal $\# :-$. Since all the literals of G have disappeared by the time we reach the bottom of the tree, there must be some step that involves resolution on the leftmost literal P_1 of G. Repeated moves can be used to bring this resolution step to the top of the tree, giving a refutation that begins with a 'good' step, and these moves do not change the height of the tree.

Now consider the rest of the tree, beginning with the outcome G_1 of the first (now good) step. It is a linear ground refutation of G_1, and it is one step shorter than the original refutation of G_0. This suggests an inductive argument; we can prove by induction on n that every linear refutation of length n can be arranged to obey left-to-right order. The base case $n = 0$ is trivial, because the 0-step derivation of $\# :-$ from itself is already an SLD–refutation. For the step case, we first bring the right resolution step to the top of the tree by using a number of our moves, then apply the induction hypothesis to all but the first step of the tree. This gives an SLD–refutation of G_1, and putting back the first step gives an SLD–refutation of G. Finally, this result extends to general resolution through the lifting lemma.

As we shall see later, SLD–resolution can be implemented in an especially efficient way using a stack to hold the literals in the current goal. At each resolution step, we pop a literal from the stack, match it with the head of a program clause by unification, and if this is successful, push instances of the literals in the body of the clause. This is the method used by Prolog.

Although this method can be implemented efficiently, and every goal has an SLD–refutation if it has any refutation at all, the search for a refutation can sometimes be much more difficult with SLD–resolution than if the literals are taken in a more 'intelligent' order. For example, consider using the clause

$grandparent(A, C) :- parent(A, B), parent(B, C).$

to solve the goal $\# :- grandparent(X, fred)$. Expanding the *grandparent* literal gives

$\# :- parent(A, B), parent(B, fred).$

A strictly left-to-right strategy would continue by solving the leftmost literal *parent*(A, B). Effectively, the strategy would be to enumerate all pairs (A, B) where A is a parent of B, and check each of them to see if B is a parent of *fred*. This is much less effective than the alternative strategy of solving the literal *parent*(B, *fred*) first (it can have at most two solutions), then looking for solutions of *parent*(A, B) once the value of B is known. The left-to-right strategy fails because it leads us to solve a literal that contains no information that is specific to the goal being solved.

For this goal, it would be better to write the definition of *grandparent* in the logically equivalent form

$$grandparent(A, C) :- parent(B, C), parent(A, B).$$

since the left-to-right order would then choose the correct literal to solve first. But of course, that would not be any good if the goal were

$$\# :- grandparent(mary, X).$$

In the absence of an intelligent selection strategy, Prolog programmers sometimes need to write several versions of a definitions, each working well with a particular pattern of known and unknown arguments. Often, however, the variety of patterns that actually occurs in the execution of a program is not very great, and a single ordering of literals will work for all of them.

7.3   Search trees

We have shown that it is sufficient to use linear derivations, and to adopt the Prolog strategy of working from left to right. The only remaining choice we have in constructing a refutation for a goal is which clause to use in each step. The possible choices can be shown as a *search tree*, in which the original goal is shown at the root, and the children of each node are the goals that can be derived from it by using various clauses in a single step of SLD–resolution.

As an example, Figure 7.5 shows the search tree for the goal

$$\# :- append(A, B, 1:2:nil).$$

with the usual two clauses for *append*. Each arc is labelled with the clause and matching substitution that is used. Thus either of the clauses may be used on the original goal. The clause (app.1) leads to an immediate solution, with $A = nil$ and $B = 1:2:nil$, and the clause (app.2) has a matching substitution with $A = 1:A_1$ and leads to the new goal $\# :- append(A_1, B, 1:nil)$. The new goal generated by using (app.2) can itself be resolved with either clause, leading to the solutions $A = 1:nil$, $B = 2:nil$ and, after another step, $A = 1:2:nil$, $B = nil$.

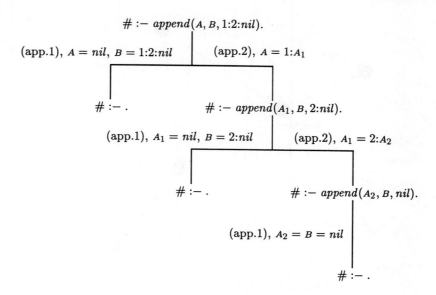

Figure 7.5: *Search tree for an append goal*

In this search tree, all the branches are finite and end in the empty goal. More typical search trees have branches that end in failure, that is, a goal that is not empty but matches no program clause. They may also have infinite branches that correspond to infinite sequences of resolution steps that never lead to failure or success.

Here is a program whose search tree has branches that end in failure, and also infinite branches that can be followed forever. It describes the problem of making a journey on a small airline serving European capitals (see Figure 7.6 for a map).

flight(*london, paris*) :− .
flight(*london, dublin*) :− .
flight(*paris, berlin*) :− .
flight(*paris, rome*) :− .
flight(*berlin, london*) :− .

journey(A, A) :− .
journey(A, C) :− *flight*(A, B), *journey*(B, C).

The first few clauses define a relation *flight*(A, B) that is true if there is a direct flight from A to B with seats available. The last two clauses define a relation *journey*(A, B) that is true if it is possible to make a journey of zero or more flights from A to B. One possible journey begins and ends at A without taking

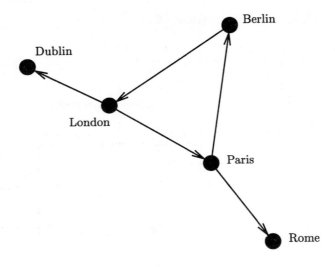

Figure 7.6: *Map of airline flights*

any flights. Other journeys begin with a flight from A to another city B, and continue with a further journey from B to the final destination C. Figure 7.7 shows the search tree when this program is used to execute the goal

> # :– *journey(london, rome).*

To save space, the city names are represented by their initial letters, *d*, *l*, *r*, etc. The diagram shows three finite branches and an infinite branch.

The leftmost branch (1) ends in failure. It corresponds to a decision to fly first from London to Dublin. Since there are no available flights out of Dublin, this leads to immediate failure. The next branch (2) ends in success, and corresponds to flying from London to Paris, then from Paris to Rome. Next to it is a failure branch (3) that represents an attempt to fly from London to Rome via Paris, then continue on a circular tour that ends in Rome. Since Rome (like Dublin) is a dead end, the branch ends in failure. Finally, branch (4) represents a decision to fly round the circuit London–Paris–Berlin–London. After doing this, we are left with the same problem we started with, namely the goal

> # :– *journey(london, rome).*

The search tree below this point is a copy of the entire search tree, which is therefore infinite. The whole search tree contains an infinite number of success nodes, each representing a sequence of flights that goes round the circuit

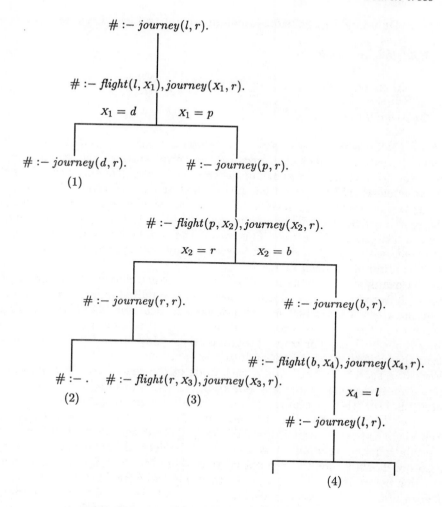

Figure 7.7: *Search tree for* $\# :- flight(london, rome)$.

a different number of times before finally ending in Rome. It also contains an infinite branch that corresponds to flying round the circuit forever.

What will happen in practice when we try to solve a goal that has an infinite search tree? The answer depends on the *search strategy* that is used to explore the tree. Prolog's search strategy is *depth-first*. It chooses one child of the root node, and explores that child and all its descendants before considering any of its other children. In other words, the search is a pre-order traversal of the search tree. In Prolog, the order of visiting the children of a node corresponds to the order in which clauses appear in the program. Thus, in the example, a flight from

London to Dublin will be considered before a flight to Paris, because the clause

> *flight*(*london, dublin*) :− .

appears earlier in the program than the clause

> *flight*(*london, paris*) :− .

As we shall see in the last part of this book, depth-first search can be implemented easily and efficiently, because the entire state of the search can be represented by a single active path in the tree. However, depth-first search spoils the completeness of SLD–resolution. If the search tree contains an infinite branch, then depth-first search will never reach any node that comes after that branch in the search order. That is, any node that would be to the right of the infinite branch in a diagram of the tree. This means that a search tree may contain one or more success nodes, but depth-first search may not find them because it gets stuck on an infinite branch first.

In the example, the existence of an infinite branch does not prevent depth-first search from finding the solutions, because the infinite branch is the rightmost one in the tree. This is just a fortunate coincidence, and a different order for the clauses in the *flight* relation would prevent the Prolog search strategy from finding any solutions. For some, programs, there may be no fixed order for the clauses that allows depth-first search to find solutions.

We call a search strategy *fair* if each node in the search tree is visited eventually, even if the search tree has infinite branches. An example of a fair search strategy is breadth-first search, which visits all the nodes on each level of the tree before beginning to visit the nodes on the next level. Thus breadth-first search visits the original goal, then all the goals that can be derived from it by one resolution step, then all the goals that can be derived in two resolution steps, and so on. For any node in the search tree, there are only finitely many nodes that come before it in this ordering, so the node will eventually be visited.

Depth-first search is not fair, because nodes that are to the right of an infinite branch are never visited, no matter how long the search continues. One solution to this problem is to abandon depth-first search in favour of a fair search strategy such as breadth-first search. Another solution, more practical for Prolog programmers, is to rewrite the program so that its search space no longer contains infinite branches. We shall look at techniques for doing this for graph-searching programs in Chapter 9.

7.4   Answer substitutions

So far, our proof methods have been rather unsatisfying as ways of executing logic programs, because they have enabled us to say whether a goal can be solved, but have not given any information about what values for the variables lead to a solution. This information is implicitly present in the unifying substitutions that are computed as part of resolution, and we now look at ways of extracting the information from a refutation as an 'answer substitution', as Prolog does when it displays the answer to a goal.

DEFINITION

Let T be a program and $G = (\# :- P_1, \ldots, P_n)$ be a goal. An *answer substitution* for G with respect to T is a substitution s such that $T \models P_i[s]$ for each i.   □

The idea is that composing all the unifiers along the spine of an SLD–refutation will give us an answer substitution. Actually, this 'extracted' substitution is not quite what we want, because it may involve variables that were not in the original goal, but were introduced from a program clause. So we define also the substitution that is 'computed' by a refutation, in which these extra variables have been removed.

DEFINITION

The substitution s *extracted* from a derivation tree D for a program T is defined as follows:

- If $D = leaf(C[w])$, where C is a program clause and w is a renaming, then $s = w$.
- If $D = fork(C, D_1, D_2)$, then $s = s_1 \triangleright r$, where s_1 is the substitution extracted from D_1 and r is the unifying substitution of the resolution step which derived C.

The substitution *computed* by a refutation D of a goal G is the substitution $s \upharpoonright vars(G)$, where s is the substitution extracted from D.   □

In this definition, the notation $s \upharpoonright A$ stands for the *restriction* of a substitution s to a set of variables A. It is defined by

$$(s \upharpoonright A)(x) = \begin{cases} s(x), & \text{if } x \in A \\ x, & \text{otherwise} \end{cases}$$

Thus $s \upharpoonright A$ is the substitution that agrees with s on variables in the set A, and leaves other variables unchanged. The substitution extracted from a refutation D is thus the composition of all the unifiers along the leftmost branch of D, restricted to the set of variables that actually appear in the goal G at its top. Given these definitions, two questions naturally arise:

- Are the substitutions computed by refutations of a goal G correct answer substitutions for G?

- Can every correct answer substitution for G be obtained as the substitution computed by a refutation of G?

These questions correspond closely to the concepts of soundness and completeness of inference rules. The first question is answered positively by the following theorem:

THEOREM [Answer correctness of resolution]
Let D be a refutation of $T \cup \{G\}$, and let r be the substitution computed by D. Then r is an answer substitution for G with respect to T.

Proof: We shall show by induction that the substitution s extracted from D is an answer substitution for G. Since r agrees with s on the variables that actually occur in G, the theorem follows from this. For simplicity, we assume that the top node of the SLD–refutation D is $leaf(G)$ (with no renaming).

We argue by induction on the length of D. If D has length zero, then it consists of the single node $leaf(\# :-)$ and G is the empty goal $\# :-$. For this goal, any substitution is (vacuously) an answer substitution. If D has non-zero length, suppose that the result holds for all shorter SLD–refutations. Consider the first resolution step in D, and suppose it combines the goal

$$G = (\# :- P_1, \ldots, P_n)$$

with the clause

$$C = (P :- Q_1, \ldots, Q_m)$$

by matching P and P_1 with unifier r. The outcome of this step is the goal

$$G' = (\# :- Q_1, \ldots, Q_m, P_2, \ldots, P_n)[r].$$

The remainder of the refutation D is an SLD–refutation of G' one step shorter than D, so we may assume that the substitution s' extracted from it is an answer substitution for G'. The substitution extracted from D itself is $s = r \triangleright s'$.

Now let M be a model of T, and let g be any ground substitution. We are assuming that s' is an answer substitution for G'. Thus

$$\models_M Q_j[r][s'][g] \text{ for all } j, \ 1 \le j \le m,$$

and so

$$\models_M Q_j[s][g] \text{ for all } j, \ 1 \le j \le m.$$

Because $\models_M C$, and so by substitution $\models_M C[s]$, it follows that $\models_M P[s][g]$, or equivalently that $\models_M P_1[s][g]$. Also, $\models_M P_i[s][g]$ for $2 \le i \le n$. Since M and g

are arbitrary, we may conclude that $T \models P_i[s]$ for each i. Hence s is an answer substitution for G. ☐

So the answers computed by refutations are correct. Now for the other question: Can all correct answers be obtained in this way? The answer is a qualified 'yes'. If s is an answer substitution for G, then there is a refutation of G that computes an answer substitution r such that $s = r \triangleright k$ for some k. If r is an answer substitution, so is $r \triangleright k$ for any k, so this is acceptable.

THEOREM [Answer completeness of resolution]
Let s be an answer substitution for a goal G with respect to a program T. Then there is an SLD-refutation D of $T \cup \{G\}$ such that the substitution r computed by D satisfies $s = r \triangleright k$ for some substitution k.

Proof: Let $vars(G) = \{V_1, \ldots, V_n\}$, and let the alphabet of T and G be L. Invent n new constant symbols $a_1, \ldots, a_n$ not in L. Let m be the substitution $\{V_1 \leftarrow a_1, \ldots, V_n \leftarrow a_n\}$, and consider the ground goal $G[s \triangleright m]$ over the extended alphabet $L \cup \{a_1, \ldots, a_n\}$.

Let $G = (\# :- P_1, \ldots, P_n)$. Because s is an answer substitution for G, it follows that $\models_M P_i[s]$ and so $\models_M P_i[s \triangleright m]$ for each i and each model M of T, and so $T \cup \{G[s \triangleright m]\} \models \#$. Hence by refutation completeness, there is an SLD–refutation D_0 of $G[s \triangleright m]$. Because $G[s \triangleright m]$ is a ground goal, D_0 computes the identity substitution. The only places that the new constants a_i appear in the refutation are along the spine, because these constants do not appear in any clause of the program T. So we can replace them by the original variables V_i to obtain an SLD–refutation D of $G[s]$ that also computes the identity substitution.

The refutation D begins with $G[s]$, an instance of G. Now apply the lifting lemma to obtain an SLD–refutation D' of G that has the same length as D. In fact, the refutation D' constructed in the proof of the lifting lemma computes a substitution r' such that $s \triangleright r = r' \triangleright k$, where r is the substitution computed by D (actually $r = I$) and k is another substitution. This fact can be proved by induction on the length of D. We conclude that $s = r' \triangleright k$ as required. ☐

Summary

- Any derivation from a program can be put into linear form, in which one of the inputs to each resolution step is a clause taken from the program.
- A refutation that is in linear form can be rearranged so that subgoals are solved in left-to-right order.
- From any refutation, we can extract a substitution that answers the goal. The substitutions that can be obtained in this way correspond exactly with the correct answers to the goal.

Exercises

7.1   Reduce the derivation of $reverse(X_1{:}X_2{:}nil, X_2{:}X_1{:}nil)$ given in Chapter 6 to the form of a derivation by SLD–resolution.

7.2   Define a relation $palin(A)$ that is true of the list A is a palindrome, that is, if it reads the same backwards as forwards. For example, $1{:}2{:}3{:}2{:}1{:}nil$ is a palindrome, but $1{:}2{:}3{:}2{:}nil$ is not. Show the sequence of goals that are derived in a successful execution of the goal $\# :- \ palin(1{:}X{:}Y{:}Z{:}nil)$. What answer substitution is computed?

Chapter 8

Negation as failure

So far, we have treated in our theory only logic programs that are composed entirely of Horn clauses, and have disallowed the use of the connective **not**. In Chapter 2, we saw that negation was useful in expressing the operation of relational difference, and – unlike the 'or' connective involved in relational union – it cannot be avoided by rewriting the program. We therefore need to extend our theory to cover negation, and we shall do so using the technique of *negation as failure*. The idea is that, at least for some formulas P, if we attempt to prove P and fail to do so, it is reasonable to deduce that **not** P is true.

In the next section, we apply this idea to the situation where goals may contain uses of **not**, although the logic program itself contains only pure Horn clauses. Section 8.2 extends this to allow **not** to be used in the bodies of program clauses also. Finally, Section 8.3 explains how our semantic theory can be extended to cover negation.

8.1 Negation in goals

The goal $\# :- member(5, 1{:}2{:}3{:}4{:}nil)$ asks whether 5 is a member of the list $1{:}2{:}3{:}4{:}nil$. Prolog executes this goal by comparing 5 with each number in the list and, finding that it is different from each of them, gives the answer 'no'. This suggests a method for executing goals that involves negation, such as $\# :- \mathbf{not}\, member(5, 1{:}2{:}3{:}4{:}nil)$: delete the **not** and execute the plain goal that results. If Prolog answers 'no' for the plain goal, give the answer 'yes' for the negated goal, and if Prolog answers 'yes' for the plain goal, give the answer 'no' for the negated goal. This method also gives the correct answer for a goal like $\# :- \mathbf{not}\, member(2, 1{:}2{:}3{:}4{:}nil)$ that ought to fail. Prolog finds that 2 *is* a member of $1{:}2{:}3{:}4{:}nil$, so it gives the answer 'yes' to the plain goal $\# :- member(2, 1{:}2{:}3{:}4{:}nil)$. Our method then tells us to answer 'no' to the negated goal.

This method is called *negation as failure*. It relies on the completeness of the resolution method used to execute goals. If the goal has an answer, then we know that resolution will find it. Consequently, when resolution fails to find an answer, we may deduce that there is none, and thus that the literal in the goal is false in the least model M_0 of the program. Thus negation as failure interprets **not** with respect to the least model, and relies on the closed world assumption, that the literals that are true in the intended use of the program are exactly the ones that are true in its least model, and thus may be derived from it by resolution.

Negation as failure works properly only for ground literals. If execution of a non-ground goal $\# :- P$ succeeds, we may conclude only that *some* ground instance of P is true in the least model M_0, and not that *every* ground instance is true; thus it would not be valid to conclude that every ground instance of **not** P is false, and doing so can lead to wrong answers. For example, consider the goal

$$\# :- \textbf{not } member(x, 1{:}2{:}3{:}4{:}nil), x = 5. \tag{$*$}$$

We expect this goal to have the answer $x = 5$, because 5 is not a member of the list $1{:}2{:}3{:}4{:}nil$. But if negation as failure is used to execute this goal, together with Prolog's left-to-right strategy, then the following is what happens: the subgoal **not** $member(x, 1{:}2{:}3{:}4{:}nil)$ is the first to be executed. Negation by failure requires that we execute the goal $\# :- member(x, 1{:}2{:}3{:}4{:}nil)$ in its place and reverse the result. Now this goal has several solutions, including $x = 1$, so the goal succeeds, and we make the negated literal fail. Consequently, the whole goal $(*)$ fails, although we expected it to succeed.

We could try executing the goal

$$\# :- x = 5, \textbf{not } member(x, 1{:}2{:}3{:}4{:}nil).$$

instead. This time, it is the subgoal $x = 5$ that is executed first. It succeeds, setting x to 5 and leaving the new goal

$$\# :- \textbf{not } member(5, 1{:}2{:}3{:}4{:}nil).$$

As we have seen, this goal succeeds under negation as failure, and the final result is the correct answer $x = 5$. In Prolog, it is the programmer's responsibility to ensure that any negated literal has become a ground literal before it is selected for execution. As the program is written, the literal may contain variables, but these variables must have been given ground values by the rest of the program before the literal is reached in the usual left-to-right execution order.

Because they must become ground before they begin to be executed, negated literals can never contribute anything to the answer substitution of a program, but can only be used to test values found elsewhere. This places a restriction on the use of negated literals in programs, but it is one that is satisfied when negation is used to compute the difference of two relations as in the database queries of Chapter 2. For example, the following goal asks for programs that are used by Mike, but not by Anna on the same machine:

$$\# :- uses(mike, PROGRAM, MACHINE),$$
$$\textbf{not } uses(anna, PROGRAM, MACHINE).$$

If this goal is executed in left-to-right order, then a successful attempt to solve the first subgoal *uses(mike, . . .)* results in specific values for the variables *PROGRAM* and *MACHINE*, and the function of the subgoal **not** *uses(anna, . . .)* is to apply a further test to these known values.

8.2 Negation in programs

So far we have restricted negation to goals that are ground literals, but it is also useful to write program clauses that have negated literals in their bodies. In database queries, this allows us to define views using relational difference, and then use these views in formulating further views and queries.

As another example of negation inside program clauses, here is a program that defines the relation *subset(A, B)* that holds between known lists *A* and *B* if every member of *A* is also a member of *B*:

$$subset(A, B) :- \textbf{not } nonsubset(A, B).$$

$$nonsubset(A, B) :- member(X, A), \textbf{not } member(X, B).$$

The relation *nonsubset(A, B)* holds if *A* is *not* a subset of *B*. This is so exactly if there is a member *X* of *A* that is not a member of *B*. The relation *subset(A, B)* holds exactly if the relation *nonsubset(A, B)* does not hold.

This program can be used to check that one list is a subset of another, and it does so by checking the members one by one. For example, consider the goal

$$\# :- subset(2{:}4{:}nil, 1{:}2{:}3{:}4{:}nil). \tag{1}$$

We first expand the *subset* literal to obtain

$$\# :- \textbf{not } nonsubset(2{:}4{:}nil, 1{:}2{:}3{:}4{:}nil). \tag{2}$$

Now we use negation as failure, and try instead to solve the goal

$$\# :- nonsubset(2{:}4{:}nil, 1{:}2{:}3{:}4{:}nil). \tag{3}$$

which is immediately expanded into

$$\# :- member(X, 2{:}4{:}nil), \textbf{not } member(X, 1{:}2{:}3{:}4{:}nil). \tag{4}$$

The execution continues by solving the first subgoal $member(X, 2{:}4{:}nil)$ to give the solution $X = 2$. We next try to solve the goal

$$\# :- \textbf{not}\ member(2, 1{:}2{:}3{:}4{:}nil). \tag{5}$$

As we saw in the preceding section, this goal fails, and this means that $X = 2$ is not a solution of (4). We try again with the other solution to the subgoal $member(X, 2{:}4{:}nil)$, that is, $X = 4$. This leads to the goal

$$\# :- \textbf{not}\ member(4, 1{:}2{:}3{:}4{:}nil). \tag{6}$$

which also fails. This exhausts the members of $2{:}4{:}nil$, so the goal (4) fails, and so does (3). So by negation as failure, (2) succeeds, and so does the original goal (1). Thus negation as failure executed the goal (1) by checking that each member of the list $1{:}2{:}nil$ is also a member of $1{:}2{:}3{:}4{:}nil$.

For the execution of a subgoal **not** P to work properly, it is necessary that P should have become a ground literal before negation as failure is applied to it, for the same reason that negation as failure could only be used for ground literals in goals. In the *subset* example, if lists A and B are known, then solving the subgoal $member(X, A)$ makes X known, and the negated subgoal **not** $member(X, B)$ is then ground, so negation as failure can be used. If either of the lists A or B were not completely known, however, the negated subgoal would not become ground, and negation as failure could not soundly be used.

It is worth comparing the program for *subset* with an alternative definition that uses recursion instead:

$subset(nil, B) :- .$

$subset(X{:}A, B) :- member(X, B), subset(A, B).$

Unlike the program that uses negation, this program *can* be used to generate subsets of a given set, and unlike the other program, this one depends on the fact that sets are represented by lists. The program with negation depends only on the existence of a *member* relation defined on sets, and it would continue to work without change if sets were represented by (say) binary trees instead of lists, provided a suitable *member* relation were defined.

8.3   Semantics of negation

The semantics of programs that include negation poses a problem. Unlike programs without negation, they do not necessarily have least models in the sense of Section 5.3. Consider, for example, the program that contains the single clause

$$p :- \textbf{not}\ q. \tag{*}$$

Here p and q are relation symbols with no arguments. This has a model in which p is true and q is false, and also a model where p is false and q is true. Neither of these models is smaller than the other, and their 'intersection' – in which both p and q are false – is not a model.

One solution to this problem is to consider only *stratified* programs, where the relations can be separated into layers, with relations in higher layers being defined in terms of the ones in lower layers. Mutual recursion is allowed among the relations in any layer, but any use of negation must refer to a relation in a lower layer than the one being defined. For example, the program for *subset* is stratified: *member* is in the lowest layer, *nonsubset* (which uses **not** *member*) in a layer above it, and *subset* (which uses **not** *nonsubset*) in a third layer.

A stratified program has a *natural* model that is built up as follows: the first layer contains no negation at all, so we take the least model of that. Now we treat relations from the first layer and their negation as fixed, and take the least model of the second layer that is consistent with them. In this way we can take least models of each successive layer, and finally build a model for the whole program.

For example, the single clause (∗) is a stratified program with two layers. In the lower layer is the relation q (for which there are no clauses). In the natural model, q is false. In the upper layer is p, which is defined in terms of the negation of q. It is true in the natural model, because **not** q is true. An example of a program that is not stratified is the single clause

$$p :\!- \textbf{not}\, p. \tag{∗∗}$$

This fails to be stratified because the clause defines p in terms of **not** p, and that cannot possibly refer to a lower level than the one containing p. Interestingly enough, this program only has one model, the one in which p is true.

Summary

- Negation as failure is a way of adding negation to Horn clause programs.
- It works for negated ground literals, and treats them with respect to the least model of the program.
- The meaning of a program that contains negated literals in its clauses can be explained by dividing the program into layers.

Exercises

8.1 A route-finding program for American cities uses a list like

north:*east*:*west*:*north*:*nil*

to represent a path that goes North for one block, then East for a block, then West for a block, and finally North again. This path can be optimized to *north:north:nil*, because the instructions to go East and then immediately West again can be deleted without affecting the feasibility of the path or its starting and finishing points.

a. Define a relation *optstep(A, B)* that holds if path *B* is the result of deleting from path *A* a successive pair of moves in opposite directions.

b. Use negation as failure to define a relation *optimize(A, B)* that holds if path *B* can be obtained from path *A* by repeated application of *optstep*, but cannot be further optimized in this way. Your program should correctly answer questions like

$$\# :- optimize(north\!:\!east\!:\!west\!:\!north\!:\!nil, B).$$

where the first argument is a ground term.

c. Write another definition of *optimize(A, B)* by direct recursion on *A*. Compare the efficiency of this definition with your answer to part (b).

Chapter 9

Searching problems

In Chapter 7, we used the problem of planning a sequence of airline flights to illustrate the concept of search trees. In this chapter, we take a closer look at this problem and, more generally, the problem of finding paths in a directed graph.

Like a map of the airline network, a directed graph consists of a collection of places or *nodes* and some connections or *arcs* from one node to another. We call the graph *directed* because these arcs have a direction, and there can be an arc from A to B without there being an arc from B to A.

In searching problems, we are interested in exploring the nodes that can be reached from a specified starting node by following the arcs. The graph may have physical locations as its nodes and physical connections as its arcs, or it may be more abstract. An example is the famous 'water jugs' problem. We are given two jugs, one that holds seven litres of water and another that holds five litres. We are allowed to fill the jugs from a tap, empty them into the sink, or pour water from one jug to another, and we are required to measure out four litres of water. We can represent this problem as searching a graph in which the nodes are labelled by the amount of water in each jug, and the arcs show the possible moves. For example, there is an arc from the node $(5, 2)$ to the node $(3, 5)$ that corresponds to pouring water from the larger jug to the smaller one until the smaller jug is full. The problem is to find a path in the graph from the starting node $(0, 0)$ to the node $(4, 0)$ in which the large jug contains four litres of water.

These problems all concern the *transitive closure* of a directed graph, a new graph that shares the same nodes as the original graph, but has an arc from A to B exactly is there is a *path* from A to B in the original graph. Another way of describing the transitive closure is to say it is the smallest graph (in the sense that it has fewest arcs) that contains all the arcs of the original graph, but is also transitive in the sense that whenever there is an arc from A to B and an arc from B to C, there is also an arc from A to C. A useful variation on this theme is the *reflexive–transitive closure* of a graph, which also has an arc from each node A to itself.

9.1   Representing the problem

In logic programming, we can represent a directed graph by a relation $arc(A, B)$ that holds if there is an arc on the graph from A to B. In simple examples, we could define this relation by explicitly listing all the arcs, but in more complicated situations, the *arc* relation might be defined by a program. Logic programming allows us to use the same graph-searching program, however the *arc* relation is defined.

In terms of *arc*, we can define another relation $connected(A, B)$ that represents the reflexive–transitive closure. One way to do this makes explicit the fact that $connected(A, B)$ holds if there is a path in the graph from A to B. In the following program, a path of n arcs is represented by a list of $n + 1$ nodes, with each node connected to the next by an arc:

$connected(A, B) :- ispath(P), first(P, A), last(P, B).$

$ispath(A{:}nil) :- .$
$ispath(A{:}B{:}P) :- arc(A, B), ispath(B{:}P).$

$first(A{:}P, A) :- .$

$last(A{:}nil, A) :- .$
$last(A{:}P, B) :- last(P, B).$

The program becomes shorter and more efficient if we combine the three conditions on P that are specified in the definition of *connected* into one relation $path(A, B, P)$, defining it directly by recursion:

$connected(A, B) :- path(A, B, P).$

$path(A, A, A{:}nil) :- .$
$path(A, C, A{:}B{:}P) :- arc(A, B), path(B, C, B{:}P).$

The *path* relation is often useful in itself, because it can not only determine whether A and B are connected, but also return an explicit path between them. If the path is not required, we can simplify the program still further, like this:

$connected(A, A) :- .$
$connected(A, C) :- arc(A, B), connected(B, C).$

These three ways of defining the *connected* relation are equivalent. This can be shown using the program transformation methods that are the subject of Chapter 13.

An alternative way to define the *connected* relation is by writing directly the fact that it is a reflexive and transitive relation containing *arc*:

> *connected*(A, C) :— *connected*(A, B), *connected*(B, C).
> *connected*(A, B) :— *arc*(A, B).
> *connected*(A, A).

As a Prolog program, this definition is much less effective than the definitions above. Consider what happens if we try to solve a goal such as

> # :— *connected*(*start*, *finish*).

in which *start* and *finish* are constants. Assuming there is no direct arc from *start* to *finish*, we must use the first clause to expand the goal into

> # :— *connected*(*start*, B_1), *connected*(B_1, *finish*).

This can be expanded by using the first clause again, generating

> # :— *connected*(*start*, B_2), *connected*(B_2, B_1), *connected*(B_1, *finish*).

Obviously, this expansion process could go on forever, leading to an infinite branch in the search tree. By way of contrast, our earlier definitions of *connected* always generate an *arc* subgoal as the first one to be solved after each expansion step. This means that, at least for finite graphs without cycles, the expansion process must eventually terminate.

Although this definition is not useful as a Prolog program, it gives us an opportunity to be precise about what is meant by defining the reflexive–transitive closure as the 'smallest' relation with certain properties. As the program demonstrates, the properties in question can be expressed as a Horn-clause program, and the results of Section 5.3 guarantee that this program has a smallest model. In this model, *connected* is interpreted as the smallest reflexive and transitive relation that contains the given *arc* relation.

We can also check that the two definitions of reflexive–transitive closure are equivalent. Let r_1 be the relation that holds between two nodes if there is a path from one to the other, that is, r_1 is the relation defined by our first series of programs for *connected*. It is easy to see that r_1 is reflexive (because A:*nil* is a path from A to A) and transitive (because a path from A to B can be joined with a path from B to C to make a path from A to C), and that it contains the *arc* relation. But the relation r_2 defined by the new program is the smallest relation that is reflexive and transitive and contains *arc*. So r_1 contains r_2.

Conversely, if r_2 is the relation defined by the new program, then it satisfies the clauses of our original program. The clause

> *connected*(A, A) :— .

is true of r_2 because this is one of the clauses defining r_2, and the clause

$$connected(A, C) :- arc(A, B), connected(B, C).$$

is true of r_2 because it includes *arc* and is transitive. Thus r_2 is one of the relations that satisfy the clauses of our original program, so it contains r_1, the smallest such relation.

9.2   Avoiding cycles

The first series of programs in the preceding section work reasonably well for searching finite graphs that have no cycles, that is, where there is never any non-trivial path from a node to itself. Such graphs result in search trees that are finite. If the graph has cycles, however, these programs behave badly, because the cycles in the graph lead to infinite branches in the search tree, and Prolog's depth-first strategy can lead it to get stuck exploring an infinite branch. We saw an example of this in Section 7.3.

There are two solutions to this problem with depth-first search. One is to abandon Prolog in favour of an implementation of logic programming that has a fair search strategy, such as breadth-first search. This solution sounds drastic, but it can be made feasible by using Prolog as a vehicle for implementing fair searching. Prolog systems often include non-logical features that make this easier, but we look at a simple way of doing it in the next section.

Another way of avoiding the problems of depth-first search is to rewrite our programs so that the search tree no longer contains infinite branches. For graph searching, we can use the technique of *loop avoidance*. We replace the relation *connected*(A, B) with a new relation *conn1*(A, B, S), for S a list of nodes, that holds if A is connected to B by a path that does not visit any member of S at an intermediate point. In writing a recursive definition of this relation, we can add each node visited to the list S of nodes to avoid later in the search. This ensures that no cyclic paths are considered. Here is the program:

$$conn1(A, A, S) :- .$$

$$conn1(A, C, S) :-$$
$$arc(A, B),$$
$$\textbf{not } member(B, S),$$
$$conn1(B, C, B{:}S).$$

The *connected* relation can now be defined like this:

$$connected(A, B) :- conn1(A, B, B{:}nil).$$

It is easy to extend this program to compute a path from A to B instead of just finding whether on exists.

With this modified program, the search tree for a finite graph is finite, even if the graph has cycles. This is because the number of nodes in the list s increases by one in each successive level of the search tree, until s contains every reachable node in the graph. For example, in the airline flight problem shown in Figure 7.6, the beginning goal would be

> $\# :- conn1\,(london, rome, london{:}nil).$

Taking the flight from London to Paris leads to the new goal

> $\# :- conn1\,(paris, rome, paris{:}london{:}nil).$

There are now two possibilities. Taking the flight from Paris to Rome leads to the new goal

> $\# :- conn1\,(rome, rome, rome{:}paris{:}london{:}nil).$

that is solved immediately. Taking the flight from Paris to Berlin leads to the goal

> $\# :- conn1\,(berlin, rome, berlin{:}paris{:}london{:}nil).$

The important point is that it is not now possible to take the flight from Berlin to London, because London is on the list of places that have already been visited. Thus Berlin becomes a dead end in the search tree, and the whole search tree is made finite.

This technique of loop avoidance can also be used to solve the 'water jugs' problem. We can represent a state of the system in which the large jug contains X litres and the small jug contains Y litres by the term $state(X, Y)$. The arc relation can be defined using the built-in arithmetic relations of picoProlog. Here is one clause that says it is possible to pour water from the large jug into the small one until the small jug is full:

> $arc(state(X, Y), state(U, 5)) :-$
> $\quad plus(X, Y, Z), plus(U, 5, Z).$

The two $plus$ literals in the body of this clause state that the total amount of water Z must be the same before and after the transfer. PicoProlog allows only non-negative integers, so the final amount U in the large jug cannot be negative. Other clauses for arc model the filling of the jugs from the tap and their emptying into the drain, and other kinds of transfer from one jug to the other.

9.3   Bounded and breadth-first search

Another method for removing infinite branches from the search tree is to place a bound on the number of arcs to be traversed. The effect is to cut off the search tree below a certain depth. Here is the definition of a relation $conn2(A, B, N)$, for N a natural number, that holds if there is a path from A to B of at most N arcs:

$$conn2(A, A, N) :- .$$

$$
\begin{aligned}
conn2(A, C, N) :&- \\
&plus(N_1, 1, N), \\
&arc(A, B), \\
&conn2(B, C, N_1).
\end{aligned}
$$

Again, this program can easily be extended to return a path instead of just finding whether one exists.

To use this program, we have to choose a suitable value for N. If the graph being searched has a known *diameter*, that is, a known upper bound on the shortest path length from one node to another, then that provides a reasonable value for N. Otherwise, we can use a technique called *iterative deepening*. This means trying first a small value of N. If this does not work, we try successively larger values until we find one that does give a solution. It is possible to write an outer Prolog program that calls the searching program iteratively, and stops when a solution is found.

An attraction of iterative deepening is that it can be used with any combinatorial search problem, not just graph searching. Any Horn clause program can be modified to place a bound on the number of resolution steps. If the bound is exceeded in executing a goal, the goal is made to fail. The idea is to replace each relation $r(X_1, \ldots, X_k)$ with a new relation $r1(X_1, \ldots, X_k, B_0, B)$ that holds if the corresponding instance of r holds, and it is solved in at most B_0 resolution steps, and B is the difference between B_0 and the number of resolution steps actually used.

If the original program contains the clause

$$r(X, Z) :- q(X, Y), r(Y, Z).$$

then the modified program will contain the following clause:

$$
\begin{aligned}
r1(X, Z, B_0, B) :& - \\
&plus(B_1, 1, B_0),\, q1(X, Y, B_1, B_2),\, r1(Y, Z, B_2, B).
\end{aligned}
$$

We first count one resolution step for using the clause, and pass to the $q1$ subgoal the number of steps remaining. It returns the number of steps left after it has been solved, and we pass these to the recursive $r1$ subgoal for its use. Finally, *r1* returns the number of steps still unused, and these are passed back to the original caller of *r1*.

By making this modification systematically to every clause in the program, we obtain a version of the program that performs bounded search. An outer wrapper can turn this into a program that searches by iterative deepening.

The method of breadth-first search can be simulated inside a Prolog program if we change slightly the way the graph is represented. In place of the relation $arc(A, B)$, we use a relation $next(A, S)$ that holds if S is the list of immediate neighbours of A, that is, a list that contains in some order all the nodes B such that $arc(A, B)$. Pure logic programming allows us to define the *arc* relation in terms of the *next* relation like this:

$$arc(A, B) :- next(A, S), member(B, S).$$

However, we cannot define *next* in terms of *arc* directly, although many Prolog systems provide a built-in relation *listof* that makes it possible:

$$next(A, S) :- listof(B, arc(A, B), S).$$

The *listof* relation cannot, unfortunately, be defined by a logic program.

In terms of *next*, we can define a relation $reach(S, B)$, for S a list of nodes, that holds if B can be reached from any node in the list S:

$$reach(B{:}S, B) :- .$$

$$reach(A{:}S, B) :-$$
$$\quad next(A, T),$$
$$\quad append(S, T, U),$$
$$\quad reach(U, B).$$

Given a value for A, there is only one solution to the subgoal $next(A, T)$, so there is almost no branching in the search tree for this program. Instead, the program maintains an explicit list of the nodes that are adjacent to nodes that it has visited, and visits them one by one, adding their neighbours to the list.

The search is in breadth-first order, because the neighbours of each node are added to the *back* of the list of nodes to visit, so all the neighbours of the starting node will be visited before the nodes that are neighbours of these nodes in turn. Replacing the *append* literal with $append(T, S, U)$ would reverse this order, making the algorithm perform depth-first search instead, visiting the children of each node before its siblings.

Summary

- Searching a graph is an instance of the problem of computing the transitive closure of a relation. Depth-first search performs badly if the graph has cycles.
- Other search strategies, such as loop-avoidance, breadth-first search and bounded search, perform better for such problems.
- These search strategies can be simulated in Prolog by modifying the program appropriately.

Exercises

9.1   Augment the loop-avoidance algorithm so that each arc can have a name, and the relation $arc(N, A, B)$ holds if N is the name of an arc from A to B. Redefine the *conn* relation so that it assembles a list of arcs in the path by name. Complete the definition of the *arc* relation for the 'water jugs' problem, adding a name for each move. What is the shortest method for measuring four litres of water, ending in the state $state(4, 0)$?

9.2   Write a logic program to solve the following puzzle: A farmer must ferry a wolf, a goat and a cabbage across a river using a boat that is too small to take more than one of the three across at once. If he leaves the wolf and the goat together, the wolf will eat the goat, and if he leaves the goat with the cabbage, the goat will eat the cabbage. How can he get all three across the river safely?

9.3   Arithmetic expressions can be represented by terms that use the function symbols $add/2$, $subtract/2$, $multiply/2$ and $divide/2$, so that the expression $(4 + 4 * 4)/4$ would be represented by the term

$$divide(add(4, times(4, 4)), 4).$$

Define a relation $trial(E)$ that holds if E represents a well-formed arithmetic expression in which the operands are four copies of the digit 4. How many such expressions are there? [Hint: such expressions have a bounded depth and a bounded number of operators.]

9.4   The puzzle called 'Towers of Hanoi' consists of three spikes, on which five perforated discs of varying diameters can be placed. The rules state that no disc may ever be placed on top of a smaller disc. The discs are initially all on the first spike, and the goal is to move the discs one at a time so that they all end up (in decreasing order of size) on the third spike. Formulate this puzzle as a graph-searching problem. Calculate the number of states that the system can occupy, and suggest a search method that will lead to a solution in a reasonable time.

Chapter 10

Parsing

Parsing is the problem of determining whether a given string conforms to the syntax rules of a language. It is an good application for logic programming, because the rules of a language can be expressed as clauses in a logic program, and (at least in principle) parsing a string amounts to solving a goal with that logic program.

10.1 Arithmetic expressions

As an example, we shall use the following set of rules for the syntax of arithmetic expressions in the variables x and y:

$$expr ::= term \mid term \text{ '+' } expr \mid term \text{ '-' } expr$$
$$term ::= factor \mid factor \text{ '*' } term \mid factor \text{ '/' } term$$
$$factor ::= \text{'x'} \mid \text{'y'} \mid \text{'(' } expr \text{ ')'}$$

The first rule says that an expression ($expr$) may be either a term, or a term followed by a plus sign and another expression, or a term followed by a minus sign and another expression. Thus an expression is a sequence of terms separated by plus and minus signs. Similarly, a $term$ is a sequence of factors separated by multiplication and division signs. A $factor$ is either a variable ('x' or 'y'), or an expression in parentheses.

The simplest way to translate these rules into a logic program is to make each syntactic class such as $expr$ or $term$ correspond to a one-argument relation, arranging that $expr(A)$ is true if and only if the string (list of characters) A forms a valid member of the class $expr$, and so on. Because one form of expression is simply a term, we can write down the clause

$$expr(A) :- term(A).$$

$expr(A) :- term(A).$
$expr(A) :-$
    $append(B, C, A), term(B),$
    $append(\text{``+''}, E, C), expr(E).$
$expr(A) :-$
    $append(B, C, A), term(B),$
    $append(\text{``-''}, E, C), expr(E).$

$term(A) :- factor(A).$
$term(A) :-$
    $append(B, C, A), factor(B),$
    $append(\text{``*''}, E, C), term(C).$
$term(A) :-$
    $append(B, C, A), factor(B),$
    $append(\text{``/''}, E, C), term(C).$

$factor(\text{``x''}) :- .$
$factor(\text{``y''}) :- .$
$factor(A) :-$
    $append(\text{``(''}, B, A), append(C, \text{``)''}, B), expr(C).$

Figure 10.1: *First program for parsing expressions*

Another possibility for an expression is a term followed by a plus sign and another expression. This can be expressed using the *append* relation:

$expr(A) :-$
    $append(B, C, A), term(B),$
    $append(D, E, C), D = \text{``+''}, expr(E).$

To be a valid expression of this kind, a string A must split into two parts B and C, where B is a valid term, and C consists of a plus sign followed by another expression. This last condition is expressed using another instance of *append*. Fixed symbols like '+' and 'x' can be translated by constant strings. A useful notation uses double quotes for strings, so that "+" means '+':*nil* and "mike" means 'm':'i':'k':'e':*nil*. Using this notation, we can translate the whole set of rules to give the logic program shown in Figure 10.1.

This translation is correct in a logical sense, but it is very inefficient when run as a program. For example, to parse the string "x*y+x", we must use the second clause for *expr*, splitting the string into a part "x*y" that satisfies *term*, and a part "+x" that is a plus sign followed by an *expr*. The Prolog strategy uses backtracking to achieve this, splitting the input string at each possible place until it finds a split that allows the rest of the clause to succeed. This means testing each of the strings " ", "x", "x*" with the relation *term*, before finally succeeding with "x*y". Testing the subgoal *term*("x*y") leads to even more backtracking, so the whole process is extremely time-consuming.

10.2 Difference lists

An equivalent but more effective translation uses a technique called *difference lists* to eliminate the calls to *append* and drastically cut down the amount of backtracking. The idea is to define a new relation *expr2*(A, B) that is true if the string A can be split into two parts: the first part is a valid expression, and the second part is the string B. This relation could be defined by the single clause

$$expr2(A, B) :- append(C, B, A), expr(C).$$

But we can do better than this by defining *expr2* directly, without using *append* or *expr*. For example, the second clause for *expr* leads to this clause for *expr2*:

$$expr2(A, D) :- term2(A, B), eat('+', B, C), expr2(C, D).$$

Here we have used a relation *term2* that is related to *term* as *expr2* is related to *expr*, and a special relation *eat*. The whole clause can be read like this: to chop off an expression from the front of A, first chop off a term to give a string B, then chop off a plus sign from B to give a string C, and finally chop of an expression from C to give the remainder D. The technique is called 'difference lists' because the pair (A, D) represents a list of characters that is the difference between A and D. The relation *eat* is defined by the single clause

$$eat(X, A, B) :- A = X:B.$$

It is true if the string B results from chopping off the single character X from the front of A.

Other rules can be re-formulated in a similar way. For example, the rule

$$factor ::= '(' \; expr \; ')'$$

can be re-formulated as

$$factor2(A, D) :- eat('(', A, B), expr2(B, C), eat(')', C, D).$$

Figure 10.2 shows the complete set of rules translated in this style. In order to test a string such as "(x+y)-x" for conformance to the syntax rules, we formulate the query

$$\# :- expr2("x*y+x", "").$$

$expr2(A, B) :- term2(A, B).$
$expr2(A, D) :- term2(A, B), eat(`+`, B, C), expr2(C, D).$
$expr2(A, D) :- term2(A, B), eat(`-`, B, C), expr2(C, D).$

$term2(A, B) :- factor2(A, B).$
$term2(A, D) :- factor2(A, B), eat(`*`, B, C), term2(C, D).$
$term2(A, D) :- factor2(A, B), eat(`/`, B, C), term2(C, D).$

$factor2(A, B) :- eat(`x`, A, B).$
$factor2(A, B) :- eat(`y`, A, B).$
$factor2(A, D) :- eat(`(`, A, B), expr2(B, C), eat(`)`, C, D).$

Figure 10.2: *Second program for parsing expressions*

This asks whether it is possible to chop off an expression from the front of "x∗y+x" and leave the empty string; in other words, whether "x∗y+x" is itself a valid expression. Solving this goal involves backtracking among the different rules, but much less than before.

10.3   Expression trees

In applications such as compilers, it is useful to build a tree that represents the structure of the input program. In our example of arithmetic expressions, we might represent the expression "x∗y+x" by the term

$$add(multiply(vbl(x), vbl(y)), vbl(x)).$$

Representing the expression like this makes it easy to evaluate it for given values of x and y, or to translate it into machine code in a compiler.

We can extend our parser so that it can build a tree like this, in addition to checking that a string obeys the language rules. We extend the relation $expr2(A, B)$ into a new relation $expr3(T, A, B)$ that is true if the difference between string A and string B is an expression represented by T. One clause in the definition of $expr3$ is this:

$$expr3(add(T_1, T_2), A, D) :-$$
$$term3(T_1, A, B), eat(`+`, B, C), expr3(T_2, C, D).$$

As before, this says that an expression may have the form *term* '+' *expr*. The added information is that if the term on the left of '+' is represented by the tree T_1, and the expression on the right is represented by T_2, then the whole expression is represented by the tree $add(T_1, T_2)$.

Other clauses in the parser can be augmented in similar ways. One clause allows an expression in parentheses to be used as a factor; it turns into the new clause

$$factor3(T, A, D) :-$$
$$eat('(', A, B), expr3(T, B, C), eat(')', C, D).$$

The tree for the whole factor is the same as the tree for the expression inside. In this way, we can be sure that parentheses have no effect on the 'meaning' of an expression, except insofar as they affect the grouping of operators.

Once the whole parser has been augmented in this way, we can use it to analyse strings and build the corresponding tree. For example, the goal

$$\# :- expr3(T, \text{``x*(y+x)''}, \text{``''}).$$

will succeed, with the answer

$$T = multiply(vbl(x), add(vbl(y), vbl(x))).$$

Rather unusually, the parser can also be used 'backwards', producing a string from a tree. For example, the goal

$$\# :- expr3(add(vbl(x), multiply(vbl(x), vbl(y))), A,).$$

has several answers, and the first one found by Prolog is $A = \text{``x+x*y''}$. The other answers have extra parentheses added around various sub-expressions. This 'unparsing' function might be useful for generating error messages in a compiler, or for saving expression trees in a text file so they could be parsed again later.

The parser for expressions has an unfortunate flaw. The expression "x-y-x" would be assigned the tree

$$subtract(vbl(x), subtract(vbl(y), vbl(x))),$$

that is, the same tree as would be assigned to the expression "x-(y-x)". This is wrong, because the usual convention is that operators 'associate to the left', so the correct tree would be

$$subtract(subtract(vbl(x), vbl(y)), vbl(x)),$$

the same as for the expression "(x-y)-x". The problem is with the syntax rule

$$expr ::= term \text{ '-' } expr,$$

and others like it. This rule suggests that where several terms appear interspersed with minus signs, the most important operator is the leftmost one. The other minus signs must be counted as part of the *expr* in this rule, not part of the *term*, because a term cannot contain a minus sign except between parentheses.

We could correct the syntax rules by replacing this rule with

$$expr ::= expr \text{ '}-\text{' } term,$$

but unfortunately this would lead to the clause

$$expr(A, D) :- expr(A, B), eat(\text{'}-\text{'}, B, C), term(C, D).$$

This clause behaves very badly under Prolog's left-to-right strategy, because a call to *expr* leads immediately to another call to *expr* that contains less information. For example, the goal $expr(\text{"x-y"}, \text{""})$ immediately leads to the subgoal $expr(\text{"x-y"}, B)$, and so to an infinite loop. This is called *left recursion*, because the body of the rule for *expr* begins with a recursive call. Left recursion causes problems for top–down parsing methods like the one that naturally results from Prolog's goal-directed search strategy.

The solution to this problem is to rewrite the grammar, avoiding left recursion. The following syntax rules are equivalent to our original ones, in that they accept the same set of strings:

$$expr ::= term \; exprtail$$
$$exprtail ::= empty \mid \text{'}+\text{' } term \; exprtail \mid \text{'}-\text{' } term \; exprtail$$
$$term ::= factor \; termtail$$
$$termtail ::= empty \mid \text{'}*\text{' } factor \; termtail \mid \text{'}/\text{' } factor \; termtail$$
$$factor ::= \text{'x'} \mid \text{'y'} \mid \text{'('} expr \text{')'}$$

The idea here is that an *exprtail* is a sequence of terms, each preceded by a plus or minus sign. In order to build the tree for an expression, we translate the rules for *exprtail* into a four-argument relation $exprtail(T_1, T, A, B)$ that is true if the difference between A and B is a valid instance of *exprtail*, and T is the result of building the terms onto the tree T. By building on the terms in the right way, we obtain the correct tree for each expression. The complete translation of the new set of rules is shown in Figure 10.3.

10.4   Grammar rules in Prolog

The technique of building parsers by direct translation of syntax rules is so useful that many Prolog systems implement a special notation for it. In this notation, the clause

$$expr(add(T_1, T_2), A, D) :-$$
$$term(T_1, A, B), eat(\text{'}+\text{'}, B, C), expr(T_2, C, D).$$

$expr(T, A, C) :- term(T_1, A, B), exprtail(T_1, T, B, C).$

$exprtail(T_1, T_1, A, A) :- .$
$exprtail(T_1, T, A, D) :-$
    $eat('+', A, B), term(T_2, B, C),$
    $exprtail(add(T_1, T_2), T, C, D).$
$exprtail(T_1, T, A, D) :-$
    $eat('-', A, B), term(T_2, B, C),$
    $exprtail(subtract(T_1, T_2), T, C, D).$

$term(T, A, C) :-$
    $factor(T_1, A, B), termtail(T_1, T, B, C).$

$termtail(T_1, T_1, A, A) :- .$
$termtail(T_1, T, A, D) :-$
    $eat('*', A, B), factor(T_2, B, C),$
    $termtail(multiply(T_1, T_2), T, C, D).$
$termtail(T_1, T, A, D) :-$
    $eat('/', A, B), factor(T_2, B, C),$
    $termtail(divide(T_1, T_2), T, C, D).$

$factor(vbl(x), A, B) :- eat('x', A, B).$
$factor(vbl(y), A, B) :- eat('y', A, B).$
$factor(T, A, D) :-$
    $eat('(', A, B), expr(T, B, C), eat(')', C, D).$

Figure 10.3: *Final program for parsing expressions*

is written as

$$expr(add(T1, T2)) \rightarrow term(T1), ['+'], expr(T2).$$

An arrow replaces the usual ':−' sign, and means that the literals in the head and body of the clause are translated specially. Each ordinary literal in the clause has two implicit arguments for their input and output strings. Actual symbols are written in square brackets, and translate into calls to *eat*.

Many Prolog systems allow *grammar rules* like this to be included in any program, and perform the translation as the program is loaded into the Prolog system.

Summary

- Syntax rules can be represented directly as logic programs.
- The technique of difference lists makes them work well as Prolog programs for parsing.
- Parsers written in this way can also build a representation of expressions as trees.
- Many Prolog systems provide special notation for building parsers.

Exercises

10.1   Use the technique of difference lists to write a definition of the relation *flatten* (from Chapter 3) that does not use *append*.

10.2   The parser for expressions in the text does not allow spaces to appear in expressions, so that "x*y+x" is recognized as a valid expression, but "x * y + x" is not. Define a relation $space(A_0, A)$ that is true if the difference between A_0 and A consists of zero or more spaces, and use this relation to write a new parser for expressions that ignores spaces before each symbol.

10.3   Define a relation $number(N, A, B)$ that holds if the difference between A and B is a non-empty sequence of decimal digits, and the integer N is the integer value of this number. Use this relation to extend the parser for expressions to allow integer constants in addition to the existing forms of expressions.

10.4   A *good* sequence consists either of the single number 0, or of the number 1 followed by two other good sequences: thus 1:0:1:0:0:*nil* is a good sequence, but 1:1:0:0:*nil* is not. Define a relation $good(A)$ that is true if A is a good sequence. Modify your program if necessary so that the Prolog goal # :− $good(A)$ will enumerate all good sequences in order of increasing length.

Chapter 11

Evaluating and simplifying expressions

In the preceding chapter, we saw that algebraic expressions can be represented by tree-structured terms, and defined parsing relations that link the textual form of an expression with its representation as a tree. This representation of expressions as trees is an important technique in building compilers, where algorithms for checking language rules and generating object code are much more readily expressed in terms of the tree than in terms of the textual form of an expression.

This chapter introduces some of the techniques that are used to build compilers and other programs that manipulate symbolic expressions, by showing logic programs that evaluate or simplify algebraic expressions represented as trees.

11.1   Evaluating expressions

Simple arithmetic expressions are made up of operators like addition and multiplication, together with integer constants. We can represent the operators by function symbols *add* and *multiply*, and the constants directly by integers, so that the expression $3 * 4 + 5$ would be represented by the term $add(times(3, 4), 5)$.

PicoProlog provides a built-in relation $integer(X)$ that is true if X is a (positive) integer, and built-in relations $plus(X, Y, Z)$ and $times(X, Y, Z)$ that are true if Z is the result of adding or multiplying the integers X and Y. These relations allow us to define recursively a relation $value(E, V)$ that is true if V is the value of expression E:

$value(X, X) :- integer(X).$

$value(add(E_1, E_2), V) :-$
  $value(E_1, V_1), value(E_2, V_2),$
  $plus(V_1, V_2, V).$

$$value(multiply(E_1, E_2), V) :-$$
$$value(E_1, V_1), value(E_2, V_2),$$
$$times(V_1, V_2, V).$$

The value of an expression that is an integer constant is that constant itself, and the value of an expression such as $add(E_1, E_2)$ can be found by taking the values of the sub-expressions E_1 and E_2 separately, then adding them together. We could put this program together with a parser built along the lines suggested in Chapter 10 to define a relation $calculator(S, V)$ that holds if V is the value of the string S considered as an arithmetic expression:

$$calculator(S, V) :- expr(E, S,), value(E, V).$$

For example, the goal $\# :- calculator(``(3+4)*5", X)$ would give the answer $X = 35$. Our relation for evaluating expressions does not need to deal explicitly with expressions that contain parentheses, because these are handled by the parser. The tree it builds for an expression reflects the grouping that is implied by parentheses, and the evaluation is done according to this grouping structure.

The next step in sophistication is to allow expressions that contain variables as well as constants. For example, the expression $x + 3 * y$, which we can represent by the term $add(vbl(x), multiply(3, vbl(y)))$. The variables in this expression are represented by terms like $vbl(x)$. Notice that, from picoProlog's point of view, this term is a *constant* that consists of the function symbol vbl applied to the atomic constant x. The term $vbl(x)$ represents a completely known expression, whereas $vbl(X)$ is an unknown expression that might be either the expression $vbl(x)$ or the expression $vbl(y)$.

To evaluate an expression that contains variables, we need to know what value to give to each variable when it appears in the expression. This information can be represented by a list of terms $val(X, V)$ where X is a variable name like x or y, and V is an integer, its value. For example, the list

$$val(x, 3):val(y, 4):nil$$

represents the state of affairs in which x has value 3 and y has value 4. We call such a list an *assignment*.

Here is the definition of a relation $lookup(X, A, V)$, for A an assignment, that holds if A gives the value V to variable X:

$$lookup(X, A, V) :- member(val(X, V), A).$$

This definition uses the *member* relation from Chapter 3 in a clever way, because typically the variable X in the term $val(X, V)$ will be known when the *member* literal comes to be solved, but the value V will not be known. The effect is that *val*(X, V) will be matched with successive elements of the list A until an element is found that has X as its first component, and the value of V is then the corresponding second component. We could also define *lookup* by direct recursion like this:

$$lookup(X, val(X, V){:}A, V) :- \,.$$
$$lookup(X, val(Y, W){:}A, V) :- lookup(X, A, V).$$

This *lookup* relation gives us the vital ingredient needed to extend the *value* relation defined earlier, giving a relation *eval*(E, A, V) that holds if V is the value of expression E under assignment A:

$$eval(X, A, X) :- integer(X).$$
$$eval(vbl(X), A, V) :- lookup(X, A, V).$$

$$eval(add(E_1, E_2), A, V) :-$$
$$value(E_1, A, V_1), value(E_2, A, V_2), plus(V_1, V_2, V).$$

$$eval(multiply(E_1, E_2), A, V) :-$$
$$value(E_1, A, V_1), value(E_2, A, V_2), times(V_1, V_2, V).$$

The rules for addition and multiplication are as before, except that the assignment A supplied for the whole expression is passed on to the recursive calls of *eval* that deal with the operands. The real change is the clause that deals with variables, whose values are found by using *lookup* and the assignment A.

11.2 Simplifying expressions

Using terms to represent algebraic expressions makes it easy to write programs that manipulate expressions symbolically. The aim in this section will be to explore this idea by defining a relation *simplify*(E_1, E_2) that holds for expressions E_1 and E_2 if E_1 can be simplified algebraically to give E_2. Such a relation might be used in a compiler to optimize expressions, reducing the number of arithmetic operations needed to evaluate them. It can also be used to carry out a simple kind of algebraic proof, because we can prove that two expressions are equal by simplifying both of them and checking that the results are the same.

In the domain of Boolean expressions, we say that an expression is a tautology if it has value 1 or *true* whatever Boolean values are given to the variables it contains. One way of checking that an expression is a tautology is to evaluate it for every combination of values, checking that the answer is 1 each time. Another way is to simplify the expression algebraically and check that the result is the logical constant 1. The practical exercise at the end of this chapter asks you to implement both these methods.

Simplifying an expression involves some specific information about the operators that may be present in the expression. For example, we might use the fact that adding 0 to an expression or multiplying it by 1 leaves the value of the expression unchanged. We can express this information by clauses like the following:

> $simp(add(E, 0), E) :- .$
> $simp(multiply(E, 1), E) :- .$
> $simp(add(0, E), E) :- .$
> $simp(multiply(1, E), E) :- .$

These clauses form part of the definition of a relation $simp(E_1, E_2)$ that holds if E_1 can be simplified in one step to give E_2. Later, we shall use $simp$ to define our desired relation *simplify*, taking into account at that stage the possibility that simplifying an expression will take several steps, with each step leading to the next.

We might also use the fact that multiplication distributes over addition, i.e., that $a * (b + c) = a * b + a * c$, by adding the following clause to $simp$:

> $simp(multiply(A, add(B, C)),$
> $\quad add(multiply(A, B), multiply(B, C))) :- .$

Such a simplification step might be useful in proving algebraic identities, but in a compiler we might choose to use the equation the other way, thereby reducing the number of multiplications needed to evaluate the expression.

These specific rules for $simp$ contain some of the information we need about the algebraic properties of the operators, but they are not very useful on their own. For example, one of the rules will allow us to simplify $x * 1$ – represented by the term $multiply(vbl(x), 1)$ – to obtain the result x, but it will not allow us to simplify the expression $x * 1 + y$, which is represented by the term

> $add(multiply(vbl(x), 1), 0).$

This happens because the left-hand side of our simplification rule appears not as the whole expression to be simplified, but only as a sub-expression, and our rules so far work only on whole expressions.

This problem is solved by adding rules that show how to simplify expressions by simplifying their sub-expressions.

> $simp(add(A, B), add(A_1, B)) :- simp(A, A_1).$
> $simp(add(A, B), add(A, B_1)) :- simp(B, B_1).$
> $simp(multiply(A, B), multiply(A_1, B)) :- simp(A, A_1).$
> $simp(multiply(A, B), multiply(A, B_1)) :- simp(B, B_1).$

The first clause here says that if we can simplify the expression A, then we can also simplify the expression $add(A, B)$ – we simply replace A by its simplified form and leave B unchanged. The second clause says that we can simplify the same expression by replacing B instead of A with a simplified form, and the third and fourth clauses say the same things for an expression $multiply(A, B)$.

If both A and B can be simplified, say to A_1 and B_1 respectively, then the expression $add(A, B)$ can undergo two stages of simplification, giving first $add(A_1, B)$ then $add(A_1, B_1)$. Thus it is not necessary to allow explicitly for simplifying the expression $add(A, B)$ on both sides at once, provided we provide the more general facility of simplifying an expression in several steps. This facility is useful in other contexts. For example, the expression $(x + 1) * y$ can be simplified first to $x * y + 1 * y$ using the fact that multiplication distributes over addition, then in another step to $x * y + y$, using the fact that 1 is a unit element for multiplication.

We can provide this kind of multi-step simplification by using the reflexive–transitive closure of the *simp* relation, rather than *simp* itself. The relation we define should be reflexive, because the original expression may not allow any simplification, and it should be transitive, because several steps may be needed to put an expression into its simplest form. Using simply the reflexive–transitive closure of *simp* would give a relation that holds between any expression and all its simplified forms, whether they are fully simplified or still subject to further simplification. We can define a more useful relation by restricting the simplified expression to be *irreducible*, so that no more simplification is possible. Negation as failure is useful for this:

$simplify(X, Y) :- simp(X, X1), simplify(X1, Y).$
$simplify(X, X) :-$ **not** $reducible(X).$

$reducible(X) :- simp(X, Y).$

A special relation *reducible* has been introduced here: $reducible(X)$ holds if there is any Y such that $simp(X, Y)$ is true. The requirement that negated literals should be ground is satisfied in the program, because the variable Y is hidden inside the definition of *reducible*.

Summary

- Algebraic expressions can be represented as trees.
- The value of an algebraic expression can be obtained by analysing the expression recursively, calculating the value of the expression in terms of the values of its sub-expressions.
- Algebraic expressions can be simplified by applying equations as left-to-right rewriting rules.

Exercises

11.1   Using the picoProlog built-in relations *plus*, *times* and *integer*, extend the definition of the relation *value*(E, V) to allow operators *subtract*(X, Y) and *divide*(X, Y) for subtraction and division without fractional or negative results. Combine this with your answer to a previous exercise to show how the numbers from 0 to 9 can each be written using exactly four copies of the digit 4.

11.2   The value of an expression **let** $X = E_1$ **in** E_2 under an assignment A is the same as the value of E_2 under an assignment where X takes the value that E_1 is given under A, so that the expression **let** $y = x + 1$ **in** $y * y$ has value $4 * 4 = 16$ under an assignment that gives x the value 3. Define a relation *update*(A, X, V, B) that holds if B is an assignment that agrees with A except that it gives X the value V. Representing **let**-expressions by terms of the form $let(X, E_1, E_2)$, extend the *eval* relation of Section 11.1 to handle them.

Practical exercise

Boolean expressions containing operators like $\wedge$, $\vee$, $\neg$ and $\Rightarrow$ can be represented by tree structures, just like arithmetic expressions. For example, the expression $p \vee (q \wedge \neg p)$ could be represented by the term

$$or(vbl(p), and(vbl(q), neg(vbl(p)))).$$

(*neg* is used here as the name for $\neg$ to avoid confusion with picoProlog's built-in **not**.)

Write a program that checks whether a given Boolean expression is a tautology. Part of this program should be a relation *eval*(E, A, V) that holds if the Boolean expression E has truth-value V (either 0 or 1) when its variables take the values given by pairs *val*(X, U) in the list A. You will also need:

- a relation *variables*(E, B) that holds if B is the list of variables that appear in expression E, with duplicates removed. Example:

$$variables(or(vbl(p), and(vbl(q), neg(vbl(p)))), p{:}q{:}nil)$$

- a relation *assign*(B, A) that holds if A is a list of assignments for the variables in the list B, each chosen from the values 0 and 1. Examples:

$$assign(p{:}q{:}nil, val(p, 0){:}val(q, 0){:}nil)$$
$$assign(p{:}q{:}nil, val(p, 0){:}val(q, 1){:}nil)$$
$$assign(p{:}q{:}nil, val(p, 1){:}val(q, 0){:}nil)$$
$$assign(p{:}q{:}nil, val(p, 1){:}val(q, 1){:}nil)$$

These three relations *eval*, *variables* and *assign* then allow us to build a tautology-checker as follows:

$tautology(E) :-$ **not** $falsifiable(E).$

$falsifiable(E, B) :- variables(E, B), assign(B, A), eval(E, A, 0).$

That is, a formula is a tautology if it is not falsifiable, and a formula is falsifiable if there is a way of assigning values to the variables that occur in it that makes the formula have the value 0. An optional extension to this part of the exercise would be to build a parser for Boolean expressions, using the methods of Chapter 10, and integrate it with the tautology checker.

Another possibility is to build a program that simplifies Boolean expressions using algebraic rules. Some of the rules that could be included are that 1 is a unit element for $\land$ and a zero element for $\lor$, and vice versa:

$$P \lor 0 = P = 0 \lor P$$
$$P \lor 1 = 1 = 1 \lor P$$
$$P \land 0 = 0 = 0 \land P$$
$$P \land 1 = P = 1 \land P$$

Other useful rules are that $\land$ distributes over $\lor$, and $\lor$ distributes over $\land$:

$$P \land (Q \lor R) = (P \land Q) \lor (P \land R)$$
$$P \lor (Q \land R) = (P \lor Q) \land (P \lor R)$$

You could also add de Morgan's laws, and the equation $\neg\neg P = P$, but adding the fact that $\lor$ and $\land$ are commutative results in disaster (Why?).

Lengthy sequences of simplifications will cause picoProlog to run out of memory, because the program requires too much information to be saved in case backtracking is needed. The following definition of the *simplify* relation is equivalent to the one in the text, except that it produces only one simplified form of an expression, and it does not consume more and more storage space if simplifying an expression takes many steps:

$simplify(X, Y) :- onestep(X, X1, F), simplify1(F, X1, Y).$

$onestep(X, Y, yes) :- simp(X, Y), !.$
$onestep(X, X, no) :- .$

$simplify1(yes, X, Y) :- simplify(X, Y).$
$simplify1(no, X, X) :- .$

Some programming tricks have been used to make this program more efficient. These tricks depend on Prolog's cut operation (!), which is explained in Section 14.3.

- The cut operation reduces the amount of potential backtracking in the program, on the assumption that we are only interested in finding one simplified form of a given expression, and not all possible simplified forms. This means that picoProlog does not need to store information that is used in backtracking.
- Adding the cut makes it possible to delete the test that the final expression is irreducible, because the control behaviour of the program ensures that simplification steps will be taken for as long as they are possible.
- Most importantly, the program has been rearranged so that the main relation *simplify* is recognized as being 'tail recursive'. This makes it possible for picoProlog to treat the recursive definition of *simplify* as if it were a loop, saving the stack space that would be needed to execute a truly recursive relation.

The efficient program is less easy to understand than the original one, but this does not matter much, because we can keep the original program as a specification for what the optimized program should do, and the optimization affects only one small part of the whole program for simplifying expressions: all the specific knowledge about algebra is contained in the relation *simp*, and that is unaffected by this optimization.

Chapter 12

Hardware simulation

This chapter shows how logic programming can be used to build simple simulations of CMOS logic circuits. These circuits are built from two types of transistors: *p–transistors* and *n–transistors* (see Figure 12.1). Each transistor has three wires called the *source*, the *gate* and the *drain*. In the simple model of transistor behaviour that we shall use, a *p*–transistor acts as a switch that connects the source and drain together if the gate is connected to the ground rail (which represents logic 0). If the gate is connected to the power rail (representing logic 1), then the source and drain are not connected together. With an *n*–transistor, the roles of logic 0 and logic 1 are reversed, and it is when the gate is connected to the power rail that the transistor connects its source and drain together.

This model of CMOS logic ignores the fact that transistors are really analogue devices that can respond to voltages intermediate between the two supply rails. It also ignores dynamic effects that depend on timing and the storage of charge, modelling only the *stable states* of a circuit. All these simplifications mean that the simulations we shall build are not very accurate. The most we can hope for is that combinational circuits that do not work in our simulation are guaranteed not to work in practice. This is better than nothing, because it allows us to use simulation as a way of testing circuit designs and finding at least some of the mistakes in them.

The simplest CMOS circuit is the inverter shown in Figure 12.2. This circuit contains two transistors, a *p*–type and an *n*–type. The *n*–transistor is arranged so that it connects the output z to logic 0 when it conducts, and it does so when its gate, connected to the input A, is a logic 1. The *p*–transistor has a symmetrical function, and connects z to logic 1 whenever the input A is at logic 0. Together, the two transistors ensure that the output is connected to the appropriate logic level whatever level is present at the input.

We can build a simulation of this circuit using logic programming. The first step is to build simulations of individual transistors. A *p*–transistor is simulated by defining a relation $ptran(S, G, D)$ that is true if there is a stable state of a

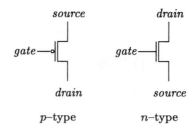

Figure 12.1: *p– and n–transistors*

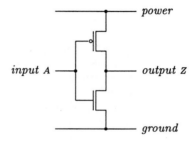

Figure 12.2: *CMOS inverter*

p–transistor in which the signals at the source, gate and drain are *S*, *G* and *D* respectively. There are two stable states for the *p*–transistor. In one state, the gate is connected to ground, so the transistor is conducting, and the source and drain have the same voltage. In the other state, the gate is connected to the power rail, so the transistor is not conducting, and the source and drain may have different voltages. These stable states are reflected in the following definition of *ptran*:

> $ptran(X, 0, X) :- .$
> $ptran(X, 1, Y) :- .$

In the first clause, the requirement that the source and drain have the same voltage is reflected by using the same variable *X* for both arguments. An *n*–transistor is modelled by the relation *ntran*(S, G, D), defined as follows:

> $ntran(X, 1, X) :- .$
> $ntran(X, 0, Y) :- .$

This simply reverses the roles of 0 and 1.

Apart from the wires, the only other components in the inverter circuit are the power and ground rails, and we can simulate them with two relations $pwr(X)$ and $gnd(X)$, defined like this:

$$pwr(1) :- \; .$$
$$gnd(0) :- \; .$$

Actually, we could manage without these relations and just substitute 0 and 1 wherever they are needed, but using these relations allows a more systematic way of connecting circuits together.

We are now ready to put the components together to make a simulation of the inverter circuit. The inverter has two external connections, so it is simulated by defining a relation *inverter* with two arguments, so that $inverter(A, Z)$ is true if there is a stable state of the circuit in which the input has voltage A and the output has voltage Z. A circuit is in a stable state if all its components are stable, and every wire carries the same voltage at all its connections. The *inverter* relation is defined as follows:

$$inverter(A, Z) :-$$
$$pwr(P), gnd(Q),$$
$$ptran(P, A, Z),$$
$$ntran(Z, A, Q).$$

The body of this clause contains one literal for each component, and variables are used instead of wires to join the components together. For example, point P of the circuit is connected to the power rail and to the source of the p–transistor, so P appears as the argument of the pwr literal and as the first argument of the $ptran$ literal. Internal connections are neatly hidden, because some of the variables that appear in the clause body do not appear as arguments of the clause head.

Having defined this relation, we can ask questions about the stable states of the circuit. For example, this goal asks what the output may be if the circuit is stable with input 1:

$$\# :- inverter(1, Z).$$

The only answer is $Z = 0$, because the n–transistor conducts, connecting the output to ground. We can also supply a value for the output and ask what values of the input would lead to a stable state:

$$\# :- inverter(A, 0).$$

The only answer is $A = 1$, because if A were zero, then the p–transistor would conduct, connecting the output to power.

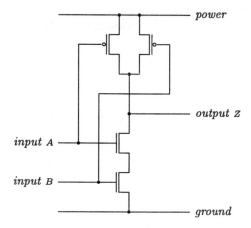

Figure 12.3: *NAND gate*

This bi-directional behaviour of the simulation is useful in some ways, because it extends the variety of questions we can ask about the circuit. In other ways it is a disadvantage, because it reveals that our model of CMOS circuits does not distinguish properly between inputs and outputs. If we make A the input and Z the output, the circuit of Figure 12.2 works correctly as an inverter, with the transistors driving the output to the opposite logic level to the input. But if we try to make A the output and Z the input, the circuit fails to work, because transistors cannot drive their gates. Our simulation does not reflect this fact.

Nevertheless, it is interesting to build simulations of more complex circuits. Figure 12.3 shows a NAND gate with two inputs A and B and one output Z. The output is logic 1 unless both inputs are at logic 1, in which case the output is logic 0. The circuit contains two p–transistors in parallel that are responsible for driving the output high when either one input or the other is low. The two n–transistors in series are responsible for driving the output low when both the inputs are high.

Here is a clause that simulates the NAND circuit:

$$nand(A, B, Z) :-$$
$$pwr(P), gnd(Q),$$
$$ptran(P, A, Z), ptran(P, B, Z),$$
$$ntran(Z, A, R), ntran(R, B, Q).$$

Like the inverter simulation, this definition of $nand(A, B, Z)$ can be used forwards to calculate the output Z from the inputs A and B, or backwards to to find what values of the inputs can lead to a given output.

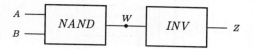

Figure 12.4: *AND gate*

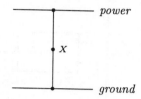

Figure 12.5: *Short circuit*

The next step in building simulations is to put together small circuits like our NAND gate and inverter to make larger circuits. For example, Figure 12.4 shows how a NAND gate and an inverter can be connected to make an AND gate, whose output is logic 1 exactly if both inputs are a logic 1. To build a simulation of the AND gate, we define $and(A, B, Z)$ in terms of the *nand* and *inverter* relations:

$and(A, B, Z) :-$
    $nand(A, B, W),$
    $inverter(W, Z).$

The *and* relation simulates our circuit by simulating the individual transistors that make it up, but we have constructed it by putting together larger building blocks.

What happens if we try to simulate a short circuit like the one shown in Figure 12.5? The simulation of this circuit is defined by

$short(X) :- pwr(X), gnd(X).$

With this definition, the goal $\# :- short(X)$ has no answers. This means that the circuit has no stable states, and current will always continue to flow. Our simple physical model of CMOS logic does not cover this situation. In reality, the current that flows may be so large that the circuit overheats.

A similar phenomenon occurs if we try to connect the output of an inverter back to its input, as shown in Figure 12.6. This circuit is simulated by the goal $\# :- inverter(X, X)$. Again, this goal has no solutions, indicating that the circuit

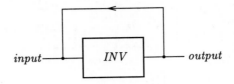

Figure 12.6: *Inverter with feedback*

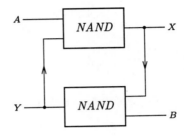

Figure 12.7: *A flip-flop*

has no stable states. In practice, the circuit will either oscillate, or it will enter a state in which both transistors of the inverter are partially conducting, and the output is at an unpredictable voltage intermediate between logic 0 and logic 1. Neither outcome is covered by our model.

Summary

- The stable states of a single transistor can be modelled by a logic program.
- Circuits that contain many transistors can be modelled by defining new relations in terms of the transistor relations, using variables to represent the wires.
- Simulations of complex circuits can be made by combining relations in a way that reflects the hierarchical structure of the circuit itself.

Exercises

12.1   Write a program that simulates the circuit shown in Figure 12.7, in which two NAND gates are connected in a ring. Determine the stable states of the circuit and explain why it can be used to build computer memory.

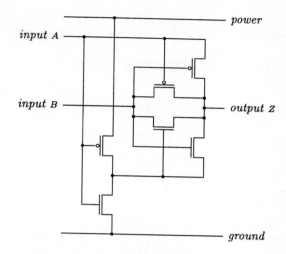

Figure 12.8: *An XOR gate*

12.2 Figure 12.8 shows a clever implementation of an XOR gate using only six transistors. (Both transistors in the parallel pair are needed because of electrical effects that are not captured in our simulations.) Build a logic program that simulates the circuit, and show that the output z is at logic 1 if exactly one of the inputs A and B are at logic 1.

Chapter 13

Program transformation

We have seen that only SLD–resolution is needed to execute logic programs, and that it involves only resolution steps in which one of the input clauses is a goal, and the other is a clause from the program. In this chapter, we look at an application for the more general kind of resolution in which both inputs may be proper clauses. The application is transforming a logic program to obtain another program with the same meaning. The hope is that, if the transformation is carried out with the right intuitions, then the new program will be more efficient than the old one.

Although pure logic cannot help us to estimate whether a transformed program is more efficient than the original one, it can guarantee that the transformed program gives the same answers. The reason for this is simple; if we derive each clause in the new program from the clauses of the original program, then any conclusion derived from the new program could also be derived from the original program by joining the derivations together.

13.1   Unfolding and symbolic execution

The simplest kind of transformation is to unfold a program, replacing a call to a relation by the body of a clause. The following three clauses define a relation $ord(A)$ that is true if A is an ordered list of numbers:

$$ord(nil) :- . \hspace{4cm} \text{(ord.1)}$$
$$ord(X{:}nil) :- . \hspace{3.6cm} \text{(ord.2)}$$
$$ord(X{:}Y{:}A) :- X < Y, ord(Y{:}A). \hspace{1.5cm} \text{(ord.3)}$$

The first two clauses deal with the special cases where A has zero or one elements, and the third deals with lists of two or more elements. Such a list is ordered if the first element is less than the second and the tail of the list is also ordered.

If this definition of *ord* were used in a program that often tested short lists to see if they were ordered, then it might be more efficient to treat lists of length 2 as a special case also. We can derive a clause that covers exactly this case by using resolution on the clauses in the definition. Taking clauses (ord.2) and (ord.3), we can match them up like this:

$$ord(X{:}Y{:}A) :- X < Y, ord(Y{:}\ A\ )$$
$$ord(U{:}nil) :-$$

The matching substitution is $\{A \leftarrow nil, U \leftarrow Y\}$, and the resolvent is the clause

$$ord(X{:}Y{:}nil) :- X < Y.$$

This is precisely the special case we wanted.

This kind of unfolding is similar to the transformation we can do to ordinary imperative programs by expanding subroutine calls in-line. The benefits and costs are the same, in that we save the cost of a subroutine call or resolution step at the expense of making the program larger. More radical transformations can be achieved by unfolding a program, rearranging the result, then folding again.

13.2 Fold–unfold transformation

Here is a definition of the relation $elem(A, N, X)$ that is true when the element of the list A at position N is X, counting from zero:

$$elem(X{:}A, 0, X) :- .\qquad\text{(elem.1)}$$
$$elem(X{:}A, s(N), Y) :- elem(A, N, Y).\qquad\text{(elem.2)}$$

In place of the built-in numbers of Prolog, this definition uses a number system in which zero is represented by the term 0, and $N+1$ is represented by the term $s(N)$ – so 3 would be represented by $s(s(s(0)))$. This number system would be very inefficient if we actually used it in a program, but it will make the transformation we are about to do more convenient. In terms of *elem*, we can define a relation $consec(X, Y, A)$ that is true if X and Y are consecutive elements of A:

$$consec(X, Y, A) :- elem(A, N, X), elem(A, s(N), Y).\qquad\text{(consec.1)}$$

Now the challenge is this: to design a version of *consec* that does not use *elem*. We can begin by resolving (consec.1) with a variant of (elem.1):

$$consec(X, Y, A) :- elem(\ A,\ N, X), elem(A, s(N), Y).$$
$$elem(Z{:}B, 0,\ Z) :-$$

This generates the resolvent

$$consec(X, Y, X{:}B) :- elem(Z{:}B, s(0), Y).$$

Two more resolution steps, one with (elem.2) and another with (elem.1) allow us to derive the clause

$$consec(X, Y, X{:}Y{:}C) :- .$$

This clause is one of the clauses in our desired definition of *consec*, covering the case that the first element selected is the very first element of the list.

Another clause can be obtained by resolving (consec.1) with (elem.2):

$$consec(X, Y, A) :- elem(\ A,\quad N,\quad X\ ), elem(A, N, s(X))$$
$$\overline{\quad elem(Z{:}B, s(M), W)\quad} :- elem(B, M, W)$$

The resolvent is

$$consec(X, Y, Z{:}B) :- elem(B, M, X), elem(Z{:}B, s(s(M)), Y).$$

Now we resolve again with (elem.2), this time choosing the second *elem* literal. The result is

$$consec(X, Y, Z{:}B) :- elem(B, M, X), elem(B, s(M), Y).$$

The body of this clause is just a variant of the body of (consec.1), so we make a final *folding* step, replacing the body with a call to *consec*:

$$consec(X, Y, Z{:}B) :- consec(X, Y, B).$$

We have now derived two clauses that together make up a new definition of *consec*:

$$consec(X, Y, X{:}Y{:}C) :- . \hspace{5cm} \text{(consec.2)}$$
$$consec(X, Y, Z{:}B) :- consec(X, Y, B). \hspace{3cm} \text{(consec.3)}$$

This new definition is more efficient than the old one, even ignoring the inefficiency caused by using terms to represent numbers. To find two consecutive elements of a list, the old definition would count the position of one element, then count again to find the other one, requiring two traversals of the list. The new definition finds both elements in a single traversal, saving about half the work.

The steps in deriving the new program from the old one have, with one exception, been steps of resolution between clauses drawn from the old program. The exception is the folding step, which uses the definition of *consec* backwards. Our definition of *consec* tells us that the clause

$$consec(X, Y, Z{:}B) :- elem(B, M, X), elem(B, s(M), Y).$$

follows from the clause

$$consec(X, Y, Z{:}B) :- consec(X, Y, B).$$

But we want to know the converse! Although there are models of the program in which the first of these clauses is true but the second is false, we are interested in the least model of the program, where the ground atoms that are true are exactly those that can be derived from the program. In this model, the folding step is justified, because we know that an atom $consec(X, Y, B)$ can be derived only by using the clause (consec.1).

Logically speaking, what we have done is this: if T_0 is the program containing (consec.1) together with the definition of *elem*, and T_1 is the program containing (consec.2) and (consec.3), we have shown that any ground atom P that can be derived from T_1 could also be derived from T_0. In short, we have shown that T_1 gives no answers that would not also be given by T_0. The new program is at least *partially* correct, in that all the answers it gives are correct.

We can check that the new program is *totally* correct, giving all the answers that could be given by the original program, by examining the search tree in the old program for the goal # :- $consec(X, Y, A)$, shown in Figure 13.1. At each node of the tree all matching clauses are shown, and we can check that every path has been covered by the clauses we have derived. So if any pair of elements X and Y can be shown to satisfy $consec(X, Y, A)$ using the old program, they can be shown to do so using the new program also.

13.3 Improving the *reverse* program

So far, our transformations have used only unfolding and folding, staying entirely within the logic of Horn clauses. More sophisticated transformations may need us to apply laws that cannot be expressed purely as Horn clauses.

The *reverse* program from Section 5.1 provides an example:

$$reverse(nil, nil) :- . \tag{rev.1}$$
$$reverse(X{:}A, C) :- reverse(A, B), append(B, X{:}nil, C). \tag{rev.2}$$

$$append(nil, B, B) :- . \tag{app.1}$$
$$append(X{:}A, B, X{:}C) :- append(A, B, C). \tag{app.2}$$

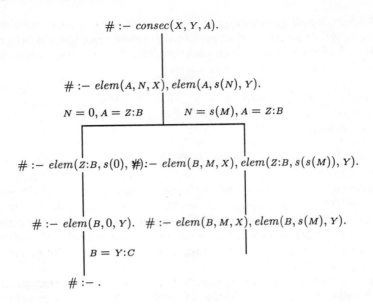

Figure 13.1: *Search tree for* # :− *consec*(X, Y, A).

Although it is a simple definition of *reverse*, this program is rather inefficient, because it repeatedly uses *append* to add elements to the end of the reversed list. This makes the running time of the program quadratic in the length of the input list. We can derive a more efficient program for *reverse* by transformation.

The first step is to introduce a new relation *revapp* that combines *reverse* and *append*, perhaps inspired by the body of clause (rev.2):

$$revapp(A, C, D) :- reverse(A, B), append(B, C, D).$$

We can now start to unfold. Resolving the definition of *revapp* with (rev.1) gives the new clause

$$revapp(nil, C, D) :- append(nil, C, D).$$

in which the matching substitution has filled in the first argument with the specific value *nil*. We can resolve this with (app.1) to obtain the clause

$$revapp(nil, C, C) :- .$$

that deals directly with the case that *revapp*'s first argument is *nil*.

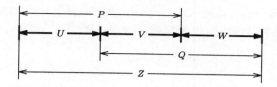

Figure 13.2: *Associativity of append*

What if the first argument is non-*nil*? We can resolve the definition of *revapp* with (rev.2) to obtain

$revapp(X{:}E, C, D) :-$
     $reverse(E, F), append(F, X{:}nil, B), append(B, C, D).$

So far we have used just Horn clause reasoning, but the next step uses the fact that *provided P and Q do not appear elsewhere in the clause*, the two literals

$append(U, V, P), append(P, W, Z)$

can be replaced by the two literals

$append(V, W, Q), append(U, Q, Z).$

As Figure 13.2 shows, this transformation uses the fact that appending lists is an associative operation. A formal proof of this fact would need induction on lists.

Applying the transformation results in the following clause:

$revapp(X{:}E, C, D) :-$
     $reverse(E, F), append(X{:}nil, C, G), append(F, G, D).$

The term $X{:}nil$ now appears as the first argument of *append*, so we can use the definition of *append* to unfold the literal and solve it. In two resolution steps, we derive first

$revapp(X{:}E, C, D) :-$
     $reverse(E, F), append(nil, C, H), append(F, X{:}H, D).$

and then

$revapp(X{:}E, C, D) :-$
     $reverse(E, F), append(F, X{:}C, D).$

The final step is to notice that the body of this clause is an instance of the body of the clause defining *revapp*, so we can fold to obtain

$$revapp(X{:}E, C, D) :- revapp(E, X{:}C, D).$$

The final part of the transformation process is to show that reverse can be defined in terms of *revapp*. This requires another law, that the literal $append(A, nil, B)$ can be interchanged with $A = B$, in other words, that *nil* is a right unit for the append operation. We apply this law as follows: start with the (evidently true) clause

$$reverse(A, B) :- reverse(A, C), C = B.$$

Now replace $C = B$ by the equivalent *append* literal:

$$reverse(A, B) :- reverse(A, C), append(C, nil, B).$$

Finally, fold with the definition of *revapp*:

$$reverse(A, B) :- revapp(A, nil, B).$$

This completes the derivation of a definition of *reverse* that does not use *append*:

$$reverse(A, B) :- revapp(A, nil, B). \tag{rev.3}$$

$$revapp(nil, B, B) :- . \tag{revapp.1}$$
$$revapp(X{:}A, B, C) :- revapp(A, X{:}B, C). \tag{revapp.2}$$

This program can solve a goal $\# :- reverse(A, B)$, where A is a list of length n, in $n + 2$ resolution steps: (rev.3) is applied first, followed by n applications of (revapp.2) that reduce A to *nil*, and finally an application of (revapp.1). This is much more efficient than the quadratic version of *reverse* we began with.

Summary

- Unfolding allows special-case clauses to be derived from a program by symbolic execution.
- Folding, combined with unfolding, allows programs to be transformed to improve their pattern of recursion.
- More general transformations combine folding and unfolding with the use of algebraic properties of the relations involved.

Exercises

13.1   Use unfolding to derive a clause for the *ord* relation that deals with lists of length 3.

13.2   Write a definition of *consec* in terms of *append*, and use program transformation to derive from it the same direct recursive definition of *consec* that was derived in the text.

13.3   Use program transformation to show the equivalence of the first and second definitions of *connected* given in Section 9.1.

13.4   A *path* in a binary tree is a list of tokens, each *l* or *r*. For example, the path *r:l:nil* is a path in the tree

$$fork(tip(1),$$
$$fork(fork(tip(2), tip(3)),$$
$$tip(4)))$$

that leads to the sub-tree *fork(tip(2), tip(3))*.

  a. Define by recursion a relation *select*(T, P, U) that holds if P is a path in the tree T that leads to sub-tree U.
  b. Define a relation *replace*(T, P, U, T') that holds if T' is the result of replacing in T the sub-tree selected by P with the new sub-tree U.
  c. Find a non-recursive definition of *select* in terms of *replace*.
  d. The relation *change* is defined by

$$change(T, U, U', T') :-$$
$$select(T, P, U), replace(T, P, U', T').$$

By unfolding and folding, transform this definition of *change* into a recursive definition that does not use the auxiliary relations *select* and *replace*.

Chapter 14

About picoProlog

The remainder of this book contains a description of picoProlog, a simple but complete implementation of a logic programming language similar to Prolog. The main differences are that real Prolog has a more flexible – and thus more complicated – syntax, and that implementations of real Prolog come with a larger selection of 'built-in' relations. Many of these relations have no real meaning in terms of logic, but perform useful functions connected with input/output and so on. Despite the small size of the picoProlog implementation presented here (it consists of about 2000 lines of Pascal), it runs at a useful speed, and can be used to run all the logic programs contained in earlier chapters of the book.

The implementation is an *interpreter*, that is, a program that inputs a logic program and carries out directly the actions required to execute it. Many Prolog implementations also include a *compiler*, a program that translates a logic program into machine code that when it is run carries out the actions described by the logic program. As with any language implementation, compiling logic programs instead of interpreting them can provide an immense improvement in execution speed, because the analysis of what actions are needed to execute the program is carried out once and for all by the compiler, and object code that is generated specially for each program can achieve these actions faster than the general-purpose code in an interpreter. For simplicity, in this book we consider only an interpreter, although many of the data structures used to represent logic programs and states of execution would be the same in a compiler-based implementation.

There are several reasons to present an implementation of logic programming in a book that also discusses the theory behind logic programs and the practice of writing them. One reason is to complete the story behind the proof theory of Horn clause programs contained in Chapters 5 to 7, by showing that SLD–resolution can be used as the basis of an efficient execution mechanism, and confirming that the actions of a Prolog system can (with a few reservations) be viewed as symbolic reasoning using resolution.

Another purpose is to give the reader some understanding of the cost in space and time of executing typical logic programs. Too many Prolog programs are unnecessarily cramped in style, because their designers suspect that any program that does not closely resemble a conventional, imperative program will be hopelessly inefficient. Often, the reverse is true, and a program that exploits the unique features of logic programming can be made to work well. Such a program is often faster than an equivalent program written in a more imperative style. This is particularly likely if the 'imperative' program relies on the non-logical features of many Prolog systems, which can be used to simulate the effect of the assignment command of imperative programming, but only in a very inefficient way.

The first part of this chapter is a summary of the picoProlog language, and can be used as a manual for the picoProlog system. Chapters 15 and 16 describe in more detail the most interesting parts of the system, the part that implements depth-first search of the SLD–tree of a goal, and the part that implements substitutions and unification. Chapter 17 contains notes on the Pascal dialect in which the interpreter is written and the macro processor that is used to extend Pascal for present purposes. The chapter also describes the supporting parts of the picoProlog system, such as the syntax analyser that parses picoProlog programs. Chapter 18 describes three optimizations that are included in the picoProlog interpreter. Though not essential to a working Prolog system, these optimizations greatly reduce the execution time and memory needs of Prolog programs. In particular, they allow programs that have a simple iterative form to run in constant space.

14.1 The picoProlog language

The input to picoProlog is a program written in an ASCII variant of the notation we have been using throughout this book. Here is a summary of the syntax of the language:

$$
\begin{aligned}
program &::= \{\ clause\ \} \\
clause &::= [\ atom\ |\ `\#\text{'}\ ]\ `:\!-\text{'}\ [\ literal\ \{\ `,\text{'}\ literal\ \}\ ]\ `.\text{'} \\
literal &::= [\ `\text{not}\text{'}\ ]\ atom \\
atom &::= compound\ |\ term\ `=\text{'}\ term \\
term &::= primary\ [\ `:\text{'}\ term\ ] \\
primary &::= compound\ |\ variable\ |\ number\ |\ string\ |\ char\ |\ `(\text{'}\ term\ `)\text{'} \\
compound &::= ident\ [\ `(\text{'}\ term\ \{\ `,\text{'}\ term\ \}\ `)\text{'}\ ]
\end{aligned}
$$

As in our earlier discussion of parsing (Chapter 10), each equation defines a certain class of phrases in the language. Here we use a few extra notations for convenience: [*stuff*] stands for an optional occurrence of *stuff*, and the notation

{ *stuff* } stands for 'zero or more' occurrences of *stuff*. In particular, the notation *term* { ',' *term* } stands for one or more instances of *term* separated by commas. Various sorts of primitive symbols are not defined by the syntax summary above:

- an *ident* is any non-empty sequence of letters, digits and underscore characters that begins with a lower-case letter.
- a *variable* is any non-empty sequence of letters, digits and underscore characters that begins with an upper-case letter or an underscore.
- a *number* is any non-empty sequence of digits.
- a *string* is any sequence of characters other than the double-quote character ("), enclosed in double-quotes.
- a *char* is any single character, enclosed in single quotes.

Numbers and characters are atomic objects in picoProlog. Strings are equivalent to lists of characters, so that the string "mike" is a shorthand for the list written 'm':'i':'k':'e':nil. This means that ordinary list-processing relations like *append* and *reverse* work equally well on strings. The routine that prints answers to queries in the picoProlog system examines each list to see if it is actually a string, and if so it uses string notation to print it.

Another thing not shown in the syntax summary is the fact that comments can appear in picoProlog programs. Like the comments of Pascal, they begin with (* and end with *). Comments do not nest, and may appear anywhere a blank space would be allowed.

14.2   Built-in relations

The picoProlog language has a number of built-in relations.

- The relation $plus(X, Y, Z)$ holds if X, Y and Z are numbers and $X + Y = Z$. The relation $times(X, Y, Z)$ holds if X, Y and Z are numbers and $X \times Y = Z$. These relations are implemented in such a way that any two of X, Y and Z can be specified, and picoProlog will find the third number (if any) that completes the equation. If fewer than two values are known at the time picoProlog tries to solve the goal, a run-time error occurs.
- The relation $integer(X)$ is true if X is a known integer, and the relation $char(X)$ is true if X is a known character. Both relations are judged false if X is an unknown variable at the time of solving the goal, even though there are many substitutions for X that would make them true.
- If P is a term that would be a valid literal, then the relation **not** P is true if attempting to prove P results in failure, and it is false if attempting to prove P results in success. Provided P is a ground literal at the time of solving the goal, this is an implementation of negation as failure. If P is not a valid literal (for example, if it is a number or an unknown variable),

a run-time error occurs. If P is a valid literal but is not ground, the results are unpredictable.

- The relation $X = Y$ is defined exactly as if the picoProlog program contained the clause $X = X :-$. It is provided as a built-in relation for the sake of convenience.
- The relation *false* (with no arguments) is defined to be always false, just as if it were defined by the empty set of clauses. It is provided as a built-in relation for convenience. PicoProlog reports an error if a program contains a call to any other relation with no clauses, because that is usually a mistake.
- The relation '!' (with no arguments) is the cut symbol. Its effect is described in the next section.

Most Prolog implementations have many more built-in relations than are provided by picoProlog. The small number of built-in relations in picoProlog provide a guide to the way others are implemented.

14.3 The cut symbol

The cut symbol '!' may appear as a literal in the body of a goal or clause. It is treated by picoProlog as if it is logically true, but it has the side-effect of causing picoProlog to discard certain alternatives to the derivation that lead to the cut. This effect is most easily explained through an example:

$$p(X) :- q(X).$$
$$p(X) :- r(X, Y), !, s(Y).$$
$$p(X) :- t(X).$$

This definition has three clauses, and picoProlog's top-to-bottom rule for trying clauses means that they will be tried in the order that they are written. In solving the goal $\# :- p(\mathit{fred})$, picoProlog will reach the second clause only if the first clause has failed because $q(\mathit{fred})$ is false. If it reaches the cut symbol, then it has just found the first solution to the literal $r(\mathit{fred}, Y)$, and if the cut symbol were not there, it would be just about to attempt the literal $s(Y)$ for some value of Y. At this point, picoProlog is exploring a particular derivation, but it is keeping several alternatives for later exploration if this one fails. There may be other solutions of $r(\mathit{fred}, Y)$; there may be derivations that use the third clause in the definition of p, and there may be alternatives to the derivation that lead to the goal $\# :- p(\mathit{fred})$ in the first place.

The cut symbol discards all but the last group of alternatives; that is, it discards all the alternatives that have been created since the $p(\mathit{fred})$ literal was selected for execution. This means that if the $p(\mathit{fred})$ literal is going to be solved at all, it will be by solving $s(Y)$, with the current value for Y that was obtained by solving $r(\mathit{fred}, Y)$. Alternative derivations that were created *before* the selection of the $p(\text{fred})$ literal are not discarded by the cut, and neither are alternatives (such as alternative ways of solving $s(Y)$) that are created after the cut has been executed.

There are several reasons for introducing cut symbols into a program. Discarding alternatives to the current derivation can allow picoProlog to reclaim the storage space that is used to save them, and to save the time that would be spent in exploring them. It may be that we know these alternatives cannot lead to a solution, so that discarding them does not affect the set of solutions generated by the program, or it may be that we are interested only in the first solution found by the program, and do not care if other solutions are discarded. In that case, adding cuts to the program can make it more efficient without affecting its proper functioning.

For example, in the program for $p(X)$, we might know that the value of X would always be supplied, and that no value of X can lead to both a solution of $r(X, Y)$ and a solution of $t(X)$. Perhaps $r(X, Y)$ can be satisfied only if X is an even number (and for only one value of Y), and $t(X)$ is satisfied only if X is odd. In that case, the cut symbol shown in the program would not discard any alternatives that could possibly lead to a solution. When the cut symbol is reached, we know that X is even, and in that case the third clause for p cannot possibly be used. Discarding this alternative instead of exploring it saves the time that would be wasted in trying to solve $t(X)$ for an even value of X, and allows the space needed to record the alternative to be reclaimed and re-used.

A common use of cuts is in recursive definitions that define a relation on lists by pattern matching. For example, here is a version of *append* that has a cut in one of its clauses:

$$append(X{:}A, B, X{:}C) :- \ !, append(A, B, C).$$
$$append(nil, B, B) :- \ .$$

This definition is useful if *append* is always used in such a way that the first argument is known (i.e., it is not a variable). If the head of the first clause matches the goal, we know that the first argument of *append* is of the form $X{:}A$, so it cannot match the *nil* that appears in the head of the second clause. This makes the cut harmless, because we know that the second clause will only be discarded if it cannot match the goal. It is also beneficial, because it saves the time needed to match the second clause, and it allows storage space to be recovered. In fact, the cut makes it possible for picoProlog to recover *all* the working space needed for *append*. We can also see that if the second clause matches a goal, then the first clause cannot match. However, there is no need for a cut in the second clause, because if picoProlog reaches the second clause, then it has already tried and discarded the first one.

Adding a cut like this spoils the generality of the *append* program, because we cannot use the version that contains a cut to split a list into two parts. The cut discards all but the first solution to a goal like

$\# :- append(A, B, 1{:}2{:}3{:}4{:}nil).$

That is, it discards all but the solution with $A = 1{:}2{:}3{:}4{:}nil$ and $B = nil$. An application that needed to do both jobs would need two versions of *append*, one with the cut and one without.

Whether it is actually necessary to include cuts like this one depends on the sophistication of the Prolog implementation being used. Many systems are able to determine by analysing the program that the second clause cannot match if the first argument of *append* is known and the first clause matches, so they are able to achieve the same efficiency without an explicit cut. With such systems, the same version of *append* can be used both to join lists and to take them apart, without any loss of efficiency. Even in picoProlog, the *indexing* feature described in Chapter 18 means that (at least in simple situations like this one) the cut is not needed.

The use of cuts to improve the efficiency of a program is easy to defend on practical grounds. A less defensible use of cuts is to cover up a logical error in the program. For example, suppose we define $max(X, Y, Z)$ to be true if Z is the maximum of X and Y:

$max(X, Y, X) :- geq(X, Y).$
$max(X, Y, Y) :- lt(X, Y).$

(where *geq* means 'greater or equal' and *lt* means 'less than'). This program is designed to be used when the first two arguments are known integers, and the third is an unknown variable, intended to receive the output. As a first step in improving the efficiency, we notice that it is pointless to try the second clause if the test $geq(X, Y)$ has succeeded. So we can add a cut like this:

$max(X, Y, X) :- geq(X, Y), !.$
$max(X, Y, Y) :- lt(X, Y).$

This cut improves the efficiency of the program without affecting its logical meaning. But now we see that if the second clause is tried at all, then it must be because the test $geq(X, Y)$ has failed. In that case, the test $lt(X, Y)$ is bound to succeed, and we may as well delete it, like this:

$max(X, Y, X) :- geq(X, Y), !.$
$max(X, Y, Y) :- .$

This last change improves the speed of the program a little more, but it means that we can no longer read and understand the meaning of each clause separately, because the second clause says something that is true only if we have already tried and rejected the first clause. Also, the program works properly only if the first and second arguments of *max* are known and the third is unknown at the time the clauses are used. If we ask

$$\# :\!- max(4, 3, 3).$$

then the execution goes like this: the goal does not match the head of the first clause, because the first and third arguments in the goal are different. So the first clause is discarded, and we try the second clause. This matches, so we produce the answer 'yes'. Of course, the correct answer is 'no', because the maximum of 4 and 3 is not 3 but 4.

Cuts of the first kind, which discard no solutions at all, or discard only solutions that are actually correct but not of any interest, are often called *green* cuts. Cuts of the second kind, like the one in our *max* program, are called *red* cuts. They discard solutions that would otherwise be found by the program, but are incorrect in terms of the problem to be solved. Red cuts tend to make programs more difficult to understand, and it is best to avoid them if the efficiency gain is minor, as it would be in the *max* example. In other situations, the saving of work may be much larger than avoiding a superfluous test $lt(X, Y)$, and then the use of a red cut may be justified.

14.4   Implementation overview

PicoProlog is implemented by a program of about 2000 lines, written in a subset of standard Pascal. The program is divided into 20 modules that are largely independent of each other (see Table 14.1). Because the picoProlog program is written in Pascal, the boundaries of these modules are not marked formally in the source code, and they cannot be checked by the compiler, but this does not reduce the benefits of designing the program in a modular way.

Some of these modules implement general-purpose facilities that are either not provided in standard Pascal, or are provided in a form that is not quite the one we need. Among these, the *string buffer* module provides storage for variable-length character strings, and the *character input* module provides simple input of characters from text files and the keyboard. The *memory allocation* module manages the blocks of storage that are used to store the picoProlog program and the data structures that represent an executing goal.

Other modules use standard compiler techniques to analyse the syntax of a picoProlog program and build a data structure that represents it internally. There is a *symbol table* that stores information about each identifier or variable name that appears in the program, and an additional table of *variable names* that records information about the variables that appear in the present goal or clause. The picoProlog program is divided into meaningful tokens by the *scanner*, and the tokens are assembled into goals and clauses by a *parser*,

1. Coding conventions
2. Error handling
3. String buffer
4. Representation of terms
5. Memory allocation
6. Character input
7. Representation of clauses
8. Stack frames and interpreter registers
9. Symbol table
10. Building terms on the heap
11. Printing terms
12. Scanner
13. Variable names
14. Parser
15. Trail
16. Unification
17. Interpreter
18. Built-in relations
19. Garbage collection
20. Main program

Table 14.1: *Modules of picoProlog*

which constructs an internal representation of the program that is later used to execute it.

The most interesting parts of the implementation are those that execute goals. At each stage, the state of execution is recorded in a stack, and there is a module that defines the layout of *stack frames*, each representing a goal that has been derived from the original goal by SLD–resolution. The main *interpreter* manipulates this stack in order to execute the goal by depth-first search, and calls the *unification* algorithm to match goal literals against the heads of clauses. An extra stack, called the *trail*, records which variables in the picoProlog program have had values assigned to them by the unifying substitution in each resolution step, so that these assignments can be removed when the execution backtracks.

A few more modules complete the implementation. There is a collection of procedures for *building terms* that is used by the parser, and a procedure for *printing terms* that is used to display the answers when execution succeeds. Another module implements the *built-in relations*. Finally, there is a *garbage collector* that recycles storage that has been allocated but is no longer accessible.

The next few chapters describe the implementation of picoProlog in more detail. Chapter 15 explains how to use a stack to represent the state of a depth-first search, and Chapter 16 explains how substitution and unification are implemented. The crucial question in both these chapters is how the abstract structures of logic can be made concrete in computer memory in an efficient way, so that each step in the execution of a picoProlog program has a cost that is proportionate to the progress it achieves.

Chapter 17 is a more concrete account of picoProlog, including notes on the macro processor that is used to implement small extensions to Pascal, and information about the supporting routines (such as the parser) that complement the execution mechanism described in the earlier chapters. Chapter 18 describes some refinements that make picoProlog more efficient: the garbage collector, an indexing scheme and the optimization of tail recursion.

A complete listing of the source code of picoProlog appears in Appendix C, and Appendix D contains a cross-reference listing that lists the line numbers where each identifier is used. For details of how to get a machine-readable copy of the source code, see the Preface.

Chapter 15

Implementing depth-first search

The basis of the picoProlog interpreter is an implementation of a depth-first search in the search tree of a goal. This chapter contains an outline of the algorithms and data structures used in the implementation. We begin by showing the very simple search algorithm as a logic program, then describe how the algorithm can be translated into Pascal, and how the state of the search can be represented so that each resolution step has a small, fixed cost. Finally, we discuss some optimizations to the algorithm and some details of the choice of data structures.

15.1 Depth-first search

Given a logic program P, we can define a binary relation $\vdash$ on goals as follows:

> $G \vdash G'$ if and only if G' is obtained from G by a step of SLD–resolution with a clause from the program.

The problem solved by the picoProlog interpreter is this: given a goal G_0, find whether there is an SLD–refutation of G_0; that is, whether $G_0 \vdash^* \heartsuit$, where $\heartsuit = (\# :-)$ is the empty goal, and $\vdash^*$ is the reflexive–transitive closure of $\vdash$. Actually, we are also interested in the answer substitutions computed by SLD–refutations of G_0, but we can add them later. Thus the problem to be solved by the picoProlog interpreter is an instance of the graph-searching problems discussed in Chapter 9, and it uses one of the searching methods studied there, depth-first search. We begin with a version of the program from Section 9.3, in which we imagine that the goals of one logic program have been represented by terms that can be manipulated by another logic program:

$exec(G_0) :- dfs(G_0:nil).$

$dfs(G{:}S) :- success(G).$
$dfs(G{:}S) :- next(G, A), append(A, S, S_1), dfs(S_1).$

Here $exec(G_0)$ is the relation that is true if the goal represented by G_0 has an SLD–refutation, and $dfs(s)$ is true of a list of goals s if any one of them has an SLD–refutation. The program uses the two relations $success(G)$, true if G represents the empty goal, and $next(G, A)$, true if A is the list of goals G' such that $G \vdash G'$.

We shall begin our development of picoProlog by translating this logic program into Pascal. At first, we shall use an extended version of Pascal that has sequences as a data type, with a number of built-in operations. Later we shall explain how these sequences can be represented and manipulated using the data types and operations of standard Pascal. The advantage of presenting the picoProlog system in this way is that it allows us to separate the explanation of the broad strategy for implementing logic programming from the details of how to fit the data structures into computer memory.

We shall use a number of simple operations on sequences in our initial designs. We write $\langle x_1, x_2, \ldots, x_n \rangle$ for the sequence s that contains the n elements x_1, x_2, $\ldots$, x_n in that order. We write $length(s)$ for its length n, and for $1 \leq i \leq n$, we write $s(i)$ for the element x_i that appears in position i of s, counting from 1. If s is non-empty, then $head(s) = x_1$ is the first element of s, and $last(s) = x_n$ is its last element. The sequence $tail(s) = \langle x_2, \ldots, x_n \rangle$ contains all elements of s but the first, and $front(s) = \langle x_1, \ldots, x_{n-1} \rangle$ contains all elements of s but the last. We write $s \frown t$ for the concatenation of sequences s and t, a sequence that contains all the elements of s in their original order, followed by all the elements of t.

Figure 15.1 shows a translation of this logic program into our extended dialect of Pascal. The program uses a Boolean function $success(G)$ that returns *true* if G is the empty goal, and a sequence-valued function $next(G)$ that returns – in some order – the list of goals G' such that $G \vdash G'$. There are two invariants that are maintained in the program:

- Every goal G in the sequence s is derivable from the original goal G_0, that is, $G_0 \vdash^* G$.
- If G_0 has a refutation, so does some goal G in the sequence s, that is, if $G_0 \vdash^* \heartsuit$ then $G \vdash^* \heartsuit$ for some $G \in s$.

These invariants are first established by the initialization $s := \langle G_0 \rangle$, and they are maintained by the assignment

$$s := next(G) \frown tail(s)$$

in the loop body, so they are true throughout execution of the loop, and remain true at its end. If the loop terminates, then either *found* is true, or $s = \langle \rangle$. If *found* is true, then $head(s)$ is the empty goal, and the first invariant tells us that

```
function Execute(G₀: goal): boolean;
    var s: sequence of goal;
        G: goal;
        found: boolean;
begin
    s := ⟨G₀⟩; found := false;
    while (s ≠ ⟨⟩) ∧ ¬ found do begin
        G := head(s);
        if success(G) then
            found := true
        else
            s := next(G) ⌢ tail(s)
    end;
    Execute := found
end;
```

Figure 15.1: *Depth-first search*

$G_0 \vdash^* \heartsuit$, so the search has succeeded. If s is empty, then the second invariant tells us that G_0 has no refutation, so the search has ended in failure.

This reasoning from invariants allows us to conclude that the depth-first search procedure is *partially* correct, in the sense that *if* the procedure terminates, then the answer – yes or no – that it gives is the right one. Unfortunately, depth-first search is not *totally* correct, because it may fail to terminate even if the goal G_0 has a solution. The search may become stuck in an infinite branch of the search tree, and never find solutions that are present in other branches.

15.2 Representing the goal list

In the depth-first search algorithm, the sequence s contains goals that are waiting to be investigated. Solving any one of these goals would complete a solution of the original goal. The sequence variable behaves like a stack, in that each step in the search involves 'popping' the first element of s, and 'pushing' in its place the list of goals that can be derived in a single resolution step. An efficient implementation of picoProlog must make the operations needed in each resolution step as cheap as possible, so we must look for an appropriate way of representing s to make this pushing and popping quick.

The representation used in picoProlog (and in most other Prolog implementations) depends on the insight that s is always made up of fragments of $next(G)$ for various goals G. For example, suppose that initially $s = \langle G_0 \rangle$, and suppose that $next(G_0) = \langle G_1, G_2, G_3, G_4 \rangle$, $next(G_1) = \langle \rangle$, $next(G_2) = \langle H_1, H_2 \rangle$, and $next(H_1) = \langle K_1, K_2, K_3 \rangle$. Then successive values of s after each iteration of the loop will be

$$\langle G_0 \rangle$$
$$\langle G_1, G_2, G_3, G_4 \rangle$$
$$\langle G_2, G_3, G_4 \rangle$$
$$\langle H_1, H_2, G_2, G_3, G_4 \rangle \quad = \langle H_1, H_2 \rangle \,\widehat{}\, \langle G_2, G_3, G_4 \rangle$$
$$\langle K_1, K_2, H_2, G_2, G_3, G_4 \rangle = \langle K_1, K_2 \rangle \,\widehat{}\, \langle H_2 \rangle \,\widehat{}\, \langle G_2, G_3, G_4 \rangle.$$

At each stage, the value of s is made up by concatenating *suffixes* of the various sequence $next(G)$ where $G = G_0$, G_2, or H_1. By a suffix of a sequence t, we mean a sequence v such that $t = u \,\widehat{}\, v$ for some u. In general, the sequence s can be written in the form

$$s = s_n \,\widehat{}\, s_{n-1} \,\widehat{}\, \ldots \,\widehat{}\, s_1,$$

where each s_i is a suffix of $next(G)$ for some goal G. If s has this form, so does the new sequence $next(G) \,\widehat{}\, tail(s)$ that is assigned to s in the loop body. If s_n is non-empty, then this new sequence can be written as

$$next(G) \,\widehat{}\, tail(s_n) \,\widehat{}\, s_{n-1} \,\widehat{}\, \ldots \,\widehat{}\, s_1.$$

This insight suggests that, instead of representing s directly (say by a linked list), we should store the sequence of sequences $ss = \langle s_1, \ldots, s_{n-1}, s_n \rangle$ of which s is made up, because this grows or shrinks by only one element per resolution step. This indirect way of representing s will be an economical one provided that we can find a good way of representing the sequences s_i that are suffixes of $next(G)$ for a goal G, and we turn to this problem next.

For any goal G, let $proc(G)$ be the list of program clauses for the relation that is named in the first literal of G. These are the clauses that can potentially be used in the first step of solving G. Then $next(G)$ is the sequence of clauses obtained by resolving G with successive elements of $proc(G)$, and collecting the resolvents from those resolution steps that do not fail. This allows us to represent $next(G)$ and its suffixes by ordered pairs (G, t), where t is a suffix of $proc(G)$. Building a pair like this does not require that we immediately compute the resolvents of G with each program clause, as would be required if we represented $next(G)$ directly. Also, there are very few possible sequences $proc(G)$ – just one for each relation in the program – so these sequences can be computed in advance. We should use a representation for these lists of clauses that makes it easy to take suffixes, for example, linked lists.

Combining these two decisions – to represent s as a sequence of sequences, and to represent the individual sequences as (G, t) pairs – leads us to consider representing s as a stack of *frames*, with each frame containing a goal and a list of clauses. As we develop the implementation further, we shall add more fields to each frame, but the essential meaning of a stack frame will remain the same: it represents the sequence of goals that can be obtained by resolving a certain goal with each member of a list of clauses, and solving any one of these goals completes the solution of the original goal G_0.

A particular benefit of this representation is that resolution steps are delayed until their results are needed. It may happen that a solution is found before some of the goals in $next(G)$ are reached in the search. In this case, any effort spent in computing these goals would be wasted, and our representation avoids this waste.

Resolution is still needed when we need to know *explicitly* what goal is the head of the sequence s, so that it can be stored as part of a new frame, or tested to see if it is the empty goal. To allow for this, we introduce a new variable *current* that represents explicitly the first element of s, and a flag *ok* to say whether *current* is valid. If *ok* is true, then the sequence s consists of the explicit goal *current*, followed by all the goals stored in *stack*. Otherwise, s consists of just the goals in *stack*, disregarding the contents of *current*. Adding the *current* variable also makes it possible to represent the initial state, where $s = \langle G_0 \rangle$: we just set *current* to G_0 and *stack* to the empty sequence.

15.3 Representing goals

In the preceding section we chose a way of representing sequences of goals that allowed the operations we needed to be implemented cheaply. But goals are themselves sequences of literals, and we must also choose a representation for them that makes resolution efficient.

When a goal $\# :- P_1, P_2, \ldots, P_n$ takes part in a resolution step, the first literal P_1 is replaced by the body of a program clause to give a new goal, say

$$\# :- Q_1, \ldots, Q_m, P_2, \ldots, P_n.$$

If we consider the first goal to be (in effect) the sequence $\langle P_1, P_2, \ldots, P_n \rangle$, then we can write this new goal as

$$\langle Q_1, \ldots, Q_n \rangle \frown \langle P_2, \ldots, P_n \rangle.$$

The unifying substitution must be applied to this new goal, but let us ignore that for the moment. Substitution apart, the operation of replacing the head of a sequence with another sequence is the same one that we saw with lists of goals. Just as the list of goals waiting to be solved is made up of suffixes of procedures, so each goal is made up of suffixes of clause bodies.

We can exploit this fact as follows: instead of storing a complete goal in each frame, we store just the first few literals, together with directions for where to look for the rest of the goal. The literals that are stored directly are the remaining

Frame 3:

$goal = \langle Q_2, \ldots, Q_m \rangle$

$parent = 1$

$proc = $ procedure for Q_2

Frame 2:

$goal = \langle Q_1, Q_2, \ldots, Q_m \rangle$

$parent = 1$

$proc = $ rest of procedure for Q_1

Frame 1:

$goal = \langle P_1, P_2, \ldots, P_n \rangle$

$parent = 0$

$proc = $ rest of procedure for P_1

Figure 15.2: *Stack layout*

part of the first clause body that makes up the goal. The rest of the goal is made up of parts of clause bodies from further down the stack, so the 'directions' lead to a *parent* frame, another stack frame where the next part of the goal can be found.

To continue the example, suppose the first resolution step (using the clause $P_1 :- Q_1, Q_2, \ldots, Q_m$) is followed by another one that uses the unit clause $Q_1 :- .$ Then the stack will look like Figure 15.2. Frame 3 contains a representation of the goal

$$\# :- Q_2, \ldots, Q_m, P_2, \ldots, P_n.$$

The first few literals are stored in the frame itself, and the rest are found in frame 1, the parent of frame 3.

Frame 1 contains the sequence $\langle P_1, P_2, \ldots, P_n \rangle$, but P_1 is the literal that took part in the resolution step that created frame 2 and lead to frame 3. So in the goal that is represented by frame 3, this literal is replaced by the subgoals Q_1, $Q_2, \ldots, Q_m$, and we can ignore it. The parent of frame 1 is shown as frame 0, because there are no more literals in the goal.

In general, a goal will consist of pieces from many clauses, and there will be a longer chain of pointers to parent frames. The goal consists of all the literals from its own frame, followed by all literals but the first from each succeeding parent frame.

15.4 Answer substitutions

We have been ignoring the fact that the unifying substitution must be applied to the new goal after each resolution step. This means that the result of a resolution step cannot be formed just by concatenating pieces of the goal and clauses that were the inputs of the resolution step, and our representation will need to be changed to reflect this fact. A solution to this problem is not to store the goal itself, but to store separately the current answer substitution and a goal to which the substitution should be applied to get the current goal. At each resolution step, we add the unifying substitution to the accumulated answer by composing them, but leave for the future the task of applying the substitution to the new goal. The answer substitution could be applied to each literal just before it takes part in a future resolution step, or (as we shall see in the next chapter) the task of applying the substitution could be merged with the task of computing a unifier, so that the substitution does not have to be carried out separately.

To use this idea, we must add another field to each stack frame that will contain the answer substitution built up so far, which should be applied to the goal as part of future resolution steps. Frames nearer the top of the stack represent the results of carrying out more resolution steps than those further down the stack, so they will contain more specific answer substitutions. For the present, we will postpone the question of how substitutions are represented, and just imagine that our programming language has a type *subst* of substitutions, and also has the operations on substitutions that we need, such as applying a substitution to a term, unifying two terms to give a substitution, or composing two substitutions to give a third one.

15.5 Depth-first search revisited

We now apply the ideas we have discussed so far by showing a version of the depth-first search algorithm that uses the data structures we have designed. It differs from the code shown in Appendix C in several respects:

- Substitutions are treated here as an *abstract data type* provided with the operations we need. We discuss the implementation of this data type in Chapter 16, and that implementation is used in the code.
- Sequences or lists, which we use to represent goals, clauses and stacks, are also treated as an abstract data type, with operations like *head*, *tail* and concatenation (^). The choice of appropriate representations of these sequences, say as arrays or linked lists, is discussed in Section 15.7.
- The program fragments given here use the record types of Pascal to represent objects with several components. In the code of Appendix C, macros are used in place of these record types. We shall later define these macros so that records can be represented as segments of a large array.

The interpreter operates on a stack of *frames*, each one a record with this type:

```
type frame = record
      f_goal: goal; f_answer: subst;
      f_parent: integer;
      f_retry: sequence of clause;
   end;
```

The program uses several variables:

```
var
   stack: sequence of frame;
   ok: boolean;
   current: goal; answer: subst;
   goalframe: integer;
   proc: sequence of clause;
```

The sequence *stack* is the stack of frames. The Boolean flag *ok* indicates whether the other variables have any significance; it is true just after a successful resolution step, and false if a resolution step has just failed. When *ok* is true, *current* contains the first part of the goal currently being solved, and *answer* contains the answer substitution built up so far. The rest of the current goal is found in a chain of stack frames linked by their *parent* fields, starting at *stack(goalframe)*. The variable *proc* has significance only within the main loop of the interpreter; there, it contains a list of clauses that have yet to be tried on the current goal.

The top level of the interpreter algorithm is contained in procedure *Execute*:

```
procedure Execute(G_0: goal);
begin
   stack := ⟨⟩; ok := true;
   current := G_0; answer := I; goalframe := 0;
   while true do begin
      if ok then begin
         if current = ⟨⟩ then return;
         proc := Proc(current)
      end
      else begin
         Backtrack;
         if ¬ ok then return;
      end;
      Step;
      if ok then Unwind
   end
end;
```

Each iteration of the main loop carries out one resolution step. The first part of the loop body finds the goal that should take part in the step and the list of clauses *proc* that have yet to be tried on it. If *ok* is true, this is the new goal that was generated in the last resolution step, and all the clauses from its procedure have yet to be tried. Otherwise, there is no current goal, and the procedure *Backtrack* is called to reset the stack to a previous state. It resets *current* to a previously saved value, and sets *proc* to the list of clauses that were not tried before. On return from *Backtrack*, the value of *ok* indicates whether it succeeded in finding a place to begin searching again.

The next part of the loop body is a call to the procedure *Step*, which carries out a resolution step between the goal and the first clause of *proc*. It sets *ok* to false if the step fails, and true if it succeeds. In that case, it updates *current*, *goalframe* and *answer* to represent the new goal and answer substitution. Finally, if the step succeeds, a procedure called *Unwind* is called. This unwinds the chain of parent pointers, until it finds a frame where there are still literals to be solved, or it reaches the end of the chain. This ensures that the variable *current* contains the empty sequence only if the current goal is itself empty.

There are two ways that *Execute* can return. One way is if *current* becomes empty, indicating success. The other way is if *Backtrack* fails to find an unexplored alternative after a resolution step has failed. This means that the entire search tree for the goal has been explored without finding a solution, so the whole execution has ended in failure.

We now look at the details of carrying out a resolution step, as implemented by the procedure *Step*.

```
procedure Step;
    var unifier: subst;
begin
    if proc = ⟨⟩ then
        ok := false
    else begin
        PushFrame;
        ok := Unifier(Apply(head(current), answer),
                            Apply(head(proc).c_lhs, answer), unifier);
        if ok then begin
            current := head(proc).c_rhs;
            answer := answer ▷ unifier
        end
    end
end;
```

On entry to this procedure, *current* contains the first part of a goal, and *proc* contains a list of clauses that have not yet been tried on it. Our job here is to try the first of these clauses, saving the rest in a stack frame to be tried later.

The procedure first deals with the case that the *proc* is empty; in that case, the attempt at resolution fails. Otherwise, it calls *PushFrame* to create a new frame on the stack. This frame will contain the current values of the interpreter variables, together with the tail of *proc*. Then it calculates the results of applying the current answer substitution to the first literal of the goal and the head of the first clause in *proc*, and tries to unify them. If the unification succeeds, the new goal is the right-hand side of clause, followed by the rest of the previous goal. The new answer substitution is obtained by composing the old answer substitution with the unifier that was just computed.

Creating a new frame on the stack is simple, because we just need to make a frame record that contains copies of the current values of the interpreter variables and add it to the end of *stack*:

```
procedure PushFrame;
   var f: frame;
begin
   f.f_goal := current;
   f.f_answer := answer;
   f.f_parent := goalframe;
   f.f_retry := tail(proc);
   stack := stack ⌢ ⟨f⟩;
   goalframe := length(stack);
end;
```

If a resolution step fails, we need to find an earlier goal that still has untried clauses. This is achieved by the *Backtrack* procedure:

```
procedure Backtrack;
begin
   while (stack ≠ ⟨⟩) ∧ ¬ ok do begin
      current := last(stack).f_goal;
      answer := last(stack).f_answer;
      goalframe := last(stack).f_parent;
      proc := last(stack).f_retry;
      stack := front(stack);
      ok := (proc ≠ ⟨⟩)
   end
end;
```

The loop repeatedly discards the top frame from the stack until either the stack is empty, or a frame is found with a non-empty *f_retry* field.

After a successful resolution step, *Unwind* is called. The new goal is represented as the literals in *current*, followed by the uncompleted parts of goals in a chain of ancestor frames, linked together by their *parent* fields. If the clause used in the resolution step was a unit clause, *current* will now be empty, even though there are still unsolved literals further along the chain. *Unwind* searches the chain until either it finds a frame that contains some literals that are still to be solved, or it reaches the end of the chain, meaning that the new goal is actually empty.

During the search, it may be that a frame that has been completed is the top one on the stack, and that it contains no alternative clauses that have yet to be tried. If so, then we say that the corresponding clause has *succeeded determinately*, and the top frame can be discarded, because it will be never be needed again. This 'success-popping' gives an important efficiency improvement, because it means that solving a subgoal will leave nothing behind on the stack unless there is a possibility of backtracking. In effect, subgoals that succeed determinately behave like subroutine calls in conventional programming languages. One way of ensuring that a subgoal succeeds determinately is to place appropriate cuts in the clauses that are used solve it.

```
procedure Unwind;
    var parent: integer;
begin
    while (current = ⟨⟩) ∧ (frame > 0) do begin
        current := tail(stack(goalframe).f_goal);
        parent := stack(goalframe).f_parent
        if (goalframe = length(stack)
               ∧ (stack(goalframe).f_retry = ⟨⟩) then
            stack := take(stack, goalframe − 1);
        goalframe := parent
    end
end;
```

This completes the implementation of depth-first search.

15.6 Choice points

In the *Backtrack* procedure, frames are removed from the stack one at a time, until a frame is uncovered that contains untried clauses. Several frames may be thrown away in this process, and it is pointless to remove them one at a time if they could all be removed together. This suggests that it might be worth keeping track of the latest *choice point*, that is, the nearest frame to the top of the stack that contains some untried clauses. Then *Backtrack* could go straight to the right frame.

We can do this by adding an interpreter variable *choice* that contains the index of the choice point, or zero if there have been no choices so far. To enable the value of this variable to be restored on backtracking, we also add a field *choice* to each frame that records the value of *choice* when the frame was created. The *Backtrack* procedure can now be rewritten like this:

```
procedure Backtrack;
   var prev: integer;
begin
  ok := (choice > 0);
  if ok then begin
      current := stack(choice).f_goal;
      answer := stack(choice).f_answer;
      goalframe := stack(choice).f_parent;
      proc := stack(choice).f_retry;
      prev := stack(choice).f_choice;
      stack := take(stack, choice − 1);
      choice := prev
  end
end
```

The *take* function is defined so that $take(s, k)$ contains the first k elements of sequence s. If $s = \langle x_1, x_2, \ldots, x_n \rangle$ and $0 \leq k \leq n$ then

$$take(s, k) = \langle x_1, x_2, \ldots, x_k \rangle.$$

Take is used here to discard the part of the stack that has been added since the last choice point.

Keeping track of the latest choice point costs some time and some space, and it would not be worthwhile if the only benefit were a slight increase in the efficiency of backtracking. The real benefits will be revealed in the next chapter, where we discuss the representation of terms and substitutions. In short, we shall be able to treat variables in an especially efficient way on backtracking of they have been created since the last choice point. Recording the last choice point also provides a way to implement the cut symbol. When a cut is executed, the *choice* variable is simply reset to the value it had when the frame for the current goal was created. This causes any choice points that have occurred since then to be ignored in backtracking, thereby fixing the choices that have been made.

15.7   Choosing representations

The decisions we have made about representing states of the interpreter have introduced several kinds of sequences and lists. The entire state of the interpreter is a sequence of stack frames, each frame contains a list of untried clauses, and each goal or clause body is a list of literals. Because the sequence types we have used are not really part of Pascal, we must choose a real Pascal data type to represent each kind of sequence. There are several Pascal types to choose from: a sequence can be represented by an array, or a linked list, or even by a file. Each choice makes some operations on the sequence efficient, and some less efficient. For example, an array makes it easy to find an element of the sequence by numerical index, but hard to add a new element at the front. A linked list makes it easy to add new elements in any position, but harder to find an element by number.

Here are the choices of representation that picoProlog uses for each kind of sequence:

- Interpreter states are represented by linked lists of stack frames. We add to each stack frame a pointer to the immediately preceding frame, so the whole stack is linked by pointers from the back to the front. This makes it easy to add and delete frames at the end of the stack.

  We have described the *parent* and *choice* fields of stack frames as the numeric indexes of frames in the stack, and finding elements by number is not very efficient with linked lists. To avoid this problem, we can replace these fields by pointers to stack frames.

  It would also be possible to represent the stack as an array of frames, and the *parent* and *choice* fields could then remain as simple indexes. PicoProlog does not use this solution, because it would mean allocating a fixed amount of storage for the array, whereas using a linked list allows storage for stack frames to be allocated from the same pool that is used for other kinds of object.

- Lists of clauses are represented by linked lists. This makes it efficient to take the head and tail of a list of clauses. In a resolution step, we try matching with the clause at the head of the list, and save the tail of the list for use on backtracking. This representation also makes it easy to add more clauses to the procedure for a relation as picoProlog reads in its program from a file.

- The lists of literals in goals (and clause bodies) are represented by segments of a large array A. Each segment contains a series of pointers to the literals of a goal, and is terminated by a null pointer. A goal is represented by a starting index s in the large array, and the literals of the goal extend from that point as far as the next null pointer. The literals in the goal starting at s are

$$A[s], A[s+1], \ldots, A[s+n-1],$$

where $A[s+n]$ is the first null pointer following $A[s]$. This representation makes it easy to find the head and tail of a goal: the head of the goal starting at s is $A[s]$, and its tail is the goal starting at $s+1$. The empty goal is represented by an index s such that $A[s]$ is a null pointer.

Summary

- Prolog uses depth-first search, implemented using a stack.
- For efficiency, resolution steps are delayed until their results are needed.
- Goals and lists of clauses can be represented in a way that allows resolution to use little time and storage.

Chapter 16

Representing terms and substitutions

The discussion of depth-first search in Chapter 15 ignored the question of how terms and substitutions should be represented, pretending that data types of terms and substitutions were available in our extended dialect of Pascal, together with operations such as unifying two terms to give a substitution, or applying a substitution to a term. We now turn to the problem of implementing these data types.

In picoProlog, terms are represented as reference-linked tree structures. Space for these structures is allocated from two storage pools:

- the *heap* area holds the clauses that make up the picoProlog program. The contents of this area do not change as a goal is executed.
- the *global stack* area holds terms that are created during execution of a goal. Space is allocated from this area as new terms are created in resolution steps, and space is released when backtracking happens, and terms that have been created during recent resolution steps are no longer needed.

In addition to these two storage pools, there is also a *local stack* area, used to allocate storage for stack frames.

16.1 Representing terms

The conventional techniques of Pascal programming provide a natural way to represent terms as reference-linked tree structures. Each term is represented by a variant record with a tag that identifies the kind of term, and other fields that give information relevant to terms of that kind (see Figure 16.1).

- Compound terms have *kind* = *FUNC*; they have a function symbol *func* and a number of arguments, each one a term itself. The arguments are

```
type
  term = ↑blob;
  blob = record
    case kind: (FUNC, INT, CHRCTR, CELL, REF) of
    FUNC:
      (func: symbol;
        arg: array [1 .. MAX] of term);
    INT:
      (ival: integer);
    CHRCTR:
      (cval: char);
    CELL:
      (val: term);
    REF:
      (index: integer);
    end;
```

Figure 16.1: *Representation of terms*

represented by an array *arg* of pointers to other records. Ideally, this array
of pointers would have a different size in different records, because different
function symbols may have different numbers of arguments, but Pascal does
not allow that, so the array is shown here as always having a fixed size *MAX*.
* Other kinds of term like integers (with *kind* = *INT*) and characters (with
  kind = *CHRCTR*) have a field that contains the value, a simple integer or
  character.
* Variables are represented by two kinds of records. Those with *kind* = *REF*
  are the variables that appear in program clauses, and those with *kind* =
  CELL are variables that have been introduced during execution of a goal.
  The interpretation of the *index* and *val* fields of these records is explained
  later, in Section 16.2. Together, these two kinds of record allow an efficient
  representation of the answer substitution for the derivation currently being
  explored, and efficient renaming of variables in a program clause that is
  used to extend the derivation.

As we shall see in Chapter 17, the pointers and record structures of Pascal do
not provide quite what we need for implementing picoProlog, because there is
no provision for variable-size arrays, and because Pascal forces on us a storage
allocation mechanism for pointers (via *new* and *dispose*) that is not adequate for
our needs. For the present, we ignore these difficulties; later, I shall explain how
they can be overcome by replacing records and pointers by segments of a large
array and indexes into the array, thereby getting round the limitations of Pascal.

16.2 Substitutions

Although substitutions were defined in Chapter 4 as infinite functions from variables to terms, the substitutions we encounter in executing picoProlog programs actually affect only a finite number of variables, so it is sufficient to represent the substitution as a finite mapping, ignoring all the variables that have not so far been used in the execution.

There are several ways in which these finite mappings could be stored. For example, we could use an array $a[1..MAXVARS]$ of terms to represent a mapping, so that $a[i]$ is the term that should be substituted for the variable numbered i. This representation can be made to work, but it does not take into account the main operation on substitutions that is needed in picoProlog. That operation is *composition*, and specifically the operation

$$r := r \triangleright \{x \leftarrow u[r]\}$$

where r is a Pascal variable that holds the current answer substitution, and $\{x \leftarrow u[r]\}$ is a fragment of a unifier that is being computed during a resolution step. This operation is costly if the substitution r is represented by an array a, because it requires the new fragment of substitution $w = \{x \leftarrow u[r]\}$ to be applied to each element $a[i]$:

for $i := 1$ **to** *MAXVARS* **do** $a[i] := Apply(a[i], w)$

This takes time that is (at the very best) proportional to the number of variables in use.

A better way of representing substitutions takes into account the fact that the unification algorithm builds them up by successive composition. Instead of directly storing the function that maps variables to the terms that are substituted for them, we store a *binding function* from which this information can be recovered. Like a substitution, a binding function maps variables to terms, but it is used differently. The difference is most easily seen by comparing the operation $t[r]$ of applying a substitution r to a term t with the operation $t\langle b\rangle$ of applying a binding function b to the same term. Here is the definition of $t[r]$, copied from Section 4.4:

$$v[r] = r(v)$$
$$f(t_1, \ldots, t_k)[r] = f(t_1[r], \ldots, t_k[r]).$$

Compare this with the following definition of $t\langle b\rangle$:

$$v\langle b\rangle = \begin{cases} b(v)\langle b\rangle, & \text{if } v \in \text{dom } b \\ v, & \text{otherwise} \end{cases}$$
$$f(t_1, \ldots, t_k)\langle b\rangle = f(t_1\langle b\rangle, \ldots, t_k\langle b\rangle).$$

The big difference is in the way variables are treated. The substitution r gives directly the term to be substituted for a variable v, but the binding function gives a term $b(v)$ that needs to be subjected to substitution by b again to obtain the final answer $b(v)\langle b\rangle$. This recursive substitution stops with variables that are outside the domain of the function b, since for them $v\langle b\rangle$ is simply equal to v.

We say a substitution r is represented by a binding function b if $t[r] = t\langle b\rangle$ for all terms t. It is not immediately obvious that all the substitutions we need can be represented by binding functions, nor that the definition of $t\langle b\rangle$ is sufficiently well-founded to serve as an implementation of the operation $t[r]$. The calculations involved in verifying this are too complicated to give here, but it is nevertheless true that every answer substitution computed in picoProlog can be represented by a binding function, and that the definition of $t\langle b\rangle$ can be used to extract answer substitutions from the binding functions that represent them.

The major advantage of using binding functions rather than using substitutions directly is that the operation

$$r := r \triangleright \{x \leftarrow u[r]\}$$

that is used in the unification algorithm can be replaced by

$$b := b \cup \{X \mapsto u\},$$

the operation of extending the function b so that it maps X to the term u. If b itself is represented (say) by an array, then this operation can be carried out by changing a single element of the array, which is much cheaper than applying the new substitution to every element. The conditions under which this representation works can be expressed in terms of the substitution r that b represents. They are as follows: that r is *idempotent*, i.e., $r \triangleright r = r$, that $X[r] = X$, and that X does not occur in $u[r]$. Luckily, all three conditions are met whenever this operation is needed in picoProlog.

Another advantage of binding functions is that the operation $b := b \cup \{X \mapsto u\}$ is reversible by removing X from the domain of b again, an operation we may write as

$$b := b \backslash \{x\}.$$

If b is represented by an array, this corresponds to resetting the appropriate element of the array to a null value.

In the algorithm for depth-first search developed in Chapter 15, we kept a substitution in each stack frame, so that the current answer substitution could be restored to its former value on backtracking. The fact that extending a binding function is a reversible operation makes this unnecessary, and we need keep only the current answer substitution itself. If we need them, previous answer substitutions can be recovered by undoing the intervening binding operations, provided we keep a record of which variables have been added to the binding function at each stage. In picoProlog, this set of variables is recorded in a special stack called the *trail*.

Keeping only one answer substitution means that we need to represent only a single binding function b. This means that b can be stored by having a single term-valued field *val* in the record for each variable v. If v is in the domain of b, then this field contains $b(v)$; otherwise it contains *nil*.

16.3 Renaming

So far, we have been ignoring the problem of renaming the variables in program clauses. Before a clause can be used in a resolution step, its variables must be renamed, so that they are different from the variables that have appeared in earlier steps of the derivation. This is particularly obvious if the same clause is used more than once in a derivation, because without renaming the variables in the clause would have to take the same values each time the clause was used.

A naive way of implementing renaming would be to copy out each clause before it was used, systematically replacing each variable with a fresh one. This would be time-consuming, taking a time that was proportional to the size of the clause. What is worse, the effort of copying out the clause might be completely wasted, because the head of the clause might fail to match the current goal, causing the resolution step to fail and the clause to be discarded immediately.

We need a way to implement renaming without copying, with a cost that is proportional to the number of different variables in the clause, rather than the size of the whole clause. This is achieved by the following plan: before saving a clause as part of the program, we replace all its variables by numbered markers, represented by nodes with *kind = REF*. For example, the familiar clause

$$append(X{:}A, B, X{:}C) :- append(A, B, C)$$

would be stored as

$$append(@1{:}@2, @3, @1{:}@4) :- append(@2, @3, @4),$$

where the symbol @i means a *REF* node with *index = i*. To make a renamed variant of a clause stored in this way, we make an array of n fresh variables (where n is the number of variables in the original clause), and pair it up with the stored form of the clause.

Storage for this array of fresh variables can conveniently be allocated as part of a stack frame, since renaming always takes place as part of a resolution step that creates a new frame. The local variables are elements of an array *local* that we now add to each stack frame. Thus a variant of the clause is represented by a pair (c, f), where c is the stored *skeleton* of the clause – with *REF* nodes in place of the variables – and f is the address of a local stack frame that contains the fresh variables $f{\uparrow}.local[1], \ldots, f{\uparrow}.local[n]$. Creating such a pair is relatively cheap, since the skeleton can be shared by all instances of the clause.

Using clauses that are represented by (c, f) pairs requires a change throughout the interpreter. Every clause, and every term that may be part of a clause, must be accompanied by a pointer to the stack frame that contains its variables. Parts of the interpreter such as the unification algorithm, or the subroutine that prints out a term, need a frame pointer as an extra argument. Whenever they encounter a *REF* node, they look up the corresponding variable in the stack frame and use that instead.

A problem arises when a term that is part of a clause is to be assigned as the value of a variable, because we have not provided space to store the frame that goes with the term. There are two solutions to this problem: one is to add a field to each variable for storing the frame part of the (c, f) pair. This approach is called 'full structure-sharing'. Its advantage is that it is never necessary to make a copy of a term, but making it work well requires a careful analysis of the Prolog program to determine which variables need space on the global stack, and which can exist purely on the local stack.

We shall adopt the other approach, called 'copy-on-use'. In this scheme, variables have only a single field that contains a term. If a term that comes with a frame pointer is to be assigned to the variable, it is necessary to make a copy of the term in the global stack, with *REF* nodes replaced by the actual variables from the stack frame. This approach requires some copying of terms, but for many programs it is as effective as full structure-sharing, without the need for a complex analysis of the Prolog program.

16.4   Printing terms

The subroutine *PrintTerm* prints a readable representation of a term. It nicely illustrates the combined effect of our two mechanisms for representing substitutions, using binding functions and *val* fields to represent answer substitutions, and using skeletons and frames to implement renaming. This subroutine is used by the picoProlog system to print the answer substitution after execution of a goal has succeeded, by printing each variable that appeared in the goal together with its image under the answer substitution.

Figure 16.2 shows a simplified version of *PrintTerm* that prints all compound terms using the basic notation $f(t_1, \ldots, t_n)$. The version incorporated into pico-Prolog itself is more complicated, because it attempts to use notations like infix ':' and '=' for appropriate terms, and to display strings in double quotes rather than as lists of characters.

Like many procedures that manipulate terms, *PrintTerm* uses the function *Deref* to handle substitution and renaming. The name of this function reflects that fact that it 'dereferences' terms by following the pointers associated with

```
procedure PrintTerm(t: term; e: frame);
   var t1: term
begin
   t1 := Deref(t, e);
   case t1↑.kind of
   FUNC:
      PrintCompound(t1, e);
   INT:
      write(t1↑.ival: 1);
   CHRCTR:
      write('''', t1↑.cval, '''');
   CELL:
      PrintVar(t1)
   end
end;

procedure PrintCompound(t: term; e: frame);
   var f: symbol; i: integer;
begin
   f := t↑.func;
   WriteString(name(f));
   if arity(f) > 0 then begin
      write('(');
      PrintTerm(t↑.arg[1], e);
      for i := 2 to arity(f) do begin
         write(', ');
         PrintTerm(t↑.arg[i], e)
      end;
      write(')')
   end
end;
```

Figure 16.2: *Code for printing terms*

CELL and REF nodes. The arguments to *Deref* are a term and a frame. Its result is also a value of type *term* that represents the same term as the arguments, but the result is never a REF node, and if it is a CELL node, then its *val* field is *nil*, so it represents a variable that is not affected by the current answer substitution. Thus the rest of the code for *PrintTerm* need not be concerned with renaming variables and applying the answer substitution.

Once *Deref* has been applied to the argument *t*, we can examine its *kind* field to determine what kind of term it is. Integers and characters are easy to print. Compound terms are printed by the *PrintCompound* routine, which calls

```
function Deref(t: term; e: frame): term;
  var t1: term
begin
  t1 := t;
  if t1↑.kind = REF then
    t1 := e↑.local[t1↑.index];
  while (t1↑.kind = CELL) ∧ (t1↑.val ≠ nil) do
    t1 := t1↑.val;
  Deref := t1
end
```

Figure 16.3: *Code for Deref*

PrintTerm recursively to print each argument. Variables that survive *Deref* are not affected by the answer substitution. PicoProlog prints them using names like 'L106' that are calculated from the address of the variable.

The code for *Deref* (Figure 16.3) reveals the steps that may need to be followed in renaming variables and applying the answer substitution. First, a term may be a *REF* node that refers to a variable in the frame. Because of the copy-on-use rule, the value of a variable cannot contain any *REF* nodes, so the frame need be used at most once. On the other hand, the *val* fields that represent the answer substitution can make a chain of many links that must be followed before the final value is found. These long chains can be made if several variables have been made to 'share' before one of them is eventually assigned a non-variable term as value.

16.5   The trail

The depth-first search algorithm of Chapter 15 saved an answer substitution in each frame. We have now decided to represent substitutions as binding functions, and have observed that the operation of extending a binding function is reversible. This means that we need keep only one answer substitution, provided we can keep track of which variable bindings must be undone in order to return to a previous state.

A good way to keep track of variable bindings is to add another stack, the *trail*, to the interpreter. It contains pointers to variables that have become bound, and we record the position of the stack pointer for the trail when each stack frame is created on the local stack. When backtracking becomes necessary, the previous binding state can be restored by popping variables off the trail stack and resetting them until the stack pointer is back where it was when the choice frame was created.

Items are added to the trail stack as variables become bound, and are removed on backtracking, so the trail stack grows and shrinks in the same way as the global stack. In picoProlog, the trail is implemented as a linked list using space allocated in the global stack area. Since each variable appears in the trail at most once, the total amount of space used for the trail is at most linear in the number of variables used in the execution.

Some variables that become bound during execution do not need to be recorded on the trail. There is no need to record the binding of variables that have themselves been created since the last choice point, since these variables will be discarded when backtracking happens, and it does not matter whether they are reset before being discarded or not. We call other variables *critical*. They *will* survive backtracking, so they need to be recorded on the trail when they become bound. Each time a variable becomes bound, we test whether it is critical and (if so) record it on the trail.

When a cut is executed, the latest choice point may be removed, so that the choice point reverts to an earlier frame. This means that variables that were critical before the cut may no longer be critical afterwards, and part of the work of executing a cut is to remove entries for these variables from the trail.

16.6 Unification

The unification algorithm used by picoProlog is similar to the one described in Section 6.1, but uses recursion in place of an explicit stack to store pairs of terms waiting to be unified. We present the algorithm here as operating on abstract substitutions by composition, though the actual program acts on binding functions by extension, as was described in Section 16.2.

The function *Unify* takes two terms as arguments, and returns a Boolean value that indicates whether the two terms can be unified. As a side effect, the value of the global variable *answer* is augmented by composing it with the most general unifier of the two terms. The initial value of *answer* is also applied to the two terms before unification, so that the statement

$$ok := Unify(t1, t2)$$

sets *ok* to *true* if $t1[answer]$ and $t2[answer]$ are unifiable, and in that case, the final value of *answer* is $answer_0 \triangleright r$, where $answer_0$ is the initial value of *answer*, and r is a most general unifier of $t1[answer_0]$ and $t2[answer_0]$. This dependence on the *answer* variable makes our version of *Unify* rather specialized, but this version is exactly the one needed in the procedure *Step* of Section 15.5, and it has the efficient implementation shown in Figure 16.4.

The function begins by applying *Deref* to both arguments. After *Deref* has done its work, the rest of the task amounts to a case analysis. If either term is a variable, then the most general unifier simply substitutes the other term for it. If neither term is a variable and they are not both integers or both characters or both compound terms, they cannot be unified. Two integers or two characters

```
function Unify(t1, t2: term): boolean;
    var u1, u2: term;
        i: integer;
        match: boolean;
begin
    u1 := Deref(t1, answer); u2 := Deref(t2, answer);
    if u1 = u2 then
        Unify := true
    else if u1↑.kind = CELL then begin
        answer := answer ▷ {u1 ← u2[answer]};
        Unify := true
    end
    else if u2↑.kind = CELL then begin
        answer := answer ▷ {u2 ← u1[answer]};
        Unify := true
    end
    else if u1↑.kind ≠ u2↑.kind then
        Unify := false
    else
        case u1↑.kind of
        FUNC:
            if u1↑.func ≠ u2↑.func then
                Unify := false
            else begin
                i := 1; match := true;
                while match ∧ (i ≤ arity(u1↑.func)) do begin
                    match := Unify(u1↑.arg[i], t2↑.arg[i]);
                    i := i + 1
                end;
                Unify := match
            end;
        INT:
            Unify := (u1↑.ival = u2↑.ival);
        CHRCTR:
            Unify := (u1↑.cval = u2↑.cval)
        end
end;
```

Figure 16.4: *Code for unification*

can be unified (by the identity substitution) if they have the same value, and not otherwise. Two compound terms can be unified if they have the same function symbol, and the arguments can be unified cumulatively, with the unifier from the first pair of arguments being applied to the rest of the arguments before unification, and so on. Because the *answer* substitution is implicitly applied to the arguments of *Unify*, this cumulative effect is achieved by making a series of recursive calls of *Unify*, one for each pair of corresponding arguments.

A vital element that is missing here is the 'occur check', that the variable v does not occur in the term w when an element $\{v \leftarrow w\}$ is added to the answer substitution. Omitting the occur check is a tradition in Prolog implementation, and it means that Prolog does not implement the logic of Horn clauses correctly. This is a great weakness, but it is partly justified by the observation that the fastest *correct* unification algorithms known are still too slow to be used in a practical Prolog implementation. We want the cost of matching a pattern such as $X{:}A$ against input data such as $3{:}1{:}4{:}1{:}nil$ to be proportional to the size of the pattern alone. Correct unification requires an occur check that also scans the whole of the input data, and this data may be arbitrarily large. In the example, before binding A to the term $1{:}4{:}1{:}nil$, it is necessary to check that this list contains no occurrences of A, and that would be bound to take proportionally more work if the list contained 1000 elements instead of just three. This explains why Prolog implementors find the compromise of omitting the occur check impossible to resist.

Summary

- Substitutions are represented in Prolog systems in a way that allows efficient composition of an existing answer substitution with a new substitution component.
- Clauses are kept as skeletons, allowing their variables to be renamed simply by allocating a frame on the stack.
- The occur check, which is needed for a correct unification algorithm, is usually omitted in Prolog implementations for the sake of speed.

Chapter 17

Implementation notes

In this chapter are collected some notes on the parts of picoProlog that surround and support the execution mechanism discussed in the preceding two chapters. There is a parser that reads picoProlog programs and builds the internal structures that represent them, with a lexical analyser and symbol table, all built using conventional compiler techniques. There are also routines that manage the different areas of storage that are used to store and execute picoProlog programs. The purpose of this chapter is to provide information that will be useful in projects that extend or improve the picoProlog system.

PicoProlog is implemented in a tiny subset of Pascal that avoids nested procedures and functions, procedures and functions that take other procedures or functions as arguments, conformant array parameters, arrays indexed by types other than *integer*, sets, typed file I/O, floating-point numbers, pointers, enumerated types, variant records, non-local **goto** statements and **with** statements. By keeping to this small subset, the author hopes to make the program easier to translate into other languages, and easier to understand by those who do not know Pascal very well.

On the other hand, we extend the Pascal subset by using macros. The source code of the picoProlog system must be passed through a simple macro processor before it is submitted to the Pascal compiler. The primary reason for this is that Pascal's record and pointer types are almost useless for the kind of programming involved in efficient implementation of Prolog. In Pascal, records have a fixed size, and there is no alternative to the primitive storage allocation facility provided by *new* and *dispose*. So instead of using records and pointers, most of the data in picoProlog is kept in a big array *mem*. Instead of records, we allocate contiguous segments of *mem*, and instead of pointers, we use indexes into the array. The segments of *mem* allocated for different records of the same kind can have different sizes, provided we take care that one record does not overlap another one.

There is a big disadvantage of this decision to ignore the data structuring features of Pascal, because in place of the usual notation $p\uparrow.val$ for the *val* field of the record pointed to by p, we are forced to write something like $mem[p+2]$. This is obscure, and likely to cause bugs if the layout of records is ever changed, especially if different kinds of record have different information at offset 2. A partial solution to this problem would be to define a family of Pascal functions for accessing the fields of each kind of record. For example, one of them would be a function *Val* that takes a pointer value p (represented by an integer), and returns the contents of the record's *val* field, taken from the *mem* array:

> **function** *Val*(p: integer): integer;
> **begin**
>   *Val* := mem[p+2]
> **end**;

This is a little inefficient, since each access to a field of a record would require a function call. More seriously, it does not provide a way of changing the fields of a record, because you cannot write an assignment like $Val(p) := 3$ and hope that it will be equivalent to $mem[p+2] := 3$. A better solution is to use macros. We could define t_val as a macro so that the expression $t\_val(p)$ is textually replaced by $mem[p+2]$ before the program is compiled. This avoids the inefficiency of a function call, and works whether the expression appears on the left-hand side of an assignment or one the right-hand side. For example, the assignment $t\_val(p) := t\_val(q)$ is textually expanded into $mem[p+2] := mem[q+2]$, a legal Pascal statement that has the desired effect.

17.1 Macros

The macro processor used for compiling picoProlog is called 'ppp' (for Pascal Pre-Processor). Pascal source code for ppp is included in the distribution kit for picoProlog. It is a simplified version of the macro processor described in Chapter 8 of the book *Software Tools in Pascal* by B. W. Kernighan and P. J. Plauger (Addison–Wesley, 1981).

A macro call looks very much like a Pascal function call: it consists of an identifier, possibly followed by a list of arguments in parentheses. To make it easier to distinguish macros from functions, most of the macros in the picoProlog code have been given names that contain an underscore character. Not all Pascal compilers allow identifiers that contain an underscore, but this does not matter, because all macro names are eliminated during the macro processing stage before the code reaches the Pascal compiler.

Whenever ppp finds an identifier that has been defined as a macro, it collects the arguments of the macro as follows: if the identifier is immediately followed by an left parenthesis, then ppp reads the following text *without expanding macros* until it finds a matching right parenthesis. Thus the whole argument list is a text in which left and right parentheses are properly nested. Inside the argument list, each argument is separated from the next by a comma that is not enclosed in parentheses. For example, if `t_arg` is defined as a macro, then the text `t_arg(t_arg(p,1),i)` is a macro call with arguments `t_arg(p,1)` and `i`. The first comma does not separate two arguments because it appears inside an inner set of parentheses.

Each macro is associated with a definition, a text that may contain the *argument markers* `$1`, `$2`, and so on up to `$9`. After collecting the arguments of a macro, ppp replaces the whole macro call with a copy of the definition, expanding each argument marker with a copy of the corresponding argument. Missing arguments are replaced by the empty text.

Continuing the example, if the `t_arg` macro is defined as `mem[$1+$2+2]`, then the macro call `t_arg(t_arg(p,1),i)` will be replaced by the text `mem[t_arg(p, 1)+i+2]`. The fact that one of the arguments contains another macro call does not affect the expansion process at this stage.

After the replacement has been made, ppp examines the whole text again to look for further macro calls. It is at this point that macro calls are recognized within the replacement text of a macro, or inside the arguments of a macro call. In the example, the nested call `t_arg(p,1)` is now expanded. Its arguments are `p` and `1`, so the call is replaced by `mem[p+1+2]`, giving the result `mem[mem[p+1+2]+i+2]`. This text no longer contains any macro calls, so it is output as the final result of macro expansion.

In the example, the expression that results from macro expansion could be simplified a little by replacing the sub-expression `p+1+2` by `p+3`. This simplification is not attempted by ppp. Although the simplified expression might be evaluated a little more quickly, the effect is not big enough to have a noticeable effect on performance. In any case, simplifications like this one are often done automatically by optimizing compilers, so there is some hope that the inefficiency will be eliminated at a later stage in the compilation process.

There are two macros that are not expanded in the usual way, but are built-in to ppp. One of these is the `define` macro that is used to define other macros. It takes two arguments, and has the effect as defining the first argument as the name of a macro, with the second argument as its definition. The `t_arg` macro that we have been using as an example would be defined like this:

```
define(t_arg, mem[$1+$2+2])
```

Each call of the `define` macro is replaced by the empty text, so no trace of the definition is left after macro expansion. If the same macro is defined several times, it is the most recent definition that is used at each point. The `define` macro can also be used with only one argument. The effect is to define the argument as the name of a macro, with the empty text as its definition.

The other built-in macro is `ifdef`. It is called with either two or three arguments. If the first argument is the name of a macro, then a call of `ifdef` is replaced by its second argument. If the first argument is not the name of a macro, then the call is replaced by the third argument if present, and otherwise by the empty text. It is particularly useful to combine `ifdef` with `define`. For example, the text

```
define(abort, goto 999)
ifdef(turbo, define(abort, halt))
```

has the effect of defining `abort` as an abbreviation for `goto 999` in most versions of picoProlog. To install the program using Turbo Pascal, we add the definition `define(turbo)` at the beginning of the program. Among other things, this causes `abort` to be redefined as a call to Turbo Pascal's built-in `halt` procedure.

A couple of extra rules about argument expansion should be mentioned. One is that the special argument marker $0 is replaced by the list of all the arguments of the macro, separated by commas. This allows a limited kind of macro with a variable number of arguments, like the following `panic` macro that prints a message and stops the program:

```
define(panic, begin writeln('Panic: ', $0); abort end)
```

Calls like `panic(n, ' is too large')` can be used to print a message that is more than a simple string. It expands to the text

```
begin writeln('Panic: ', n, ' is too large'); abort end
```

This provides a convenient way around Pascal's limitations that prohibit variable-length strings and variable numbers of arguments to procedures. Another special argument marker is $$, which expands to a single dollar sign.

Macro calls are not expanded inside Pascal string constants or inside comments delimited by curly brackets. This prevents surprises when a macro name is accidentally used inside a string, and even makes it possible to 'comment out' macro definitions.

In addition to providing a more readable way to access data structures, macros are used in the code of picoProlog to get round a few other small limitations of Pascal. We have already seen one of these, the `panic` macro. Macros also let us get round the silly restriction that labels must be numbers instead of meaningful names. We simply define a few macros that have meaningful labels as their names and expand to plain numbers:

```
define(found, 1)
define(exit, 2)
define(done, 3)
```

Then we can write `goto found` instead of `goto 1`. Many implementations of Pascal allow identifiers as labels, but using macros makes this feature available in all implementations.

One drawback of using macros is that the compiler reads a different text from the one that the programmer wrote, making its error messages a little more difficult to understand. Also, if any macro calls or replacement texts contain newline characters, then lines in the output of the macro processor may not match up with lines in the original program text, so compiler error messages that mention line numbers may be misleading. This can be frustrating, especially if the error messages are otherwise unhelpful.

17.2   String handling

Standard Pascal provides only very weak facilities for handling character strings. Many implementations of Pascal contain better facilities as extensions, but using these extensions would make picoProlog more difficult to move from one Pascal implementation to another. Instead, picoProlog includes its own simple collection of routines for handling strings.

There are two representations for strings: either as a fixed-length array of characters (a *tempstring*), or as a segment of the global array *charbuf* (a *permstring*). The *tempstring* representation is used to store the characters of a string as they are input, and the function *SaveString* (line 98) can then be used to allocate a segment of the *charbuf* array and turn the string into a *permstring*, where the string is represented by the index in *charbuf* of its first character. In both representations, the end of a string is indicated by a special character *ENDSTR*. In the ASCII character set, *ENDSTR* can be defined as the otherwise unused character $chr(0)$ with numeric value 0.

The technique of allocating segments of a large character array is useful because it makes it possible to store long strings, without wasting space if the strings turn out to be short. If most strings are stored in the *charbuf* array, then we can afford to be generous with the maximum length of a *tempstring*, and this is the only fixed limit on the length of a string.

17.3   Memory allocation

Space for the data structures described in previous chapters is allocated from three parts of a single large array *mem*. The areas are defined by the global variables *hp*, *lsp* and *gsp*:

- The *heap* area is used to store the clauses of a picoProlog program. It extends from $mem[1]$ to $mem[hp]$. During execution of a goal, the program is fixed and so the size of the heap does not change, but the heap grows upwards when the program is being input.
- The *local stack* area is used for stack frames and their local variables. It extends from $mem[hp + 1]$ to $mem[lsp]$, and grows upwards.

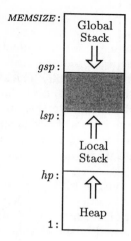

Figure 17.1: *Layout of the mem array*

- The *global stack* area is used for terms constructed during execution of a goal. It extends from $mem[gsp]$ to $mem[MEMSIZE]$ and grows downwards.

The portion of the array from $mem[lsp + 1]$ to $mem[gsp - 1]$ is free, and both the stacks can grow by occupying parts of the free portion at opposite ends. Since the heap does not change as a goal is executed, there is no need for a free space between it and the local stack.

As the picoProlog program runs, both stacks expand and contract. The local stack expands as frames are added for successive resolution steps, and contracts when a clause body is completed determinately. The global stack grows as new terms are created, and both stacks contract on backtracking. Most of the time, this stack-like behaviour is enough to ensure that some free memory is always available. However, if the stacks ever grow so large that the free area vanishes, then execution must stop for lack of memory space.

If this happens, one last possibility remains. Some of the space that has been allocated on the global stack may store terms that are no longer needed, because the local variables that pointed to them have been discarded. PicoProlog includes a *garbage collector* that traces pointers to determine which storage is really needed. It reclaims any 'garbage' space that is no longer needed, and makes it available for re-use by compacting together all the needed objects in the global stack area. More details of the garbage collector appear in Chapter 18.

17.4   Symbol table

The symbol table contains an entry for each identifier or variable name used in the picoProlog program. It is organized as a hash table, with collisions handled by searching adjacent elements of the table. The symbol table has two purposes. One is to allow symbols to be represented in the rest of picoProlog by simple numbers rather than the strings that are their names, so that comparing symbols for equality is a cheap operation. Each identifier appears just once in the symbol table, so its index can be used as a unique representation of the identifier. Two identifiers are equal if and only if they occupy the same entry in the symbol table.

The other purpose of the symbol table is to store certain information about each identifier. A function or relation symbol has a fixed number of arguments that is kept in the *arity* field of its entry in the symbol table. Relation symbols either have a list of clauses stored in the *proc* field, or have an *action* code that identifies them as built-in relations.

The primary interface to the symbol table is the function *Lookup* (line 347), which takes a name represented as a *tempstring* and returns the index of the entry for that name in the symbol table, creating a new entry if necessary. It first computes a hash function from the string, and this determines the starting point for a sequential search of the table. The search finishes when it reaches either the desired symbol, or a vacant slot, indicated by a *name* field that contains -1 instead of a valid *permstring* value. If the symbol is not found, then it is entered into the vacant slot.

Good performance for this kind of hash table depends on having plenty of vacant records where unsuccessful searches can be stopped, so *Lookup* does not allow the table to become more than *HASHFACTOR* per cent full, where *HASHFACTOR* is about 90. It is better to stop immediately than to let the system grind slowly to a halt because the table is too full.

The procedure *InitSymbols* (line 395) puts all the built-in symbols of picoProlog into the hash table using the same look-up mechanism. A few moments could be saved each time picoProlog starts by pre-computing the locations of these symbols, but the time saved would not be worth the risk of getting the locations wrong.

17.5   Lexical analysis

The parts of picoProlog that read the input program are built using similar techniques to those used in most compilers. The job is split into two parts: *lexical analysis*, which divides the input into meaningful groups of characters called *tokens*, and *syntactic analysis* or *parsing*, which assembles the stream of tokens into clauses, checking them against the grammar of the picoProlog language and building the internal structures that represent the clauses.

The job of procedure *Scan* (line 693) is to break the picoProlog program into tokens. For example, if the program begins with the clause

```
append(X:A, B, X:C) :- append(A, B, C).
```

then the first few tokens will be

```
append  (  X  :  A  ,  B  ,  X  :  C  )  :-  ...
```

A token may consist of an identifier like append or X, or a punctuation symbol of one or more characters, like (or :-. The spaces between tokens are discarded as the input is split into tokens, as are any comments that appear in the picoProlog program.

When *Scan* is called, it reads the next token from the input and sets the global variable *token* to a value that indicates what kind of token it is. Continuing, the example, if *Scan* were called repeatedly, the values returned in *token* would be

IDENT, *LPAR*, *VARBLE*, *COLON*, *VARBLE*, *COMMA*, *VARBLE*, *COMMA*, *VARBLE*, *COLON*, *VARBLE*, *RPAR*, *ARROW*, ...

The value of *token* indicates only the kind of token that was found, so all identifiers are represented by the same value *IDENT*; but there is another global variable *tokval* that *Scan* fills with the *symbol* value associated with the identifier. Variables (starting with an upper-case letter), numbers, character constants and strings are treated in similar ways. Each class is represented by a single value of *token*, but there are other global variables that return more precise information in each case. The value of a number or the ASCII code of a character constant are put in *tokival*, and there is a *tempstring* buffer called *toksval* that holds the actual characters of each string constant. The implementation of *Scan* is lengthy but fairly simple. We can usually tell from the first character of a token what kind of token it is, so *Scan* contains a big case statement that examines one character from the input. Each arm reads the remaining characters of a token, setting *token* and the other global variables appropriately.

It is convenient to let the lexical analyser read the input file as a simple stream of characters, rather than as the sequence of separate lines that is provided by the input facilities of Pascal. To perform the translation (which probably reverses a translation done by the Pascal run-time library), there is a procedure *GetChar* (line 232). The end of a line is marked by a special character *ENDLINE*, defined to be the ASCII code for newline, and the end of an input file is indicated by the special character *ENDFILE*.

GetChar also deals with switching between input from a file and input from the keyboard, and allows a single character to be 'pushed back' onto the input stream using the procedure *PushBack* (line 242). Sometimes the lexical analyser cannot recognize the end of a token without seeing the next character beyond it.

For example, the end of a number cannot be recognized except by seeing that the following character is not a digit. In such cases, the *PushBack* mechanism can be used to save the extra character to be read again as part of the next token.

17.6 Syntax analysis

The job of parsing or syntactic analysis is to take the stream of tokens produced by lexical analysis, check it against the grammar of the language, and build the internal data structures that represent each clause in the program. The method used in picoProlog is called *recursive descent*, because it is based on a set of mutually recursive procedures, each responsible for recognizing a certain class of phrases. This is the easiest way to construct a parser by hand, without the aid of special software tools. Since the picoProlog language has a fairly simple syntax, it is quite easy to build a parser from scratch in this way.

In the method of recursive descent, the parser contains one procedure for each kind of phrase in the grammar given in Section 14.1: one procedure *ParseClause* for clauses, another called *ParseTerm* for terms, one called *ParseFactor* for factors, and so on. The job of each procedure is to 'consume' the tokens that make up one instance of its kind of phrase. The procedure is called in a situation where the *token* variable contains the first token of a phrase. It fetches more tokens by calling *Scan*, and when it returns, *token* contains the first token *after* the phrase.

Just as a phrase belonging to one class is made up from elements that are phrases of other kinds, so the analysis procedures call each other in a mutually recursive way to analyse sub-phrases. For example, a compound term may have arguments that are themselves terms, so the procedure *ParseCompound* calls *ParseTerm* to analyse each argument. Each of these arguments may be a compound term itself; if so, then *ParseTerm* calls *ParseCompound* recursively to analyse it. The pattern of recursive calls in the parser exactly mirrors the pattern of recursion on the grammar it is designed to recognize.

Here is a simple implementation of the *ParseCompound* procedure:

```
{ ParseCompound – parse a compound term }
procedure ParseCompound;
begin
  Eat(IDENT);
  if token = LPAR then begin
    Eat(LPAR);
    ParseTerm;
    while token = COMMA do
      begin Eat(COMMA); ParseTerm end;
    Eat(RPAR)
  end
end;
```

This procedure corresponds to the grammar rule

$$compound ::= ident \, [\, `(' \, term \, \{ \, `,` \, term \, \} \, `)' .$$

Each item in the rule that corresponds to a single token has been replaced by a call to the procedure *Eat* (line 851), which checks that the current value of *token* is as expected, and uses *Scan* to get the next token. The two occurrences of *term* have been replaced by calls to the *ParseTerm* procedure. The square brackets (meaning an optional phrase) correspond to an **if** statement, and the curly brackets (meaning a repeated phrase) correspond to a **while** loop in the analysis procedure. In both cases, the condition is expressed in terms of the next token from the input.

There are two differences between this way of building parsers and the translation of grammar rules into logic programs that we discussed in Chapter 10. First, the sequence of tokens that makes up the input is not represented by an explicit list, but by the sequence of values taken by the *token* variable as the *Scan* procedure is called repeatedly. Second, Pascal has nothing corresponding to the backtracking of Prolog, so each decision about which rule to use has to be made irrevocably, knowing only the first token of a phrase. For example, in *ParseCompound*, the decision whether the term has arguments is made by testing whether the next token is an opening parenthesis, and the decision whether there are further arguments is made each time by testing whether the next token is a comma. Not all grammars allow all necessary decisions to be made just by looking at the next token, but picoProlog (by design if not by accident) does allow this, making recursive descent an appropriate choice of analysis method.

Full Prolog implementations typically use a different parsing method call *operator precedence* parsing, because the full syntax of Prolog includes many kinds of infix operators, and even allows the Prolog programmer to define new operators. It is difficult to handle this using recursive descent alone.

There are a couple more things to explain about the parser in picoProlog: how it builds the internal structures that represent the clauses it has read, and what happens if there is a syntax error in the input. The data structures are built by making each analysis procedure into a parameterless *function* that returns a representation of its phrase. Each function receives representations of its sub-phrases as the results of the other analysis procedures it calls, and receives information about identifiers and constants from the lexical analyser in the global variables *tokval*, etc. It uses these to construct the representation of the whole phrase, which it returns as its own result. For comparison with the simple code above, the full version of *ParseCompound* appears at line 863 of Appendix C.

The parser builds each clause in the heap area, and replaces the variables in the input clause with *REF* nodes, ready for the clause to be used with the renaming scheme explained in Chapter 16. The procedure *VarRep* (line 811) manages a little table of variable names that gives the correct index for each variable in the present clause. If the clause is a goal, this table is saved during the execution of the goal, and used by the function *ShowAnswer* (line 821) to display the answer substitution in the familiar '*VAR* = *value*' form.

If an input clause contains syntax errors, the parser adopts a simple strategy for recovery, implemented by procedures *ShowError* (line 665) and *Recover* (line 675). After printing an error message, they set a flag *errflag* to prevent a cascade of further error messages, then discard characters up to the next full stop (or, if input is from the keyboard, the end of the line). The *token* variable is set to *DOT*, the code for a full stop.

To make this strategy work, the analysis routines are written in such a way that they will not scan past a full stop. The result is that all the active analysis procedures will exit without consuming any more tokens, and control returns to the procedure *ReadClause* (line 963), the outermost layer of the parser. Here *errflag* is reset, and the process of reading a clause is tried again. This recovery strategy is not perfect, because it discards the whole of any clause that contains an error, and it can be confused by stray full stop, especially full stops inside strings, but it is easy to implement and fairly effective in practice.

17.7 Trail

The trail stack is kept as a linked list using storage allocated from the global stack area. The global variable *trhead* points to the top item on the stack, and each item t contains a pointer $x\_reset(t)$ to a variable that has become bound, and a pointer $x\_next(t)$ to the item below it.

As discussed in Section 16.5, a variable need be added to the trail only is it is *critical*, that is, if it will still exist after backtracking. This observation is important for efficient use of storage, because a large fraction of bindings affect only 'local' variables of a clause that will be thrown away if the clause fails. The test whether a variable is critical is implemented in the macro *critical* (line 988) by comparing its address with the values of the local and global stack pointers at the last choice point.

There are three procedures that act on the trail. *Save* (line 990) tests if a variable is critical, and if so adds it to the trail; it is called whenever a variable becomes bound. *Restore* (line 999) undoes the bindings that have been recorded on the trail since the last choice point, restoring all variables to their previous state. *Commit* (line 1009) is called as part of executing a cut, and removes from the trail any variables that are no longer critical. This is necessary because the space occupied by non-critical variables may be reclaimed as part of success-popping, and leaving them on the trail would result in dangling pointers.

17.8   Unification

The unification algorithm is implemented in the function *Unify* (line 1083). It is exactly the algorithm explained in Section 16.6, but there are a few details of the coding that should be explained here.

To allow for success-popping, it is important that no variable is ever bound to an object with a shorter lifetime. Variables on the global stack must not point to items on the local stack, and no variable on either stack may point to other items nearer to the top of the same stack. Consequently, if two variables are to be bound together, it is necessary to compare their lifetimes and bind the one that will be discarded first. This is done in procedure *Share* (line 1075), which uses a tricky macro *lifetime* to compute a numeric measure of an object's lifetime.

17.9   Interpreter

Procedure *Execute* (line 1306) and its subroutines implement the depth-first search procedure discussed in Chapter 15. It incorporates a couple of refinements that are described in more detail in Chapter 18, but we give a brief summary here.

The first refinement is that the clauses that are tried against a goal are not all the clauses for the relevant relation, but only those that pass an initial 'filtering' test, chosen so that clauses that fail the test are certain not to solve the goal. This is implemented by a function *Search* that takes a goal and a list of clauses, and discards from the beginning of the list any clauses that fail the test. The *Search* function is used in procedure *Resume* (line 1279) to compute the initial procedure for a goal, and also in procedure *Step* (line 1227) to compute the list of clauses to be used on backtracking.

The second refinement is that a different method can sometimes be used to solve the last subgoal in a clause body. This method, called the tail recursion optimization (TRO), allows some programs to be executed in less storage space than would otherwise be needed. The refinement is implemented by adding a test to the *Step* procedure that detects when TRO can be used, and a procedure *TroStep* (line 1191) that carries out a resolution step using the improved method.

The main loop of the execution mechanism is in procedure *Resume* (line 1279). It is made into a separate procedure because the execution mechanism is called recursively as part of the implementation of the built-in relation **not**.

17.10   Built-in relations

Each built-in relation is implemented as a Boolean function with no parameters. When one of these functions is called, the arguments of the relation are available in the global array *av*. The job of the Boolean function is to return *true* if the relation is true of these arguments, and *false* if not; the function may also set the values of variables in the arguments. If the function returns *true*, it should set *current* to point to the next subgoal to be solved, usually *g_rest*(*current*). There follow brief notes on the implementation of each built-in relation:

- The cut symbol ! is implemented in *DoCut* (line 1351) by resetting the *choicepoint* variable to the value it had when the calling frame was created, thereby freezing all choices made since that time. The *Commit* operation is used to discard from the trail any bindings that are no longer critical.

- If *P* is a valid literal, then the subgoal *call*(*P*) behaves as if *P* itself appeared in place if the subgoal. This behaviour is implemented in *DoCall* (line 1360) by a trick, using a dummy clause whose body consists of a single variable.

- Negation as failure, **not** *P*, is implemented in *DoNot* (line 1376) by calling the execution mechanism recursively to solve *P*. If the recursive call ends in failure, then *DoNot* returns *true*; otherwise, it commits to the first solution and returns *false*.

- The arithmetic relations *plus* and *times* are implemented by *DoPlus* (line 1408) and *DoTimes* (line 1430). Each involves a case analysis according to which arguments are known integers and which are unknown, and in each case, the unknown arguments are calculated from the known ones.

- The relation $X = Y$ is implemented in *DoEqual* (line 1456) by unifying X and Y. If this succeeds then the unifying substitution becomes part of the answer substitution of the executing goal. This gives exactly the same effect as if the relation were defined by the clause

$$X = X :- \,.$$

so making it a built-in relation is purely a matter of convenience.

- The tests *integer*(X) and *char*(X) are implemented by *DoInteger* (line 1463) and *DoChar* (line 1470). They are implemented by a straightforward test of the *t_kind* field of the argument.

17.11 Main program

The main program of picoProlog deals with the command-line arguments and the opening of input files. Pascal provides no standard way of doing these things, so the main program uses a small collection of procedures that are not standard Pascal, but can be implemented easily with most compilers. The parameterless function

function *argc*: *integer*;

should return the number of command-line arguments, including the program name. Thus if picoProlog were started with the command

```
$ pprolog motel.pp
```

then the *argc* function would return 2. The arguments themselves are accessed using the procedure

> **procedure** *argv*(*i*: *integer*; **var** *arg*: *tempstring*);

This should store the string that is argument number *i* in the *arg* parameter, terminating it with the character *chr*(0). Arguments are numbered from zero, with argument number zero being the program name.

To open a named file for reading, the main program uses the function

> **function** *openin*(**var** *f*: *text*; **var** *name*: *tempstring*): *boolean*;

This function is passed the name of the file (terminated by *chr*(0)) as its *name* argument. It should attempt to open the file for reading and associate it with the Pascal file variable *f*, returning *true* if the file is successfully opened. If the file cannot be opened, the program should not crash, but *openin* should return *false*.

The main program uses these procedures in a straightforward way to read in the clauses from each of the files named on the command line, and finally reads a sequence of goals from the keyboard.

Chapter 18

Interpreter optimizations

In this chapter, we describe briefly three improvements that are incorporated in the picoProlog interpreter:

- *Garbage collection* for the global stack recovers storage space that has become inaccessible, but is not recovered by the usual stack-like behaviour of the storage mechanism.
- *Indexing* quickly discards from a procedure those clauses that 'obviously' fail to match a goal literal. This saves the time needed to carry out unification for those clauses, and enables the interpreter to detect that some goals are determinate without the help of cuts.
- *Tail recursion* is treated specially. When the last literal in a clause body is reached, it is sometimes possible to reclaim the stack space used by the clause before executing the literal. This allows recursive relations of a simple form to be executed in constant space.

The three refinements work well together: indexing makes more goals determinate, so their working space can be recovered early by the garbage collector, and it also makes more tail calls amenable to special treatment. These refinements are important, because they allow a Prolog system with a finite amount of storage to execute programs that have a simple pattern of recursion without any limit on the recursion depth. Broadly speaking, if a program could be written with a loop in a conventional programming language, the same program can naturally be written in Prolog in such a way that a Prolog system with these refinements can execute it in constant space.

18.1 Garbage collection

As picoProlog programs are executed, much of the storage that is allocated is reclaimed by the usual process of contracting the stacks on backtracking or determinate success. But some storage may not be reclaimed in this way, even though it has become inaccessible to the program. An example is a program like this:

$$translation(X, Z) :- analyse(X, Y), !, synthesize(Y, Z).$$

All the global stack space allocated during execution of $analyse(X, Y)$ that is not part of the immediate result Y will no longer be accessible after the cut, because even backtracking cannot then return to $analyse(X, Y)$. The purpose of the garbage collector is to reclaim this storage.

The garbage collector is the most subtle and complicated part of the picoProlog system. Because it has to analyse the whole network of pointers in the system state, it breaks all the abstraction boundaries that keep other parts of the system simple. It must do so, because it must discover what parts of the allocated storage are accessible from any part of the state.

Another source of complexity, even compared to other garbage collectors, is the kind of garbage collection that Prolog demands. We do not want to lose the advantages of stack-like reclamation of global stack space on backtracking, so the garbage collector must work by compacting all the accessible storage in a way that preserves the order of data in memory. This makes the task of the garbage collector more difficult than it would be if it simply linked the garbage into a free list, as some storage allocation schemes do.

For garbage collection to work, it must be possible to find all the pointers that lead into the global stack from outside. These pointers may be stored in the interpreter's 'register' variables such as *call* or *trhead*, or in the fields of a local stack frame. During a resolution step, pointers into the global stack are also help in the local variables of interpreter procedures like *Unify*. This would cause great problems if we allowed garbage collection to take place in the middle of a resolution step, especially because items in the global stack are moved during garbage collection. Consequently, we arrange that the garbage collector is called only at 'quiet' times, when the only pointers into the global stack are help in interpreter registers or local stack frames.

The main loop of the interpreter includes a test whether the amount of free storage left is less than a certain threshold *GCLOW*. If so, the garbage collector is called before the next resolution step begins. If storage runs out *during* a resolution step, execution of the goal is abandoned without much grace. This scheme is reasonable, because the amount of storage consumed during a resolution step is bounded by the size of the largest program clause, for global stack space is consumed by copying out parts of the clause. In theory, we could calculate this bound for each Prolog program and use it in place of the constant value *GCLOW*, but picoProlog does not bother with this. When the garbage collector runs, it must find at least *GCHIGH* words of free space, otherwise execution stops immediately. This prevents the situation where a program calls the garbage collector many times in quick succession before finally running out of space.

The garbage collector is implemented as the procedure *Collect* (line 1668), and is based on the 'LISP 2 garbage collector' described in the answer to an exercise on page 602 of the book *Fundamental Algorithms* by Donald E. Knuth (Addison–Wesley, 1973). Its work is divided into four phases:

1. Mark all accessible storage in the global stack.
2. Compute the new location of that each accessible block will have after storage has been compacted.
3. Adjust internal and external pointers to global stack items to point to the new locations of the items.
4. Compact the accessible storage towards the top of the *mem* array.

During phase 1, the accessible storage is marked by modifying the *t_kind* field of each node. During phase 2, the distance that a node will move relative to the bottom of the stack is stored in a special field *t_shift* that is added to each node for use by the garbage collector. This information is used in phase 3 to adjust pointers to the node. Further details of the implementation are contained in comments in the code.

18.2   Indexing

In solving a goal literal P, the usual method is to take the list of clauses for same relation as P (the *procedure* for P), and try them in sequence until a clause matches P. The other clauses may be tried later after backtracking. The indexing optimization works by filtering out from the procedure some of the clauses that do not match, so increasing the likelihood that each of the remaining clauses does match. There are two benefits in this: first, the test applied in filtering the list of clauses is much cheaper than allocating a frame and performing unification, so time is saved if some of the clauses for a relation can be filtered out. The second benefit is obtained after a matching clause has been found. If there are no remaining alternatives in the procedure, there is no need to mark the stack frame as a choice point, and no need to visit it again on backtracking. Filtering the list of clauses makes it more likely that there will be no alternatives that have not been discarded, and so increases the chance of avoiding backtracking.

An implementation of indexing requires a quick and effective test that compares a goal literal with the head of a clause. This test must say 'yes' when the two literals can be unified, but may say 'no' otherwise. It does not matter much if the test says 'yes' when the two literals cannot actually be unified, but it must not say 'no' if they *can* be unified. Since all the clauses in a procedure share the same relation symbol as the goal, it is pointless to use the relation symbol for filtering. Instead, picoProlog (and many other Prolog implementations) filter the clauses according to an index computed from the first argument of the relation.

The function *Key* (line 1120) computes an integer index $key(t)$ from a compound term t. The function is chosen so that if two terms t_1 and t_2 are unifiable then $key(t_1) = key(t_2)$ or $key(t_1) = 0$ or $key(t_2) = 0$. This is achieved by making $key(t)$ depend on the outermost function symbol in the first argument of t, and putting $key(t) = 0$ if the first argument of t is a variable. If a goal literal and a clause head are mapped to different non-zero integers by the *key* function, then they are not unifiable, so there is no point in trying to use the clause to solve the goal. Each clause c has the *key* value of its head stored in a field *c_key(c)*, and the function *Search* (line 1143) uses these values to find the first clause in a procedure that is not discarded by indexing. *Search* is used both to find the first clause to try when a new goal is adopted, and also to determine the list of clauses that are saved in a stack frame for use on backtracking. The effect of using *Search* in this way is the same as filtering the whole procedure all at once.

It is unfortunate that the choice of *key* function introduces an asymmetry among the arguments of a relation by treating the first argument specially, but this fits in well with the natural programming style in which the first few arguments of a relation are its usual inputs and the last few are its outputs. A relation that is defined by recursion on lists will often have a clause that applies when the first argument is *nil*, and one that applies when the first argument is *X:A*. Indexing on the outermost function symbol allows picoProlog to choose the right clause each time, and avoid backtracking to try the other clause.

18.3   Tail recursion

When the interpreter executes the last literal in a clause body, the resolution step replaces the literal by the body of the matching clause. Normally, this is represented by adding a new frame to the stack, with the current frame as its parent. The new frame contains the clause body as its goal, and the current frame contains no further subgoals to be solved. If execution of the clause body succeeds, the next subgoal to be solved will come from the parent frame of the original frame.

Under certain conditions, it is possible to release the storage occupied by the current frame *before* starting to solve the subgoals in the new frame, and to arrange that the new frame shares the same parent as the current frame. If execution of the subgoals in the new frame succeeds, control will then pass directly to the parent of the current frame. This is known as the *tail recursion optimization.*

The advantage of this optimization is particularly great in the case of relations that are defined in a 'tail recursive' way, that is, where the only recursive calls in the definition appear as the last literals in clause bodies, as in the following definition of *revapp*, taken from Section 13.3:

$$revapp(nil, B, B) :- \; .$$
$$revapp(X{:}A, B, C) :- revapp(A, X{:}B, C).$$

In this definition, the recursive call of *revapp* appears as the only literal in a clause body, so it is certainly the last one. Reversing a list with n elements leads to n recursive calls of *revapp*, and normally this would lead to n frames being created on the local stack. With the tail recursion optimization, however, the first of these frames is released at the same time that the second one is created, and the second one is released at the same time that the third one is created, and so on. The program needs no more than a certain fixed amount of local stack space, however long the list that is being reversed. The tail recursion optimization has turned the recursive behaviour of the program into a loop-like behaviour.

The tail recursion optimization cannot always be used when the last literal of a clause is being solved, because sometimes the frame that would be discarded might still be needed later for backtracking. So before deciding to use the optimization, the interpreter must check that *both* the calling relation *and* the relation being called are free from non-determinism. If there are still clauses for the calling relation that have not been tried, then backtracking may return to the current frame to try those clauses. Also, if there are alternatives to the clause that is being used to solve the tail call, then backtracking will return to the current frame to find the goal to which those alternatives should be applied. In picoProlog, a macro *tro_test* (line 1180) checks that these conditions are satisfied before the tail recursion optimization is used. It also checks that the current frame is not the bottom one on the stack, because the variables in that frame are needed to print the answer.

If the test succeeds, then the current frame will not be visited by backtracking. Before discarding it, we also need to make sure that there are no outside references to its local variables. Because the current frame is on top of the stack, and links between variables are always directed downwards in the local stack, we can be sure that any references to the current frame must come from the new frame. We can avoid such references by a dirty trick: before unifying the current subgoal with the head of the clause, we slide the current frame upwards on the stack, and allocate space for the new frame underneath it. That way, any references from one frame to the other will lead from the old frame to the new one, and the old frame can then be discarded safely. This rather convoluted manoeuvre is accomplished by the procedure *TroStep* (line 1191).

In an interpreter, the tail recursion optimization costs some time, because it is necessary to test whether it can be applied, and if so, to make the complex moves needed to discard the old frame early. In comparison, the time benefit of going straight from the new frame to the parent of the current frame on success is negligible. The real benefit of this optimization is the space it saves, because it allows simple programs – those that could be written as loops in conventional programming languages – to be executed in constant stack space. In a Prolog implementation based on a compiler, the benefit of the tail recursion optimization is even clearer, because the test whether it can be applied can be carried out once and for all by the compiler, and need not be repeated every time a relation is used by the running program.

Additional space may be saved in an implementation that also includes a garbage collector, because storage on the global stack can be reclaimed as soon as the stack frames that reference it have been discarded. The tail recursion optimization also combines well with indexing, because part of the test whether the optimization can be applied involves checking that there are no untried clauses for either the calling or the called relation, and indexing makes this more likely by discarding alternatives earlier.

18.4 A concluding example

The three refinements we have described work well together. For example, let us consider the problem of computing the sum of a list of numbers. We can define a relation $sum(A, S)$ that holds if S is the sum of list A:

$$sum(nil, 0) :- .$$
$$sum(X{:}A, S) :- sum(A, S_1), plus(X, S_1, S).$$

Using the techniques of Chapter 13, we can transform the program into the following *tail recursive* form:

$$sum(A, S) :- sum1(A, 0, S).$$

$$sum1(nil, S_0, S_0) :- .$$
$$sum1(X{:}A, S_0, S) :- plus(S_0, X, S_1), sum1(A, S_1, S).$$

The relation $sum1$ is defined so that $sum1(A, S_0, S)$ holds if S is equal to S_0 plus the sum of the elements of A. The transformed program is called tail recursive because the recursive call of $sum1$ occurs at the end of its clause.

Indexing of the first argument of $sum1$ allows picoProlog to determine which of the two clauses for $sum1$ applies to each goal, and calls to $sum1$ execute without backtracking and without creating any choice points, even without including any cuts in the program. Because there are no choice points, the tail recursion optimization applies, and the program executes in a constant amount of stack space: the stack space needed to sum a list of 1000 elements is no bigger than that needed to sum a list of 3 elements. Each recursive call of $sum1$ replaces one stack frame by another one that differs only in the values of its variables, as a subgoal of the form $sum1(X{:}A, S_0, S)$ is replaced by one of the form $sum1(A, S_1, S)$, where $S_1 = S_0 + X$. Finally, after a call to sum has succeeded, the associated frames are popped from the local stack, and the only global stack data that is accessible is the result. Any space allocated to hold intermediate results can be reclaimed by the garbage collector.

If we were to write a Pascal function to sum a list of numbers, it would probably look rather like this:

```
function Sum(a₀: list): integer;
    var a: list; s: integer;
begin
    a := a₀; s := 0;
    while a ≠ nil do begin
        s := s + head(a);
        a := tail(a)
    end
end;
```

In each iteration of the loop, the values of variables s and a change as follows: the first element of a is added to s, then the first element is removed from a. This is exactly the same change as takes place in the Prolog program as one stack frame is replaced by another.

What we have just shown is that a simple Prolog program for the same task is executed in essentially the same way. The difference in efficiency between the Pascal program and the picoProlog program is the difference between a program that is compiled and one that is interpreted. With a Prolog compiler that uses the refinements discussed in this chapter, this difference can be eliminated too, and Prolog programs can run at the almost the same speed as a Pascal program for the same problem.

Chapter 19

In conclusion

In this book, we have looked at logic programming from three complementary points of view: as a mathematical theory based on logic, as a medium for expressing the solutions of problems and as a programming language that is implemented on computers. Each of these three points of view is important in the history of logic programming.

The mathematical theory of logic programming draws on concepts from mathematical logic, and the theorems of soundness and completeness for Horn clause resolution mirror results that can be proved using similar methods in the more general setting of first order predicate calculus. It was Alan Robinson who first discovered that the single rule of Resolution was complete for the clausal form of predicate calculus, and invented the unification algorithm that is an essential part of resolution. These results were reported in the classic paper 'A machine-oriented logic based on the resolution principle'. (Details of books and papers cited here may be found in the Further Reading section below.)

Kowalski's book *Logic for Problem Solving* opened up the field by showing that many common problems from artificial intelligence had a natural representation as logic programs. As we have seen, problems like combinatorial searching and parsing have natural expressions as logic programs.

New ideas in programming are of little use unless they lead to computer programs that really work. In the case of logic programming, this means that there is a need for implementations of Prolog that work at speeds comparable to other languages. David H. D. Warren did important work here, by showing how to implement Prolog for the DEC–10 computer in a demonstrably efficient way. The data structures used in all Prolog implementations to represent goals and clauses are based on his early work. His famous article with Luis and Fernando Pereira, 'Prolog: the language and its implementation compared with Lisp', showed that Prolog programs could achieve the same order of speed as comparable programs written in Lisp, but with a versatility and elegance that the Lisp programs could not match. High-performance Prolog implementations use compilers instead of

185

the interpreter techniques we studied in picoProlog. Nevertheless, the data structures are the same, and refinements like garbage collection, indexing and optimized tail calls carry across to implementations based on compilers.

In the author's view, the true importance of logic programming should not be seen as depending solely on Prolog. Although Prolog is undeniably the most successful realization of logic programming ideas, it is weak as a programming language. It does not support notions like modularity and strong compile-time typing that help with the construction of large and reliable software, and practical details like input/output are not well integrated with the logic programming part of Prolog: hence our avoidance of them in this book. One solution to these problems with Prolog is to design new and better logic programming languages that remedy the defects and deficiencies. Recent developments in this direction have been made by P. M. Hill and J. W. Lloyd at the University of Bristol and are described in their book, *The Gödel Programming Language*.

Another view is that logic programming is just one of a network of ideas that can be used in understanding and building complex systems. Prolog can be used for prototyping, and for constructing appropriate parts of a larger system, other parts of which may be built using more traditional techniques. From this point of view, the links between logic programming and other ideas in computer science are as important as its strength as a programming paradigm in its own right. In this book, we have touched on links with databases, the theory of programming languages, theorem proving and hardware design. The techniques that we have studied in the implementation of picoProlog provide other links: with other declarative programming paradigms such as functional programming, with the type systems of programming languages like ML and with the technology of automatic theorem proving.

Further reading

Rather than attempt a comprehensive bibliography, which would run into many thousands of entries, I will restrict myself here to recommending some of the books and papers I have found helpful in studying logic and logic programming. These works themselves contain references to more sources. Besides these, there are several journals and periodic conferences that are entirely devoted to the subject. First, two book on the the theory of logic programming; the first of these is the standard account, and the second is a more accessible textbook.

- J. A. Lloyd, *Foundations of Logic Programming*, second edition, Springer-Verlag, 1987.
- C. J. Hogger, *Essentials of Logic Programming*, Oxford University Press, 1990.

The following book by Kowalski concentrates on the expression of typical artificial intelligence problems in Horn clause logic.

- R. Kowalski, *Logic for Problem Solving*, North Holland, 1979.

For programming in Prolog itself, two useful texts are

- W. F. Clocksin and C. S. Mellish, *Programming in Prolog*, Springer-Verlag, 1981.
- L. Sterling and E. Y. Shapiro, *The Art of Prolog: Advanced Programming Techniques*, MIT Press, 1986.

A lot of information about Prolog implementation techniques is contained in

- D. Maier and D. S. Warren, *Computing with Logic: Logic Programming with Prolog*, Benjamin Cummings, 1988.

The techniques used in building Prolog compilers (rather than interpreters) are covered in

- H. Aït-Kaci, *Warren's Abstract Machine: A Tutorial Reconstruction*, MIT Press, 1991.

Considered as a programming language, Prolog is relatively primitive. Some possible directions for future development are shown by the language Gödel, described in

- P. M. Hill and J. W. Lloyd, *The Gödel Programming Language*, MIT Press, 1994.

For a book on logic, with almost no reference to computer programming, the author recommends

- H. B. Enderton, *A Mathematical Introduction to Logic*, Academic Press, 1972.

This book follows the standard development of mathematical logic, from which many concepts are borrowed in the theory of logic programming. Rather charmingly, the book contains a single FORTRAN statement on page 16.

Finally, some of the primary literature on logic programming is quite easy to read, and worth looking up. A good place to start are the papers

- J. A. Robinson, 'A machine-oriented logic based on the resolution principle', *J. ACM.*, **12**, 1 (January 1965), pp. 23–41.
- M. H. van Emden and R. A. Kowalski, 'The semantics of predicate logic as a programming language', *J. ACM.*, **23**, 4 (October 1976), pp. 733–42.
- D. H. D. Warren, L. M. Pereira and F. Pereira, 'Prolog: the language and its implementation compared with Lisp', Proc. Symp. on AI and Programming Languages, *SIGPLAN Notices*, **12**, 8 (August 1977), pp. 109–15.

Appendix A

Answers to the exercises

1.1 Modify the *lounge* relation to allow two bedroom doors, but leave the *bedroom* relation unchanged:

$suite(FD, LW, BD_1, BD_2, BW_1, BW_2) :-$
    $lounge(FD, LW, BD_1, BD_2), bedroom(BD_1, BW_1), bedroom(BD_2, BW_2).$

$lounge(FD, LW, BD_1, BD_2) :-$
    $opposite(FD, LW), adjacent(LW, BD_1), adjacent(LW, BD_2).$

$bedroom(BD, BW) :-$
    $adjacent(BD, BW), BW = east.$

There are eight solutions to the goal

$\# :- suite(FD, LW, BD_1, BD_2, BW_1, BW_2).$

However, some of these describe suites that cannot be built with rectangular rooms inside a rectangular boundary.

2.1 a. Join the *manager* and *bill* relations on the *NAME* field, select the records that satisfy $AMOUNT > 10$, and then project on the *NAME* field:

$answer(NAME) :-$
    $manager(NAME), bill(NAME, NUMBER, AMOUNT), AMOUNT > 10.$

b. Join the *bill* relation with itself on the *NAME* field, select the records that satisfy $NUMBER_1 \neq NUMBER_2$, then project on the *NAME* field:

$answer(NAME) :-$
    $bill(NAME, NUMBER_1, AMOUNT_1),$
    $bill(NAME, NUMBER_2, AMOUNT_2),$
    $NUMBER_1 \neq NUMBER_2.$

c. Join the *bill* and *paid* relations on the *NUMBER* field, select the records in which the amount paid is less than amount of the bill, and finally project on the *NAME* field:

> $answer(NAME) :-$
> $\quad bill(NAME, NUMBER, AMOUNT_1),$
> $\quad paid(NUMBER, AMOUNT_2, DATE),$
> $\quad AMOUNT_2 < AMOUNT_1.$

d. Define a relation *prompt(NUMBER)* that holds if *NUMBER* is the number of a bill that was paid before February 1st. This relation can be defined by selecting from the *paid* relation and projecting on the *NUMBER* field:

> $prompt(NUMBER) :- paid(NUMBER, AMOUNT, DATE), before(DATE, feb1).$

Now define a relation *issued(NUMBER)* that is true if someone has been given a bill numbered *NUMBER*. Define it by projecting the *bill* relation on the *NUMBER* field:

> $issued(NUMBER) :- bill(NAME, NUMBER, AMOUNT).$

The difference of these two relations gives a relation *late(NUMBER)* that holds if the bill numbered *NUMBER* has been issued, but has not been paid promptly:

> $late(NUMBER) :- issued(NUMBER), \textbf{not } prompt(NUMBER).$

Finally, we can obtain the names of late payers by joining with the *bill* relation on the *NUMBER* field and projecting on the *NAME* field:

> $answer(NAME) :- bill(NAME, NUMBER, AMOUNT), late(NUMBER).$

3.1   The goal fails because their is no solution to the subgoal *member*(X, nil). This accurately reflects that fact that only non-empty lists have a maximum element.

3.2   The solution $X = 3$ is displayed twice if we use the definition of *maximum* in terms of *member* and *dominates*. This is because their are two ways of deriving the fact that 3 is a member of the list $3{:}1{:}3{:}2{:}nil$. With the direct definition of *maximum*, the solution is displayed only once.

3.3   In terms of *append* and other relations:

  a. $prefix(A, B) :- append(A, C, B).$
  b. $suffix(A, B) :- append(C, A, B).$
  c. $segment(A, B) :- prefix(C, B), suffix(A, C).$
  e. $delete(A, X, B) :- append(C, X{:}D, A), append(C, D, B).$

By recursion:

  a. $prefix(nil, B) :- .$
    $prefix(X{:}A, X{:}B) :- prefix(A, B).$
  b. $suffix(B, B) :- .$
    $suffix(A, X{:}B) :- suffix(A, B).$

c. $segment(A, B) :- prefix(A, B).$
  $segment(A, X{:}B) :- segment(A, B).$
d. $sublist(nil, nil) :- .$
  $sublist(A, X{:}B) :- sublist(A, B).$
  $sublist(X{:}A, X{:}B) :- sublist(A, B).$
e. $delete(X{:}A, X, A) :- .$
  $delete(Y{:}A, X, Y{:}B) :- delete(A, X, B).$
f. $perm(nil, nil) :- .$
  $perm(X{:}A, B) :- delete(B, X, C), perm(A, C).$

3.4   a. By recursion:

$$last(X{:}nil, X) :- .$$
$$last(X{:}A, Y) :- last(A, Y).$$

b. In terms of *append*:

$$last(A, X) :- append(B, X{:}nil, A).$$

The goal $\# :- last(A, 3)$ has infinitely many solutions of the form $A = X_1{:}X_2{:}\ldots{:}X_n{:}3{:}nil$.

3.5   With the first definition of *maximum* (the one in terms of *member* and *dominates*), the answer $X = 3$ is displayed twice, because there are two ways of showing that 3 is a member of the list $3{:}1{:}3{:}2{:}nil$, and picoProlog is enumerating *proofs* rather than the answers themselves. With the other definition of *maximum*, the answer is only displayed once, because there is only one way of deriving the answer in this case.

3.6   Because of Prolog's left-to-right rule, the clause

$$flatten(fork(L, R), C) :- flatten(L, A), flatten(R, B), append(A, B, C).$$

does not work well if only the list C is given, because it causes the subgoal $flatten(L, A)$ to be solved first, and that subgoal does not contain any of the given information. The result is that Prolog blindly tries all trees L and R, looking for pairs of trees whose flattened forms join to give C. This search will go on forever, finding only some of the correct solutions.

For this use of *flatten*, it is better to rewrite the clause as

$$flatten(fork(L, R), C) :- append(A, B, C), flatten(L, A), flatten(R, B).$$

This leads to a systematic search of the ways of splitting C into two parts A and B, followed by systematic searches for ways of building trees for the two parts.

There is a further problem: one of the ways of splitting a list into two parts is to have one part be *nil*, and the other part be the whole list. Choosing this split results in an attempt to solve the original problem as a sub-problem of itself, and hence to an infinite search. A solution to this problem is to require both parts of the split to be non-empty, like this:

$$flatten(fork(L, R), C) :- append(X{:}A, Y{:}B, C), flatten(L, X{:}A), flatten(R, Y{:}B).$$

4.1   The problem involves the five literals *valuable*, *metal*, *yellow*, *heavy* and *gold*, so the truth table has $32 = 2^5$ rows. We present it here in a compact form, allowing '*' to stand for both T and F, and using '?' to stand for an unknown result:

valuable	metal	yellow	heavy	gold	(1)	(2)	(3)
T	*	*	*	*	T	?	T
F	F	*	*	*	T	T	?
F	T	F	*	*	T	T	?
F	T	T	F	*	T	?	?
F	T	T	T	T	F	T	F
F	T	T	T	F	F	F	T

For example, the first line of this compact table stands for 16 lines of the full table, and records the fact that (1) is true whenever *valuable* is true, regardless of the values of the other literals. The table shows that (1) is false only if either (2) or (3) is false, so demonstrating that (1) follows from (2) and (3) together.

4.2   If C is a ground clause then $C[g] = C$ for any substitution g; so if $\models_M C$ then $\models_M C[g]$. Conversely, suppose that $\models_M C[g]$ for all ground substitutions g, and let g_0 be any ground substitution. Then $\models_M C[g_0]$, so $\models_M C$. We need to assume that the alphabet contains at least one constant, for otherwise there are no ground terms, and so no ground substitutions g_0.

4.3   If t is a variable Y, then Y is different from X, since X does not appear in t. Consequently

$$t[X \leftarrow u] = Y[X \leftarrow u] = Y = t.$$

If t is a compound term $f(t_1, \ldots, t_k)$ and X does not appear in t, then X does not appear in any of the t_i. So we may assume as induction hypotheses that $t_i[X \leftarrow u] = t_i$ for each i. We deduce that

$$t[X \leftarrow u] = f(t_1, \ldots, t_k)[X \leftarrow u] = f(t_1[X \leftarrow u], \ldots, t_k[X \leftarrow u])$$
$$= f(t_1, \ldots, t_k) = t.$$

This completes the proof.

4.4   We use structural induction on t. If t is a variable X, we calculate

$$X[I] = I(X) = X.$$

If t is a compound term $f(t_1, \ldots, t_k)$, and $t_i[I] = t_i$ for each i, then

$$f(t_1, \ldots, t_k)[I] = f(t_1[I], \ldots, t_k[I]) = f(t_1, \ldots, t_k).$$

This completes the proof.

4.5   We prove that the two substitutions

$$s_1 = \{X \leftarrow u]\} \triangleright \{Y \leftarrow w\},$$
$$s_2 = \{Y \leftarrow w\} \triangleright \{X \leftarrow u[Y \leftarrow w]\}$$

are equal by showing that they have the same effect on any variable V.

If v is different from both x and y, then clearly $s_1(v) = s_2(v) = v$. If v is the same as x, we find

$$s_1(x) = x[x \leftarrow u][y \leftarrow w] = u[y \leftarrow w],$$
$$s_2(x) = x[y \leftarrow w][x \leftarrow u[y \leftarrow w]] = x[x \leftarrow u[y \leftarrow w]] = u[y \leftarrow w].$$

And if v is the same as y, we find

$$s_1(y) = y[x \leftarrow u][y \leftarrow w] = y[y \leftarrow w] = w,$$
$$s_2(y) = y[y \leftarrow w][x \leftarrow u[y \leftarrow w]] = w[x \leftarrow u[y \leftarrow w]] = w.$$

5.1   Let M be a structure, and suppose $\models_M C$, where $C = (P :- Q_1, Q_2)$. Let g be any ground substitution; then $\models_M C[g]$, so either $P[g]$ is true in M, or one of $Q_1[g]$, $Q_2[g]$ is false in M. Putting this another way, either $P[g]$ is true, or one of $Q_2[g]$, $Q_1[g]$ is false. In other words, $\models_M C'[g]$, where $C' = (P :- Q_2, Q_1)$. Since this is so for any ground substitution g, it follows that $\models_M C'$.

5.2   From the given clause $P :- Q_1, Q_2$, we may derive the clause $P[s] :- Q_1[s], Q_2[s]$ by the rule of substitution. But $Q_1[s] = Q_2[s]$, so this is the same as $P[s] :- Q_1[s], Q_1[s]$. The desired result $P[s] :- Q[s]$ may be derived from this by the following *rule of direct factoring*: from $A :- B, B$ derive $A :- B$.

For soundness of this rule, let M be a structure, and suppose that $\models_M C$, where $C = (A :- B, B)$. Let g be any ground substitution. We may assume that $\models_M C[g]$, and must show that $\models_M C'[g]$, where $C' = (A :- B)$. But $C[g] = (A[g] :- B[g], B[g])$, so either $A[g]$ is true in M or one of the literals $B[g]$ is false in M (and so both are false). Hence $\models_M C'[g]$ as required.

5.3   Let M be a model of the two premises C_1 and C_2, let C' be the proposed conclusion, and let g be a ground substitution. By the rule of substitution, M is a model of $C_1[g]$ and $C_2[g]$. Hence by the rule of ground resolution, M is a model of $C'[g]$, the ground resolvent of $C_1[g]$ and $C_2[g]$ on $Q[g] = Q_j[g]$. Thus M is a model of $C'[g]$ for every g, and so M is a model of C'.

6.1   a. $\{X \leftarrow g(h(z)), Y \leftarrow h(z)\}$.
   b. There are no unifiers.
   c. $\{X \leftarrow g(a), Y \leftarrow a, z \leftarrow g(g(a))\}$.

6.2   If t and v are different constants *foo* and *baz*, and u is a variable X, then t and u have a unifier $\{X \leftarrow foo\}$, and u and v have a unifier $\{X \leftarrow baz\}$, but t and v have no unifier.

6.3   We first show that $t_1[r \triangleright s] = t_2[r \triangleright s]$. Expanding the left-hand side,

$$t_1[r \triangleright s] = f(u_1, w_1)[r][s] = f(u_1[r][s], w_1[r][s]).$$

Now $u_1[r] = u_2[r]$ because r unifies u_1 and u_2, and $w_1[r][s] = w_2[r][s]$ because s unifies $w_1[r]$ and $w_2[r]$. Also $t_2[r \triangleright s] = f(u_2[r][s], w_2[r][s])$ as above.

Now suppose p is any unifier of t_1 and t_2; we show that p factors through $r \triangleright s$. Since p unifies t_1 and t_2, it also unifies u_1 and u_2, so p factors through r, say $p = r \triangleright q$. But p also unifies w_1 and w_2, so $w_1[r][q] = w_1[p] = w_2[p] = w_2[r][q]$, and q unifies $w_1[r]$ and $w_2[r]$. Since s is the m.g.u. of $w_1[r]$ and $w_2[r]$, it follows that q factors through s, say $q = s \triangleright k$. Putting the pieces together, we find that

$$p = r \triangleright q = r \triangleright (s \triangleright k) = (r \triangleright s) \triangleright k,$$

and p factors through $r \triangleright s$. Since this happens for any unifier p of t_1 and t_2, it follows that $r \triangleright s$ is a most general unifier of t_1 and t_2.

6.4   First, $r \triangleright s$ is a unifier of $\{t_1, t_2, t_3\}$ because $t_1[r \triangleright s] = t_1[r][s] = t_2[r][s] = t_2[r \triangleright s]$ (since r is a unifier of t_1 and t_2), and $t_1[r \triangleright s] = t_1[r][s] = t_3[r][s] = t_3[r \triangleright s]$ (since s is a unifier of $t_1[r]$ and $t_2[r]$).

Moreover, $r \triangleright s$ is a most general unifier; for if p is another unifier of $\{t_1, t_2, t_3\}$ then p unifies t_1 and t_2 in particular, so p factors through r, say $p = r \triangleright q$. We now find that $t_1[r][q] = t_1[p] = t_3[p] = t_3[r][q]$, so q unifies $t_1[r]$ and $t_3[r]$, and hence q factors through the m.g.u. s, say $q = s \triangleright k$. Summarizing, $p = r \triangleright q = r \triangleright s \triangleright k$, and p factors through $r \triangleright s$.

Finally, if $\{t_1, t_2, t_3\}$ has a unifier p, then p unifies t_1 and t_2 in particular, and so they have a m.g.u. r, and p factors through r, say $p = r \triangleright q$. As above, q unifies $t_1[r]$ and $t_2[r]$, so these have an m.g.u. s, and an m.g.u. of $\{t_1, t_2, t_3\}$ is $r \triangleright s$.

6.5   a.   The relation $\preceq$ is reflexive because $t[I] = t$ and so $t \preceq t$ for any term t. Also, $\preceq$ is transitive. If $t \preceq u$ and $u \preceq w$, say $t[s] = u$ and $u[r] = w$, then $t[s \triangleright r] = t[s][r] = u[r] = w$, so $t \preceq w$. However, *preceq* is not anti-symmetric; for example, if X and Y are distinct variables, then $X \preceq Y$ (because $X[X \leftarrow Y] = Y$), and similarly $Y \preceq X$, but $X \neq Y$.

   b.   We first show that for any terms t and u, $t \sqcap u$ is a lower bound of t and u. Let s_0 be the substitution defined by

$$s_0(V) = \begin{cases} t, & \text{if } V = \phi(t, u) \\ V, & \text{otherwise.} \end{cases}$$

Then $\phi(t, u)[s_0] = t$ for all terms t and u. We now use structural induction to extend this result, showing that $(t \sqcap u)[s_0] = t$ for all t and u. It follows that $t \sqcap u \preceq t$, and the proof that $t \sqcap u \preceq u$ is similar. The actual proposition $P(w)$ proved by induction on w is the following:

> For all t and u, if $w = t \sqcap u$ then $w[s_0] = t$.

The base case occurs when w is a variable. If so, and $w = t \sqcap u$, then $w = \phi(t, u)$; we examined this case above. For the induction step, we assume that $P(w_1), \ldots, P(w_k)$ hold, and show $P(w)$ where $w = f(w_1, \ldots, w_k)$. If so, and $w = t \sqcap u$, then $t = f(t_1, \ldots, t_k)$ for some terms $t_1, \ldots, t_k$, and similarly $u = f(u_1, \ldots, u_k)$, with $w_i = t_i \sqcap u_i$ for each i. Applying the induction hypothesis, we find that $w_i[s_0] = t_i$ for each i, and so $w[s_0] = t$. This completes the proof that $t \sqcap u \preceq t$.

To show that $t \sqcap u$ is a *greatest* lower bound, suppose $w[s_1] = t$ and $w[s_2] = u$ for some term w. Define a substitution s by

$$s(V) = s_1(V) \sqcap s_2(V).$$

We claim that $w[s] = t \sqcap u$, so $w \preceq t \sqcap u$.

Again we argue by structural induction, the actual proposition $Q(w)$ proved by induction being the following:

> For all t and u, if $w[s_1] = t$ and $w[s_2] = u$, then $w[s] = t \sqcap u$.

For the base case, if w is a variable V, then

$$w[s] = s(V) = s_1(V) \sqcap s_2(V) = w[s_1] \sqcap w[s_2] = t \sqcap u.$$

For the step case, we assume that $Q(w_1)$, ..., $Q(w_k)$ hold, and show $Q(w)$ where $w = f(w_1, \ldots, w_k)$. If $w[s_1] = t$, then $t = f(t_1, \ldots, t_k)$ with $t_i = w_i[s_1]$ for each i. Also if $w[s_2] = u$, then $u = f(u_1, \ldots, u_k)$ with $u_i = w_i[s_2]$ for each i. Applying the induction hypothesis, we conclude that $w_i = t_i \sqcap u_i$ for each i, and so

$$w[s] = f(w_1[s], \ldots, w_k[s]) = f(t_1 \sqcap u_1, \ldots, t_k \sqcap u_k) = t \sqcap u.$$

This completes the proof.

c. If $u' = u[s]$ is a variant of u having no variables in common with t, and t and u' have a most general unifier r, then $t[r]$ is a least upper bound of t and u.

7.1

1. $reverse(X_1{:}A_1, C_1) :\!- reverse(A_1, B_1), append(B_1, X_1{:}nil, C_1).$	(rev.2)
2. $reverse(X_2{:}A_2, C_2) :\!- reverse(A_2, B_2), append(B_2, X_2{:}nil, C_2).$	(rev.2)
3. $reverse(X_1{:}X_2{:}A_2, C_1) :\!-$	1, 2, R
$\quad reverse(A_2, B_2), append(B_2, X_2{:}nil, B_1), append(B_1, X_1{:}nil, C_1).$	
4. $reverse(nil, nil) :\!- .$	(rev.1)
5. $reverse(X_1{:}X_2{:}nil, C_1) :\!- append(nil, X_2{:}nil, B_1), append(B_1, X_1{:}nil, C_1).$	3, 4, R
6. $append(nil, B_6, B_6) :\!- .$	(app.1)
7. $reverse(X_1{:}X_2{:}nil, C_1) :\!- append(X_2{:}nil, X_1{:}nil, C_1).$	5, 6, R
8. $append(X_8{:}A_8, B_8, X_8{:}C_8) :\!- append(A_8, B_8, C_8).$	(app.2)
9. $reverse(X_1{:}X_2{:}nil, X_2{:}C_8) :\!- append(nil, X_1{:}nil, C_8).$	7, 8, R
10. $append(nil, B_{10}, B_{10}) :\!- .$	(app.1)
11. $reverse(X_1{:}X_2{:}nil, X_2{:}X_1{:}nil) :\!-$	9, 10, R

7.2   One possibility is to define *palin* in terms of *reverse*:

$palin(A) :\!- reverse(A, A).$

We can use the following definition of *reverse* (see Chapter 13):

$reverse(A, B) :\!- revapp(A, nil, B).$

$revapp(nil, B, B) :\!- .$
$revapp(X{:}A, B, C) :\!- revapp(A, X{:}B, C).$

The following sequence of goals is derived in solving $\# :\!- palin(1{:}X{:}Y{:}Z{:}nil)$:

$\# :\!- palin(1{:}X{:}Y{:}Z{:}nil).$
$\# :\!- reverse(1{:}X{:}Y{:}Z{:}nil, 1{:}X{:}Y{:}Z{:}nil).$
$\# :\!- revapp(1{:}X{:}Y{:}Z{:}nil, nil, 1{:}X{:}Y{:}Z{:}nil).$
$\# :\!- revapp(X{:}Y{:}Z{:}nil, 1{:}nil, 1{:}X{:}Y{:}Z{:}nil).$
$\# :\!- revapp(Y{:}Z{:}nil, X{:}1{:}nil, 1{:}X{:}Y{:}Z{:}nil).$
$\# :\!- revapp(Z{:}nil, Y{:}X{:}1{:}nil, 1{:}X{:}Y{:}Z{:}nil).$
$\# :\!- revapp(nil, Z{:}Y{:}X{:}1{:}nil, 1{:}X{:}Y{:}Z{:}nil).$
$\# :\!- .$

The final step involves unifying the lists $Z{:}Y{:}X{:}1{:}nil$ and $1{:}X{:}Y{:}Z{:}nil$, yielding the answer substitution $\{Z \leftarrow 1, Y \leftarrow X\}$.

8.1   a. In terms of the relation *opposite* from Chapter 1:

$$optstep(X{:}Y{:}A, A) :- opposite(X, Y).$$
$$optstep(X{:}A, X{:}B) :- optstep(A, B).$$

or (more cleverly),

$$optstep(A, B) :- append(P, X{:}Y{:}Q, A), opposite(X, Y), append(P, Q, B).$$

b. This is an example of transitive closure (see Chapter 9):

$$optimize(A, A) :- \textbf{not } improvable(A).$$
$$optimize(A, C) :- optstep(A, B), optimize(B, C).$$

$$improvable(A) :- optstep(A, B).$$

The *improvable* relation is needed so that the test *improvable*(A) is ground whenever A is.

c. The trick is to introduce a relation *adjoin*, defined so that *adjoin*(X, A, B) is true if B is a path equivalent to $X{:}A$, but optimal if A is itself optimal:

$$optimize(nil, nil) :- .$$
$$optimize(X{:}A, C) :- optimize(A, B), adjoin(X, B, C).$$

$$adjoin(X, nil, X{:}nil) :- .$$
$$adjoin(X, Y{:}A, A) :- opposite(X, Y).$$
$$adjoin(X, Y{:}A, X{:}Y{:}A) :- \textbf{not } opposite(X, Y).$$

This solution is plainly linear in the length of A, but the previous solution is quadratic, because each optimization step is linear, and there may be $n/2$ of them.

9.1   The relation $conn(A, B, P, S)$ is defined to mean that P is a path from A to B that avoids nodes in S:

$$connected(A, B, P) :- conn(A, B, P, A{:}nil).$$

$$conn(A, A, nil, S) :- .$$
$$conn(A, C, N{:}P, S) :- arc(A, B, N), notmember(B, S), conn(B, C, P, B{:}S).$$

$$arc(empty7, state(X, Y), state(0, Y)) :- .$$
$$arc(empty5, state(X, Y), state(X, 0)) :- .$$
$$arc(pour7to5, state(X, Y), state(0, V)) :- plus(X, Y, V), leq(V, 5).$$
$$arc(pour5to7, state(X, Y), state(U, 0)) :- plus(X, Y, U), leq(U, 7).$$
$$arc(fill5from7, state(X, Y), state(U, 5)) :- plus(X, Y, Z), plus(U, 5, Z).$$
$$arc(fill7from5, state(X, Y), state(7, V)) :- plus(X, Y, Z), plus(7, V, Z).$$
$$arc(fill7, state(X, Y), state(7, Y)) :- .$$
$$arc(fill5, state(X, Y), state(X, 5)) :- .$$

$$leq(X, Y) :- plus(X, W, Y).$$

Executing the goal

$\# :- \ connected(state(0,0), state(4,0), P).$

gives the answer

$P = fill7{:}fill5from7{:}empty5{:}pour7to5{:}fill7{:}fill5from7{:}empty5{:}nil$

in addition to several longer ones.

9.2 Use (for example) the term $state(left, left, right, left)$ to name the state in which the farmer, the wolf and the cabbage are on the left bank, and the goat is alone on the right bank. The relation $opposite(A, B)$ is true if A and B are different banks of the stream:

$opposite(left, right) :- \ .$
$opposite(right, left) :- \ .$

A state is unsafe if the wolf and goat or the goat and cabbage are on the same bank, but the farmer is on the opposite bank:

$unsafe(state(A, B, B, C)) :- \ opposite(A, B).$
$unsafe(state(A, B, C, C)) :- \ opposite(A, C).$

Using negation as failure, we can now define a relation $safe(S)$ that checks whether state S is safe:

$safe(S) :- \ notunsafe(S).$

Use the term $take(X, A, B)$ to name the move of taking object X from bank A to bank B. Then we can define a relation $arc(N, X, Y)$ that is true if move N takes state X to state Y:

$arc(take(wolf, A, B), state(A, A, C, D), state(B, B, C, D)) :- \ opposite(A, B).$
$arc(take(goat, A, B), state(A, C, A, D), state(B, C, B, D)) :- \ opposite(A, B).$
$arc(take(cabbage, A, B), state(A, C, D, A), state(B, C, D, B)) :- \ opposite(A, B).$
$arc(take(boat, A, B), state(A, C, D, E), state(B, C, D, E)) :- \ opposite(A, B).$

For example, taking the wolf from A to B requires that the farmer and the wolf are on bank A beforehand, and results in both being on the opposite bank B, while the goat and cabbage do not move. With this set-up, we can use the path-finding program from the preceding exercise to solve the goal

$\# :- \ connected(state(left, left, left, left), state(right, right, right, right), P).$

9.3 Each expression must contain exactly three operators, so we define *trial* in terms of a relation $trial1(E, B_0, B)$ that is true if E is an expression containing not more than B_0 operators, and B is the number left over:

$trial(E) :- \ trial1(E, 3, 0).$

$trial1(E, B_0, B) :-$
$\quad plus(B_1, 1, B_0), trial1(E_1, B_1, B_2), trial1(E_2, B_2, B), combine(E_1, E_2, E).$
$trial1(4, B_0, B_0) :- \ .$

$combine(E_1, E_2, add(E_1, E_2)) :- .$
$combine(E_1, E_2, subtract(E_1, E_2)) :- .$
$combine(E_1, E_2, multiply(E_1, E_2)) :- .$
$combine(E_1, E_2, divide(E_1, E_2)) :- .$

There are five possible structures for an expression with three operators *op*; symbolically, they are $op(4, op(4, op(4, 4)))$, $op(4, op(op(4, 4), 4)$ and their mirror images, and the symmetrical structure $op(op(4, 4), op(4, 4))$. The operators *op* can be chosen from the four possibilities in $4^3 = 64$ ways, giving a total of $5 \times 64 = 320$ expressions.

9.4   We can represent the state as a term $towers(A, B, C)$, where A, B and C are the lists of discs on each spike, in decreasing order of size. We can define a relation $legal(X, A)$ to hold if disc X can legally be added to a spike holding discs A:

$legal(X, nil) :- .$
$place(X, Y:nil) :- less(X, Y).$

Any disc can be added to an empty spike; a disc can be added to a non-empty spike exactly if it is smaller than the top disc already on the spike. Now we can write clauses for a relation *move* like this:

$move(towers(X:A, B, C), towers(A, X:B, C), move12) :- legal(X, B).$
$move(towers(X:A, B, C), towers(A, B, X:C), move13) :- legal(X, C).$
$\ldots$

There are six such clauses altogether. To calculate the number of states, observe that we can place the largest disc on any spike, then the next smaller disc either on an empty spike or on top of the largest disc. Following this procedure, we have a free choice for each disc, so there are $3^5 = 243$ states in all. As is well known, there is a solution in $2^5 - 1 = 31$ moves. Without programming the solution explicitly, it can be found fairly quickly using loop-avoidance.

10.1

$flatten(T, A) :- flat1(T, A, nil).$

$flat1(tip(X), X:A, A) :- .$
$flat1(fork(T_1, T_2), A_0, A) :-$
    $flat1(T_1, A_0, A_1),$
    $flat1(T_2, A_1, A).$

This version of *flatten* avoids the need to append the flattened forms of the trees T_1 and T_2 in order to construct the flattened form of $fork(T_1, T_2)$.

10.2   Define *space* like this:

$space(A, C) :- eat(`\ ', A, B), space(B, C).$
$space(A, A).$

This relation can be used in a new definition of *expr* by systematically inserting calls to *space* wherever *eat* is used. For example, the clause

$$expr(add(T_1, T_2), A, D) :-$$
$$term(T_1, A, B), eat(`+`, B, C), expr(T_2, C, D).$$

becomes

$$expr(add(T_1, T_2), A, E) :-$$
$$term(T_1, A, B), space(B, C), eat(`+`, C, D), expr(T_2, D, E).$$

Alternatively, we could modify the definition of *eat* to ignore spaces itself.

10.3 It is helpful to use a relation $digit(C, K)$ that holds if the character C is a decimal digit and K is the corresponding numeric value:

$$digit(`0`, 0) :- .$$
$$digit(`1`, 1) :- .$$
$$\ldots$$

We can define a first version of *number* as follows:

$$number(A_0, A) :-$$
$$eat(C, A_0, A_1), digit(C, K), number1(A_1, A).$$

$$number1(A_0, A) :-$$
$$eat(C, A_0, A_1), digit(C, K), number1(A_1, A).$$
$$number1(A_0, A_0) :- .$$

This version does not compute the value of the number. To do that, we add *two* extra arguments to the relation *number1*, so that $number1(N_0, N, A_0, A)$ holds if the difference between A_0 and A is a (possibly empty) sequence of digits, and the value of the number composed by adding these digits after the number N_0 is N:

$$number(N, A_0, A) :-$$
$$eat(C, A_0, A_1), digit(C, K), number1(K, N, A_1, A).$$

$$number1(N_0, N, A_0, A) :-$$
$$eat(C, A_0, A_1), digit(C, K),$$
$$times(N_0, 10, N_1), plus(N_1, K, N_2),$$
$$number1(N_2, N, A_1, A).$$
$$number1(N_0, N_0, A_0, A_0) :- .$$

Extending the parser for expressions is a simple matter of adding the clause:

$$factor(N, A_0, A) :- number(N, A_0, A).$$

10.4 We just need to build a parser for the grammar

$$good ::= `0` \mid `1` \; good \; good$$

The program is as follows:

$$good(A) :- good1(A, nil).$$

$$good1(0{:}A_0, A_0) :- .$$
$$good1(1{:}A_0, A) :- good(A_0, A_1), good(A_1, A).$$

To improve the control behaviour of the goal $\# :- good(A)$ (and yield the solutions in increasing order of length), we can add a call to the *list* predicate (see page 30):

$$good(A) :- list(A), good1(A, nil).$$

Solving the goal $\# :- good(A)$ with this definition of *good* causes Prolog to generate lists A of increasing length whose elements are all unknown variables, then solve the subgoal $good1(A, nil)$. Since the length of the first argument of *good1* goes down in each recursive call, the program is well-behaved.

11.1

$$value(X, X) :- integer(X).$$
$$value(add(P, Q), Z) :- value(P, X), value(Q, Y), plus(X, Y, Z).$$
$$value(subtract(P, Q), Z) :- value(P, X), value(Q, Y), plus(Y, Z, X).$$
$$value(times(P, Q), Z) :- value(P, X), value(Q, Y), times(X, Y, Z).$$
$$value(divide(P, Q), Z) :-$$
$$\quad value(P, X), value(Q, Y), /\!\!\!\!\sim = 0, times(Y, Z, X).$$

11.2   Define *update* by

$$update(nil, X, V, val(X, V){:}nil) :- .$$
$$update(val(X, W){:}A, X, V, val(X, V){:}A) :- .$$
$$update(val(Y, W){:}A, X, V, val(Y, W){:}B) :-$$
$$\quad \textbf{not } X = Y, update(A, X, V, B).$$

Extend *eval* by adding the clause

$$eval(let(X, E_1, E_2), A, V) :-$$
$$\quad eval(E_1, A, V_1), update(A, X, V_1, B), eval(E_2, B, V).$$

12.1

$$flipflop(A, B, X, Y) :- nand(A, Y, X), nand(B, X, Y).$$

There are five stable states:

$A = 0$	$B = 0$	$X = 1$	$Y = 1;$
$A = 0$	$B = 1$	$X = 1$	$Y = 0;$
$A = 1$	$B = 0$	$X = 0$	$Y = 1;$
$A = 1$	$B = 1$	$X = 0$	$Y = 1;$
$A = 1$	$B = 1$	$X = 1$	$Y = 0.$

The use of this circuit as a memory element is explained by the existence of two stable states in which the inputs are both 1.

12.2

$$xor(A, B, Z) :\!-$$
$$pwr(P), gnd(Q),$$
$$ptran(P, A, C), ntran(C, A, Q),$$
$$ptran(A, B, Z), ntran(Z, B, C),$$
$$ptran(B, A, Z), ntran(Z, C, B).$$

The goal $\# :\!- xor(A, B, Z)$ reveals that there are four stable states, one for each combination of the inputs A and B, and the output Z always has the correct value.

13.1

$$ord(X{:}Y{:}A) :\!- X < Y, ord(Y{:} \ A \ )$$

$$ord(U{:}V{:}B) :\!- U < V, ord(V{:}B).$$

This gives the resolvent

$$ord(X{:}Y{:}V{:}B) :\!- X < Y, Y < V, ord(V{:}B).$$

Now resolve with (ord.2):

$$ord(X{:}Y{:}V{:}A) :\!- X < Y, Y < V, ord(V{:} \ B \ )$$

$$ord(W{:}nil) :\!-$$

This gives the desired special case:

$$ord(X{:}Y{:}V{:}nil) :\!- X < Y, Y < V.$$

13.2 In terms of *append*:

$$consec(X, Y, A) :\!- append(B, X{:}Y{:}C, A). \tag{1}$$

Resolving this with (app.1) gives $B = nil$, $A = X{:}Y{:}C$ and

$$consec(X, Y, X{:}Y{:}C) :\!- .$$

Resolving (1) with (app.2) gives $B = U{:}B'$, $A = U{:}A'$ and

$$consec(X, Y, U{:}A') :\!- append(B', X{:}Y{:}C, A').$$

which we can fold with (1) to give

$$consec(X, Y, U{:}A') :\!- consec(X, Y, A').$$

13.3 Define the relation *path* by

$$path(A, B, P) :\!- ispath(P), first(P, A), last(P, B).$$

Unfolding the definitions of *ispath*, *first* and *last*, followed by a folding step, then gives a direct definition of *path* by recursion. The clause

$$connected(A, B) :- path(A, B, P).$$

is obtained by folding the original definition of *connected* with the clause defining *path*.

13.4   a. The definition is by simultaneous recursion on the tree and the path:

$$select(T, nil, T) :- .$$
$$select(fork(L, R), l{:}P, U) :- select(L, P, U).$$
$$select(fork(L, R), r{:}P, U) :- select(R, P, U).$$

b. Again we use simultaneous recursion on the path and the subject tree:

$$replace(T, nil, U, U) :- .$$
$$replace(fork(L, R), l{:}P, U, fork(L', R)) :- replace(L, P, U, L').$$
$$replace(fork(L, R), r{:}P, U, fork(L, R')) :- replace(R, P, U, R').$$

c. The answers to parts (a) and (b) share a common pattern:

$$select(T, P, U) :- replace(T, P, U, T).$$

d. The transformation results in the following direct definition of *change*:

$$change(T, T, U', U') :- .$$
$$change(fork(L, R), U, U', fork(L', R)) :- change(L, U, U', L').$$
$$change(fork(L, R), U, U', fork(L, R')) :- change(R, U, U', R').$$

Using an ordinary Prolog system

Most of the programs in this book can also be run using an ordinary Prolog system, with only small changes of notation. For example, standard Prolog omits the ':−' from unit clauses, so the clause we have been writing as

$$opposite(north, south) :- \; .$$

would be written

$$opposite(north, south).$$

in Prolog. Goals are written with '?−' like this: ?− $opposite(X, Y)$.

The most significant difference between picoProlog and standard Prolog systems is that picoProlog does not provide the list notation of standard Prolog. There are two choices here: one choice is to translate the programs from the book to use the standard notation, so that the famous *append* program becomes

$$append([\,], B, B).$$
$$append([X \mid A], B, [X \mid C]) :- append(A, B, C).$$

You can then write goals like ?− $append([1, 2], [3, 4], X)$.

The other choice is to ignore Prolog's list notation, and use infix colon instead. To do this, you must declare ':' as an infix symbol by executing the goal

$$?- op(50, xfy, :).$$

Taking this approach means that programs and goals must be written as shown in this book: you cannot mix this notation with Prolog lists, because the Prolog list $[1, 2, 3]$ is not equal to the term $1{:}2{:}3{:}nil$.

Another difference between picoProlog and standard Prolog is that picoProlog provides arithmetic facilities through the built-in relations *plus* and *times*, and the facilities provided by Prolog are different. This problem is solved by adding to each program the following definitions of these relations:

$plus(A, B, C) :-$ $integer(A), integer(B), !, C$ is $A + B.$
$plus(A, B, C) :-$ $integer(B), integer(C), !, C > B, A$ is $C - B.$
$plus(A, B, C) :-$ $integer(C), integer(A), !, C > A, B$ is $C - A.$
$plus(A, B, C) :-$ $write($'Bad arguments to plus'$), nl, abort.$

$times(A, B, C) :-$ $integer(A), integer(B), !, C$ is $A * B.$
$times(A, B, C) :-$
   $integer(B), integer(C), !, C$ mod $B =:= 0, A$ is $C/B.$
$times(A, B, C) :-$
   $integer(C), integer(A), !, C$ mod $A =:= 0, B$ is $C/A.$
$times(A, B, C) :-$ $write($'Bad arguments to times'$), nl, abort.$

Most other built-in relations of picoProlog are exactly the same as the standard ones of Prolog: !, =, **not**, *call*, *integer*. Standard Prolog has no character objects, and represents characters by the integers that are their ASCII codes; thus there is no *char* relation. Finally, there is a standard built-in relation *fail* that behaves exactly like picoProlog's *false*, but any relation with no clauses behaves the same way, so you can continue to use *false*.

PicoProlog source code

pprolog.p – picoProlog interpreter

{ Copyright (C) J. M. Spivey 1992 }

{ This is the 'picoProlog' interpreter described in the book 'An Introduction to Logic
Programming through Prolog' by Michael Spivey (Prentice Hall, 1995). Copyright is
retained by the author, but permission is granted to copy and modify the program for
5   any purpose other than direct commercial gain.

The text of this program must be processed by the 'ppp' macro processor before it can
be compiled. }

program *picoProlog*(*input, output*);

define(*turbo*)

10 { tunable parameters }
const

MAXSYMBOLS = 511;	{ max no. of symbols }
HASHFACTOR = 90;	{ percent loading factor for hash table }
MAXCHARS = 2048;	{ max chars in symbols }
15 *MAXSTRING* = 128;	{ max string length }
MAXARITY = 63;	{ max arity of function, vars in clause }
MEMSIZE = 24576;	{ size of *mem* array }
GCLOW = 512;	{ call GC when this much space left }
GCHIGH = 4096;	{ GC must find this much space }

20 { special character values }

define(*ENDSTR, chr*(0))	{ end of string }
define(*TAB, chr*(9))	{ tab character }
define(*ENDLINE, chr*(10))	{ newline character }
define(*ENDFILE, chr*(127))	{ end of file }

C.1 Coding conventions

25 { We ignore Pascal's stupid rule that all global variables must be declared together at the start of the program; likewise all global types and all global constants. Many Pascal compilers relax the rule to make large programs easier to read and write; but if your Pascal compiler enforces it, you know what to do, and a text editor is the tool for the job. }

30 { Most Pascal compilers implement a 'default' part in case statements. The macro **default** should be defined as the text that comes between the ordinary cases and the default part. If the default part is like an ordinary case, but labelled with a keyword (say 'others'), then the definition of **default** should include the semicolon that separates it from the preceding case, like this: '; others:'. If your Pascal doesn't have default parts for case
35 statements, most of them can be deleted, since they are only calls to *bad_tag* put there for robustness. The only other one (in *Scan*) will need a little more work. }

ifdef (*turbo*, *define*(**default**, **else**))

{ Some Pascal implementations buffer terminal output, but provide a special procedure to flush the buffer; the *flush_out* macro should be defined to call whatever procedure is
40 necessary. A call to *flush_out* follows each prompt for input from the terminal, and the progress messages from the garbage collector. }

define(*flush_out*)

{ Pascal's numeric labels make code that uses **goto** statements unnecessarily obscure, so we define a few macros that have meaningful names but expand to plain integers that
45 can be used as labels. }

define(*end_of_pp*, 999)
define(*found*, 1)
define(*exit*, 2)
define(*done*, 3)
50 *define*(*found2*, 4)

{ When something goes drastically wrong, picoProlog sometimes needs to stop immediately. In standard Pascal, this is achieved by a non-local jump to the label *end_of_pp*, located at the end of the main program. But some Pascal compilers don't allow non-local jumps; they often provide a *halt* procedure instead. The macro *abort* should be
55 defined to do whatever is needed. }

label *end_of_pp*;
define(*abort*, **goto** *end_of_pp*)
ifdef (*turbo*, *define*(*abort*, *halt*))

{ Here are a few convenient abbreviations: }
60 *define*(*incr*, $1 := $1 + 1)   { increment a variable }
define(*decr*, $1 := $1 − 1)   { decrement a variable }
define(**return**, **goto** *exit*)   { return from procedure }
define(*skip*)   { empty statement }

C.2 Error handling

{ These macros print an error message, then either arrange for execution of a goal to
65 abandoned (by clearing the *run* flag), or abandon the whole run of picoProlog. They use the $0 feature to allow for a list of arguments.

Errors during execution of a goal are reported by *exec_error*; it sets the *run* flag to false, so the main execution mechanism will stop execution before starting on another resolution step. }

70 **var** *run*: *boolean*;   { whether execution should continue }
      dflag: *boolean*;   { switch for debugging code }

   define(*exec_error*,
        begin *writeln*; *write*('Error: ', $0); *run* := *false* **end**)
      define(*panic*, **begin** *writeln*; *writeln*('Panic: ', $0); *abort* **end**)
75 *define*(*bad_tag*, *panic*('bad tag ', $2: 1, ' in ', $1))

C.3 String buffer

{ The strings that are the names of function symbols, variables, etc. are saved in the array *charbuf*: each string is represented elsewhere by an index *k* into this array, and the characters of the string are *charbuf*[*k*], *charbuf*[*k* + 1], ..., terminated by the character *ENDSTR*. *charptr* is the last occupied location in *charbuf*.

80   In addition to these 'permanent' strings, there are 'temporary' strings put together for some short-term purpose. These are kept in arrays of size *MAXSTRING*, and are also terminated by *ENDSTR*. }

   type
      permstring = 1 .. *MAXCHARS*;
85   *tempstring* = **array** [1 .. *MAXSTRING*] **of** *char*;

   var
      charptr: 0 .. *MAXCHARS*;
      charbuf: **array** [1 .. *MAXCHARS*] **of** *char*;

   { *StringLength* – length of a tempstring }
90 **function** *StringLength*(**var** *s*: *tempstring*): *integer*;
      var *i*: 0 .. *MAXSTRING*;
   begin
      i := 0;
      while *s*[*i* + 1] ≠ *ENDSTR* **do** *incr*(*i*);
95   *StringLength* := *i*
   end;

   { *SaveString* – make a tempstring permanent }
   function *SaveString*(**var** *s*: *tempstring*): *permstring*;
      var *i*: 0 .. *MAXSTRING*;
100 **begin**
      if *charptr* + *StringLength*(*s*) + 1 > *MAXCHARS* **then**
         panic('out of string space');
      SaveString := *charptr* + 1; *i* := 0;
      repeat
105   *incr*(*i*); *incr*(*charptr*); *charbuf*[*charptr*] := *s*[*i*]
      until *s*[*i*] = *ENDSTR*
   end;

{ *StringEqual* – compare a tempstring to a permstring }
function *StringEqual*(**var** *s1*: *tempstring*; *s2*: *permstring*): *boolean*;
110   **var** *i*: *integer*;
begin
  i := 1;
  while (*s1*[*i*] ≠ *ENDSTR*) ∧ (*s1*[*i*] = *charbuf*[*s2* + *i* − 1]) **do** *incr*(*i*);
  StringEqual := (*s1*[*i*] = *charbuf*[*s2* + *i* − 1])
115 **end**;

{ *WriteString* – print a permstring }
procedure *WriteString*(*s*: *permstring*);
  var *i*: 1 .. *MAXCHARS*;
begin
120 *i* := *s*;
  while *charbuf*[*i*] ≠ *ENDSTR* **do**
    begin *write*(*charbuf*[*i*]); *incr*(*i*) **end**
end;

C.4 Representation of terms

{ It is now time to give the details of how terms are represented. Each 'term' is an index
125 into the *mem* array that points to a small block of contiguous words. The first word
indicates the number and layout of the words that follow. It packs together the size of
the node, and an integer code that determines the kind of term: *FUNC* for a compound
term, *INT* for an integer, and so on. Macros *t_kind*(*t*) and *t_size*(*t*) extract these from
the first word of a term *t*. There is also a bit in the first word that is used by the
130 garbage collector for marking. The second word of the node, *t_shift*(*t*) = *mem*[*t* + 1] is
also reserved for the garbage collector.

The layout of the remaining elements of *mem* that make up the term depends on the
t_kind field. For a *FUNC* term, there is the function symbol *t_func*(*t*), and a variable
number of arguments, which may be referred to as *t_arg*(*t*, 1), *t_arg*(*t*, 2), ..., *t_arg*(*t*, *n*)
135 where *n* is the arity of *t_func*(*t*).

For an *INT* term, there is just the integer value *t_ival*(*t*), and for a *CHRCTR* term there
is the character value *t_cval*(*t*), which is actually the code *ord*(*c*). *CELL* nodes represent
variables and have a *t_val* field that points to the value. *REF* nodes are the numeric
markers in program clauses that refer to a slot in the frame for a clause; the *t_index*
140 field is the index of the slot. *UNDO* nodes do not represent terms at all, but items on
the trail stack; they share some of the layout of terms, so that they can be treated the
same by the garbage collector. }

type
  pointer = *integer*;   { index into *mem* array }
145 *define*(*NULL*, 0)   { null pointer }

type *term* = *pointer*;
define(*t_tag*, *mem*[$1])
  define(*t_kind*, *t_tag*($1) **div** 256)   { one of *FUNC*, *INT*, ... }
  define(*t_size*, *t_tag*($1) mod 128)   { size in words }
150 *define*(*marked*, (*t_tag*($1) mod 256 ≥ 128)) { GC mark }
  define(*add_mark*, *t_tag*($1) := *t_tag*($1) + 128)

```
          define(rem_mark, t_tag($1) := t_tag($1) − 128)
          define(make_tag, 256 ∗ $1 + $2)
       define(t_shift, mem[$1 + 1])              { for use by gc }
155    define(FUNC, 1)                           { compound term }
          define(t_func, mem[$1 + 2])            {    function symbol }
          define(t_arg, mem[$1 + $2 + 2])        {    arguments (start from 1) }
       define(INT, 2)                            { integer }
          define(t_ival, mem[$1 + 2])            {    integer value }
160    define(CHRCTR, 3)                         { character }
          define(t_cval, mem[$1 + 2])            {    character value }
       define(CELL, 4)                           { variable cell }
          define(t_val, mem[$1 + 2])             {    value or NULL if unbound }
       define(REF, 5)                            { variable reference }
165       define(t_index, mem[$1 + 2])           {    index in frame }
       define(UNDO, 6)                           { trail item }
          { see later }
       define(TERM_SIZE, 3)                      { ... plus no. of args }
```

C.5 Memory allocation

170 { Storage for most things is allocated from the big array *mem*. This array is in three parts: the heap and local stack, which grow upwards from the bottom of *mem*, and the global stack, which grows downwards from the top of *mem*.

The heap stores the clauses that make up the program and running goal; it grows only while clauses are being input and not during execution, so there is no need for free space between the heap and local stack. Program clauses become a permanent part of

175 the heap, but goal clauses (and clauses that contain errors) can be discarded; so there is an extra variable *hmark* that indicates the beginning of the present clause.

The local stack holds activation records for clauses during execution of goals, and the global stack other longer-lived data structures. Both stacks expand and contract during execution of goals. Also, there is a garbage collector that can reclaim inaccessible

180 portions of the global stack. }

```
       var
          lsp, gsp, hp, hmark: pointer;
          mem: array [1 .. MEMSIZE] of integer;

          { LocAlloc − allocate space on local stack }
185    function LocAlloc(size: integer): pointer;
       begin
          if lsp + size ≥ gsp then panic('out of stack space');
          LocAlloc := lsp + 1; lsp := lsp + size
       end;

190    { GloAlloc − allocate space on global stack }
       function GloAlloc(kind, size: integer): pointer;
          var p: pointer;
       begin
          if gsp − size ≤ lsp then
195          panic('out of stack space');
```

```
        gsp := gsp − size; p := gsp;
        t_tag(p) := make_tag(kind, size);
        GloAlloc := p
    end;

200 { HeapAlloc – allocate space on heap }
    function HeapAlloc(size: integer): pointer;
    begin
        if hp + size > MEMSIZE then panic('out of heap space');
        HeapAlloc := hp + 1; hp := hp + size
205 end;

    define(is_heap, ($1 ≤ hp))              { test if a pointer is in the heap }
    define(is_glob, ($1 ≥ gsp))             { test if it is in the global stack }
```

C.6 Character input

{ Pascal's I/O facilities view text files as sequences of lines, but it is more convenient for picoProlog to deal with a uniform sequence of characters, with the end of a line indicated
210   by an *ENDLINE* character, and the end of a file by an *ENDFILE* character. The routines here perform the translation (probably reversing a translation done by the Pascal run-time library). They also allow a single character to be 'pushed back' on the input, so that the scanner can avoid reading too far. }

```
    var
215 interacting: boolean;                    { whether input is from terminal }
    pbchar: char;                           { pushed-back char, else ENDFILE }
    infile: text;                           { the current input file }
    lineno: integer;                        { line number in current file }
    filename: permstring;                   { name of current file }

220 { FGetChar – get a character from a file }
    function FGetChar(var f: text): char;
        var ch: char;
    begin
        if eof(f) then
225         FGetChar := ENDFILE
        else if eoln(f) then
            begin readln(f); incr(lineno); FGetChar := ENDLINE end
        else
            begin read(f, ch); FGetChar := ch end
230 end;

    { GetChar – get a character }
    function GetChar: char;
    begin
        if pbchar ≠ ENDFILE then
235         begin GetChar := pbchar; pbchar := ENDFILE end
        else if interacting then
            GetChar := FGetChar(input)
        else
            GetChar := FGetChar(infile)
```

240 **end**;

    { *PushBack* – push back a character on the input }
    procedure *PushBack*(*ch*: *char*);
    begin
      pbchar := *ch*
245 **end**;

C.7 Representation of clauses

{ Clauses in the picoProlog program (and goals to be executed) have head and body literals in which the variables are replaced by REF nodes. The clause itself is a segment of *mem* that has some fields at fixed offsets, followed by a variable-length sequence of pointers to the literals in the body of the clause, terminated by NULL. Goal clauses have
250 the same representation, but with *head* = NULL. Macros *c_rhs* and *c_body* are defined so that *c_rhs*(*c*) is a pointer to the beginning of the sequence of pointers that makes up the clause body, and *c_body*(*c*, *i*) is the *i*'th literal in the body itself.

Partially executed clause bodies are represented in the execution mechanism by the address of the pointer *p* to the first unsolved literal. For cleanliness, we provide macros
255 *g_first*(*p*) and *g_rest*(*p*) that respectively return the first literal itself, and a pointer that represents the remaining literals after the first one. The test for the empty list is *g_first*(*p*) = NULL.

The number of clauses tried against a goal literal is reduced by using associating each literal with a 'key', calculated so that unifiable literals have matching keys. }

260 **type** *clause* = *pointer*;
    define(*c_nvars*, *mem*[$1])   { no. of variables }
    define(*c_key*, *mem*[$1 + 1])   { unification key }
    define(*c_next*, *mem*[$1 + 2])   { next clause for same relation }
    define(*c_head*, *mem*[$1 + 3])   { clause head }
265 *define*(*c_rhs*, ($1 + 4))   { clause body (ends with NULL) }
    define(*c_body*, *mem*[*c_rhs*($1) + $2 − 1])
    define(*CLAUSE_SIZE*, 4)   { ... plus size of body + 1 }

    define(*g_first*, *mem*[$1])   { first of a list of literals }
    define(*g_rest*, ($1) + 1)   { rest of the list }

C.8 Stack frames and interpreter registers

270 { The local stack is organized as a sequence of frames, each corresponding to an active copy of a program clause. Most fields in a frame are copies of the values of the interpreter's 'registers' when it was created, so here also is the declaration of those global registers. The *tp* register that points to the top of the trail stack is declared later.

The last part of a frame is a variable-length array of cells, containing the actual variables
275 for the clause being used in the frame. The variables are numbered from 1, and each cell is of length *TERM_SIZE*, so the *f_local* macro contains the right formula so that *f_local*(*f*, *i*) is a pointer to the *i*'th cell. }

```
         type frame = pointer;
         define(f_goal, mem[$1])                    { the goal }
280  define(f_parent, mem[$1 + 1])                  { parent frame }
     define(f_retry, mem[$1 + 2])                   { untried clauses }
     define(f_choice, mem[$1 + 3])                  { previous choice-point }
     define(f_glotop, mem[$1 + 4])                  { global stack at creation }
     define(f_trail, mem[$1 + 5])                   { trail state at creation }
285  define(f_nvars, mem[$1 + 6])                   { no. of local variables }
     define(f_local, ($1 + 7 + ($2 − 1) * TERM_SIZE))
     define(FRAME_SIZE, 7)                          { . . . plus space for local variables }

     { frame_size – compute size of a frame with n variables }
     define(frame_size, (FRAME_SIZE + ($1) * TERM_SIZE))

290  var
         current: pointer;                          { current goal }
         call: term;                                { Deref'ed first literal of goal }
         goalframe: frame;                          { current stack frame }
         choice: frame;                             { last choice point }
295      base: frame;                               { frame for original goal }
         proc: clause;                              { clauses left to try on current goal }
```

{ *Deref* is a function that resolves the indirection in the representation of terms. It looks up references in the frame, and following the chain of pointers from variable cells to their values. The result is an explicit representation of the argument term; if the frame is non-*NULL*, the result is never a *REF* node, and if it is a *CELL* node, the *t_val* field is empty. }

```
     { Deref – follow VAR and CELL pointers }
     function Deref(t: term; e: frame): term;
     begin
305      if t = NULL then panic('Deref');
         if (t_kind(t) = REF) ∧ (e ≠ NULL) then
             t := f_local(e, t_index(t));
         while (t_kind(t) = CELL) ∧ (t_val(t) ≠ NULL) do
             t := t_val(t);
310      Deref := t
     end;
```

{ This is a good place to put the forward declarations of a few procedures and functions. }

```
     procedure PrintTerm(t: term; e: frame; prio: integer); forward;
     function ParseTerm: term; forward;
315  function DoBuiltin(action: integer): boolean; forward;
     procedure Collect; forward;
     function Key(t: term; e: frame): integer; forward;
```

{ In the actual definition of a procedure or function that has been declared forward, we repeat the parameter list in a call to the macro *fwd*. Standard Pascal requires this to be replaced by the empty string, but some implementations allow the parameter list to be repeated and check that the two lists agree. }

```
     define(fwd)
     ifdef(turbo, define(fwd, $0))
```

C.9 Symbol table

325 { The names of relations, functions, constants and variables are held in a hash table. It is organized as a 'closed' hash table with sequential search: this is simple but leaves much room for improvement. The symbol table is not allowed to become more full than *HASHFACTOR* per cent, since nearly full hash tables of this kind perform rather badly.

330 Each symbol has an *s_action* code that has a different non-zero value for each built-in relation, and is zero for everything else. User-defined relations have a chain of clauses that starts at the *s_proc* field and is linked together by the *c_next* fields of the clauses. }

```
type symbol = 1 .. MAXSYMBOLS;          { index in symtab }

var
    nsymbols: 0 .. MAXSYMBOLS;          { number of symbols }
    symtab: array [1 .. MAXSYMBOLS] of record
        name: integer;                  { print name: index in charbuf }
        arity: integer;                 { number of arguments or -1 }
        action: integer;                { code if built-in, 0 otherwise }
        proc: clause                    { clause chain }
    end;
    cons, eqsym, cutsym, nilsym, notsym: symbol;

    { We define selector macros for symbols, just as for terms }
    define(s_name, symtab[$1].name)
    define(s_arity, symtab[$1].arity)
    define(s_action, symtab[$1].action)
    define(s_proc, symtab[$1].proc)

    { Lookup – convert string to internal symbol }
    function Lookup(var name: tempstring): symbol;
        label found;
        var h, i: integer; p: symbol;
    begin
        { Compute the hash function in h }
        h := 0; i := 1;
        while name[i] ≠ ENDSTR do
            begin h := (5 * h + ord(name[i])) mod MAXSYMBOLS; incr(i) end;

        { Search the hash table }
        p := h + 1;
        while s_name(p) ≠ −1 do begin
            if StringEqual(name, s_name(p)) then goto found;
            decr(p);
            if p = 0 then p := MAXSYMBOLS
        end;

        { Not found: enter a new symbol }
        { Be careful to avoid overflow on 16 bit machines: }
        if nsymbols ≥ (MAXSYMBOLS div 10) * (HASHFACTOR div 10) then
            panic('out of symbol space');
        s_name(p) := SaveString(name);
        s_arity(p) := −1;
        s_action(p) := 0; s_proc(p) := NULL;
```

found:
370   *Lookup* := *p*
       end;

       type *keyword* = **array** [1 .. 8] **of** *char*;

       { *Enter* – define a built-in symbol }
       function *Enter*(*name*: *keyword*; *arity*: *integer*; *action*: *integer*): *symbol*;
375   **var** *s*: *symbol*; *i*: *integer*; *temp*: *tempstring*;
       begin
           i := 1;
           while *name*[*i*] ≠ ' ' **do**
               begin *temp*[*i*] := *name*[*i*]; *incr*(*i*) **end**;
380   *temp*[*i*] := *ENDSTR*; *s* := *Lookup*(*temp*);
           s_arity(*s*) := *arity*; *s_action*(*s*) := *action*;
           Enter := *s*
       end;

       { Codes for built-in relations }
385 *define*(*CUT*, 1)   { !/0 }
     define(*CALL*, 2)   { *call*/1 }
     define(*PLUS*, 3)   { *plus*/3 }
     define(*TIMES*, 4)   { *times*/3 }
     define(*ISINT*, 5)   { *integer*/1 }
390 *define*(*ISCHAR*, 6)   { *char*/1 }
     define(*NAFF*, 7)   { ¬ /1 }
     define(*EQUALITY*, 8)   { = /2 }
     define(*FAIL*, 9)   { *false*/0 }

       { *InitSymbols* – initialize and define standard symbols }
395 **procedure** *InitSymbols*;
           var *i*: *integer*; *dummy*: *symbol*;
       begin
           nsymbols := 0;
           for *i* := 1 **to** *MAXSYMBOLS* **do** *s_name*(*i*) := −1;
400   *cons* := *Enter*(' :   ', 2, 0);
           cutsym := *Enter*(' !   ', 0, *CUT*);
           eqsym := *Enter*(' =   ', 2, *EQUALITY*);
           nilsym := *Enter*('nil   ', 0, 0);
           notsym := *Enter*('not   ', 1, *NAFF*);
405   *dummy* := *Enter*('call   ', 1, *CALL*);
           dummy := *Enter*('plus   ', 3, *PLUS*);
           dummy := *Enter*('times   ', 3, *TIMES*);
           dummy := *Enter*('integer ', 1, *ISINT*);
           dummy := *Enter*('char   ', 1, *ISCHAR*);
410   *dummy* := *Enter*('false   ', 0, *FAIL*)
       end;

       { *AddClause* – insert a clause at the end of its chain }
       procedure *AddClause*(*c*: *clause*);
           var *s*: *symbol*; *p*: *clause*;
415 **begin**
           s := *t_func*(*c_head*(*c*));

```
         if s_action(s) ≠ 0 then begin
             exec_error('can''t add clauses to built-in relation ');
             WriteString(s_name(s))
420      end
         else if s_proc(s) = NULL then
             s_proc(s) := c
         else begin
             p := s_proc(s);
425          while c_next(p) ≠ NULL do p := c_next(p);
             c_next(p) := c
         end
     end;
```

C.10 Building terms on the heap

430 { Next, some convenient routines that construct various kinds of term in the heap area: they are used by the parsing routines to construct the internal representation of the input terms they read. The routine *MakeRef* that is supposed to construct a *REF* node in fact returns a pointer to one from a fixed collection. This saves space, since all clauses can share the same small number of *REF* nodes. }

```
type argbuf = array [1 .. MAXARITY] of term;

435 { MakeCompound – construct a compound term on the heap }
    function MakeCompound(fun: symbol; var arg: argbuf): term;
        var p: term; i, n: integer;
    begin
        n := s_arity(fun);
440     p := HeapAlloc(TERM_SIZE + n);
        t_tag(p) := make_tag(FUNC, TERM_SIZE + n);
        t_func(p) := fun;
        for i := 1 to n do t_arg(p, i) := arg[i];
        MakeCompound := p
445 end;

    { MakeNode – construct a compound term with up to 2 arguments }
    function MakeNode(fun: symbol; a1, a2: term): term;
        var arg: argbuf;
    begin
450     arg[1] := a1; arg[2] := a2;
        MakeNode := MakeCompound(fun, arg)
    end;

    var refnode: array [1 .. MAXARITY] of term;

    { MakeRef – return a reference cell prepared earlier }
455 function MakeRef(offset: integer): term;
    begin
        MakeRef := refnode[offset]
    end;
```

```
         { MakeInt – construct an integer node on the heap }
460  function MakeInt(i: integer): term;
        var p: term;
     begin
        p := HeapAlloc(TERM_SIZE);
        t_tag(p) := make_tag(INT, TERM_SIZE);
465     t_ival(p) := i; MakeInt := p
     end;

         { MakeChar – construct a character node on the heap }
     function MakeChar(c: char): term;
        var p: term;
470  begin
        p := HeapAlloc(TERM_SIZE);
        t_tag(p) := make_tag(CHRCTR, TERM_SIZE);
        t_cval(p) := ord(c); MakeChar := p
     end;

475  { MakeString – construct a string as a Prolog list of chars }
     function MakeString(var s: tempstring): term;
        var p: term; i: integer;
     begin
        i := StringLength(s);
480     p := MakeNode(nilsym, NULL, NULL);
        while i > 0 do
           begin p := MakeNode(cons, MakeChar(s[i]), p); decr(i) end;
        MakeString := p
     end;

485  { MakeClause – construct a clause on the heap }
     function MakeClause(nvars: integer; head: term;
                          var body: argbuf; nbody: integer): clause;
        var p: clause; i: integer;
     begin
490     p := HeapAlloc(CLAUSE_SIZE + nbody + 1);
        c_nvars(p) := nvars; c_next(p) := NULL; c_head(p) := head;
        for i := 1 to nbody do c_body(p, i) := body[i];
        c_body(p, nbody + 1) := NULL;
        if head = NULL then c_key(p) := 0
495     else c_key(p) := Key(head, NULL);
        MakeClause := p
     end;
```

C.11   Printing terms

{ These routines print terms on the user's terminal. The main routine is *PrintTerm*, which prints a term by recursively traversing it. Unbound cells are printed in the form
500   'L123' (for local cells) or 'G234' (for global cells): the number is computed from the address of the cell. If the frame is *NULL*, reference nodes are printed in the form '@3'. }

```
          { operator priorities }
          define(MAXPRIO, 2)                       { isolated term }
          define(ARGPRIO, 2)                       { function arguments }
505   define(EQPRIO, 2)                            { equals sign }
          define(CONSPRIO, 1)                      { colon }

          { IsString – check if a list represents a string }
          function IsString(t: term; e: frame): boolean;
             label done;
510      const limit = 128;
             var i: integer;
          begin
             i := 0; t := Deref(t, e);
             while i < limit do begin
515         if (t_kind(t) ≠ FUNC) ∨ (t_func(t) ≠ cons) then
                   goto done
                else if t_kind(Deref(t_arg(t, 1), e)) ≠ CHRCTR then
                   goto done
                else
520            begin incr(i); t := Deref(t_arg(t, 2), e) end
             end;
          done:
             IsString := (t_kind(t) = FUNC) ∧ (t_func(t) = nilsym)
          end;

525   { ShowString – print a list as a string }
          procedure ShowString(t: term; e: frame);
          begin
             t := Deref(t, e);
             write('"');
530      while t_func(t) ≠ nilsym do begin
                write(chr(t_cval(Deref(t_arg(t, 1), e))));
                t := Deref(t_arg(t, 2), e)
             end;
             write('"')
535   end;

          { PrintCompound – print a compound term }
          procedure PrintCompound(t: term; e: frame; prio: integer);
             var f: symbol; i: integer;
          begin
540      f := t_func(t);
          if f = cons then begin
                { t is a list: try printing as a string, or use infix : }
                if IsString(t, e) then
                   ShowString(t, e)
545         else begin
                   if prio < CONSPRIO then write('(');
                   PrintTerm(t_arg(t, 1), e, CONSPRIO − 1);
                   write(':');
                   PrintTerm(t_arg(t, 2), e, CONSPRIO);
550            if prio < CONSPRIO then write(')')
```

```
          end
       end
    else if f = eqsym then begin
       { t is an equation: use infix = }
555    if prio < EQPRIO then write('(');
       PrintTerm(t_arg(t, 1), e, EQPRIO - 1);
       write(' = ');
       PrintTerm(t_arg(t, 2), e, EQPRIO - 1);
       if prio < EQPRIO then write(')')
560 end
    else if f = notsym then begin
       { t is a literal 'not P' }
       write('not ');
       PrintTerm(t_arg(t, 1), e, MAXPRIO)
565 end
    else begin
       { use ordinary notation }
       WriteString(s_name(f));
       if s_arity(f) > 0 then begin
570       write('(');
          PrintTerm(t_arg(t, 1), e, ARGPRIO);
          for i := 2 to s_arity(f) do begin
             write(', ');
             PrintTerm(t_arg(t, i), e, ARGPRIO)
575       end;
          write(')')
       end
    end
  end;

580 { PrintTerm – print a term }
    procedure PrintTerm fwd((t: term; e: frame; prio: integer));
    begin
       t := Deref(t, e);
       if t = NULL then
585       write('*null-term*')
       else begin
          case t_kind(t) of
          FUNC:
             PrintCompound(t, e, prio);
590       INT:
             write(t_ival(t): 1);
          CHRCTR:
             write('''', chr(t_cval(t)), '''');
          CELL:
595          if is_glob(t) then
                write('G', (MEMSIZE - t) div TERM_SIZE: 1)
             else
                write('L', (t - hp) div TERM_SIZE: 1);
          REF:
600          write('@', t_index(t))
```

```
            default
                write('*unknown-term(tag=', t_kind(t): 1, ')*')
            end
        end
605  end;

    { PrintClause – print a clause }
    procedure PrintClause(c: clause);
        var i: integer;
    begin
610     if c = NULL then
            writeln('*null-clause*')
        else begin
            if c_head(c) ≠ NULL then begin
                PrintTerm(c_head(c), NULL, MAXPRIO);
615             write(' ')
            end;
            write(' :- ');
            if c_body(c, 1) ≠ NULL then begin
                PrintTerm(c_body(c, 1), NULL, MAXPRIO);
620             i := 2;
                while c_body(c, i) ≠ NULL do begin
                    write(', ');
                    PrintTerm(c_body(c, i), NULL, MAXPRIO);
                    incr(i)
625             end
            end;
            writeln('.')
        end
    end;
```

C.12 Scanner

630 { The *Scan* procedure that reads the next token of a clause or goal from the input, together with some procedures that implement a crude form of recovery from syntax errors.

Scan puts an integer code into the global variable *token*; if the token is an identifier, a number, or a string, there is another global variable that contains its actual value.

The recovery mechanism skips input text until it finds a full stop or (if the input was 635 from the terminal) the end of a line. It then sets *token* to DOT, the code for a full stop. The parser routines are designed so that they will never read past a full stop, and final recovery from the error is achieved when control reaches *ReadClause* again. }

```
    var
        token: integer;          { last token from input }
640     tokval: symbol;          { if token = IDENT, the identifier }
        tokival: integer;        { if token = NUMBER, the number }
        toksval: tempstring;     { if token = STRCON, the string }
        errflag: boolean;        { whether recovering from an error }
        errcount: integer;       { number of errors found so far }
```

645 { Possible values for *token*: }
    define(*IDENT*, 1)   { identifier: see *tokval* }
    define(*VARIABLE*, 2)   { variable: see *tokval* }
    define(*NUMBER*, 3)   { number: see *tokival* }
    define(*CHCON*, 4)   { char constant: see *tokival* }
650 *define*(*STRCON*, 5)   { string constant: see *toksval* }
    define(*ARROW*, 6)   { ':-' }
    define(*LPAR*, 7)   { '(' }
    define(*RPAR*, 8)   { ')' }
    define(*COMMA*, 9)   { ',' }
655 *define*(*DOT*, 10)   { '.' }
    define(*COLON*, 11)   { ':' }
    define(*EQUAL*, 12)   { '=' }
    define(*NEGATE*, 13)   { 'not' }
    define(*EOFTOK*, 14)   { end of file }

660 { *syntax_error* – report a syntax error }
    define(*syntax_error*,
        begin if ¬ *errflag* **then**
            begin *ShowError*; *writeln*($0); *Recover* **end end**)

    { *ShowError* – report error location }
665 **procedure** *ShowError*;
    begin
        errflag := *true*; *incr*(*errcount*);
        if ¬ *interacting* **then begin**
            write('"'); *WriteString*(*filename*);
670   *write*('", line ', *lineno*: 1, ' ')
        end;
        write('Syntax error - ')
    end;

    { *Recover* – discard rest of input clause }
675 **procedure** *Recover*;
        var *ch*: *char*;
    begin
        if ¬ *interacting* ∧ (*errcount* ≥ 20) **then**
            begin *writeln*('Too many errors: I''m giving up'); *abort* **end**;
680   **if** *token* ≠ *DOT* **then begin**
        repeat
            ch := *GetChar*
        until (*ch* = '.') ∨ (*ch* = *ENDFILE*)
              ∨ (*interacting* ∧ (*ch* = *ENDLINE*));
685   *token* := *DOT*
        end
    end;

    define(*is_upper*, ((($1 ≥ 'A') ∧ ($1 ≤ 'Z')) ∨ ($1 = '_')))
    define(*is_letter*, (*is_upper*($1)
690   ∨ (($1 ≥ 'a') ∧ ($1 ≤ 'z'))))
    define(*is_digit*, (($1 ≥ '0') ∧ ($1 ≤ '9')))

```
     { Scan – read one symbol from infile into token. }
     procedure Scan;
        var ch, ch2: char; i: integer;
695  begin
        ch := GetChar; token := 0;
        while token = 0 do begin
           { Loop after white-space or comment }
           if ch = ENDFILE then
700             token := EOFTOK
           else if (ch = ' ') ∨ (ch = TAB) ∨ (ch = ENDLINE) then
              ch := GetChar
           else if is_letter(ch) then begin
              if is_upper(ch) then token := VARIABLE
705           else token := IDENT;
              i := 1;
              while is_letter(ch) ∨ is_digit(ch) do begin
                 if i > MAXSTRING then
                    panic('identifier too long');
710              toksval[i] := ch; ch := GetChar; incr(i)
              end;
              PushBack(ch);
              toksval[i] := ENDSTR; tokval := Lookup(toksval);
              if tokval = notsym then token := NEGATE
715        end
           else if is_digit(ch) then begin
              token := NUMBER; tokival := 0;
              while is_digit(ch) do begin
                 tokival := 10 * tokival + (ord(ch) − ord('0'));
720              ch := GetChar
              end;
              PushBack(ch)
           end
           else begin
725           case ch of
              '(':
                 begin
                    ch := GetChar;
                    if ch ≠ '*' then begin
730                    token := LPAR;
                       PushBack(ch)
                    end
                    else begin
                       ch2 := ' '; ch := GetChar;
735                    while (ch ≠ ENDFILE) ∧ ¬ ((ch2 = '*') ∧ (ch = ')')) do
                          begin ch2 := ch; ch := GetChar end;
                       if ch = ENDFILE then
                          syntax_error('end of file in comment')
                       else
740                       ch := GetChar
                    end
                 end;
```

```
          ')': token := RPAR;
          ',': token := COMMA;
745       '.': token := DOT;
          '=': token := EQUAL;
          '!': begin token := IDENT; tokval := cutsym end;
          ':':
             begin
750             ch := GetChar;
                if ch = '-' then
                   token := ARROW
                else
                   begin PushBack(ch); token := COLON end
755          end;
          '''':
             begin
                token := CHCON; tokival := ord(GetChar); ch := GetChar;
                if ch ≠ '''' then
760                syntax_error('missing quote')
             end;
          '"':
             begin
                token := STRCON; i := 1; ch := GetChar;
765             while (ch ≠ '"') ∧ (ch ≠ ENDLINE) do
                   begin toksval[i] := ch; ch := GetChar; incr(i) end;
                toksval[i] := ENDSTR;
                if ch = ENDLINE then begin
                   syntax_error('unterminated string');
770                PushBack(ch)
                end
             end
          default
             syntax_error('illegal character "', ch, '"')
775       end
       end
    end
end;

    { PrintToken – print a token as a string }
780 procedure PrintToken(t: integer);
    begin
       case t of
       IDENT:
          begin write('identifier '); WriteString(s_name(tokval)); end;
785    VARIABLE:
          begin write('variable '); WriteString(s_name(tokval)); end;
       NUMBER: write('number');
       CHCON: write('char constant');
       ARROW: write('":-"');
790    LPAR: write('"("');
       RPAR: write('")"');
       COMMA: write('","');
```

DOT: write('"."');
COLON: write('":"');
795   EQUAL: write('"="');
STRCON: write('string constant')
default
    write('unknown token')
end
800   end;

```
        DOT: write('"."');
        COLON: write('":"');
795     EQUAL: write('"="');
        STRCON: write('string constant')
        default
            write('unknown token')
        end
800  end;
```

C.13 Variable names

{ As the parser reads an input clause, the routines here maintain a table of variable names and the corresponding run-time offsets in a frame for the clause: for each i, the name of the variable at offset i is *vartable*[i]. Each clause contains only a few variables, so linear search is good enough.

805 If the input clause turns out to be a goal, the table is saved and used again to display the answer when execution succeeds. }

```
var
    nvars: 0 .. MAXARITY;                    { no. of variables so far }
    vartable: array [1 .. MAXARITY] of symbol;   { names of the variables }
810  { VarRep – look up a variable name }
     function VarRep(name: symbol): term;
         var i: integer;
     begin
         if nvars = MAXARITY then panic('too many variables');
815      i := 1; vartable[nvars + 1] := name;    { sentinel }
         while name ≠ vartable[i] do incr(i);
         if i = nvars + 1 then incr(nvars);
         VarRep := MakeRef(i)
     end;

820  { ShowAnswer – display answer and get response }
     function ShowAnswer(bindings: frame): boolean;
         var i: integer; ch: char;
     begin
         if nvars = 0 then ShowAnswer := true
825      else begin
             for i := 1 to nvars do begin
                 writeln;
                 WriteString(s_name(vartable[i])); write(' = ');
                 PrintTerm(f_local(bindings, i), NULL, EQPRIO - 1)
830          end;
             if ¬ interacting then
                 begin writeln; ShowAnswer := false end
             else begin
                 write(' ? '); flush_out;
835              if eoln then
                     begin readln; ShowAnswer := false end
                 else
```

```
                         begin readln(ch); ShowAnswer := (ch = '.') end
                    end
840      end
       end;
```

C.14 Parser

{ Here are the routines that parse input clauses. They use the method of recursive descent, with each class of phrase recognized by a single function that consumes the tokens of the phrase and returns its value. Each of these functions follows the convention that
845   the first token of its phrase is in the global *token* variable when the function is called, and the first token after the phrase is in *token* on return. The value of the function is the internal data structure for the term; this is built directly in the heap, with variables replaced by REF nodes. Syntax errors are handled by skipping to the next full stop, then trying again to find a clause. }

```
850  { Eat – check for an expected token and discard it }
     procedure Eat(expected: integer);
     begin
         if token = expected then
             begin if token ≠ DOT then Scan end
855      else if ¬ errflag then begin
             ShowError;
             write('expected '); PrintToken(expected);
             write(', found '); PrintToken(token); writeln;
             Recover
860      end
     end;

     { ParseCompound – parse a compound term }
     function ParseCompound: term;
         var fun: symbol; arg: argbuf; n: integer;
865  begin
         fun := tokval; n := 0; Eat(IDENT);
         if token = LPAR then begin
             Eat(LPAR); n := 1; arg[1] := ParseTerm;
             while token = COMMA do
870              begin Eat(COMMA); incr(n); arg[n] := ParseTerm end;
             Eat(RPAR)
         end;
         if s_arity(fun) = −1 then
             s_arity(fun) := n
875      else if s_arity(fun) ≠ n then
             syntax_error('wrong number of args');
         ParseCompound := MakeCompound(fun, arg)
     end;

     { ParsePrimary – parse a primary }
880  function ParsePrimary: term;
         var t: term;
     begin
```

```
          if token = IDENT then t := ParseCompound
          else if token = VARIABLE then
885           begin t := VarRep(tokval); Eat(VARIABLE) end
          else if token = NUMBER then
              begin t := MakeInt(tokival); Eat(NUMBER) end
          else if token = CHCON then
              begin t := MakeChar(chr(tokival)); Eat(CHCON) end
890       else if token = STRCON then
              begin t := MakeString(toksval); Eat(STRCON) end
          else if token = LPAR then
              begin Eat(LPAR); t := ParseTerm; Eat(RPAR) end
          else begin
895           syntax_error('expected a term'); t := NULL
          end;
          ParsePrimary := t
      end;

      { ParseFactor – parse a factor }
900   function ParseFactor: term;
          var t: term;
      begin
          t := ParsePrimary;
          if token ≠ COLON then
905           ParseFactor := t
          else begin
              Eat(COLON);
              ParseFactor := MakeNode(cons, t, ParseFactor)
          end
910   end;

      { ParseTerm – parse a term }
      function ParseTerm fwd(: term);
          var t: term;
      begin
915       t := ParseFactor;
          if token ≠ EQUAL then
              ParseTerm := t
          else begin
              Eat(EQUAL);
920           ParseTerm := MakeNode(eqsym, t, ParseFactor)
          end
      end;

      { CheckAtom – check that a literal is a compound term }
      procedure CheckAtom(a: term);
925   begin
          if t_kind(a) ≠ FUNC then
              syntax_error('literal must be a compound term')
      end;

      { ParseClause – parse a clause }
930   function ParseClause(isgoal: boolean): clause;
          label done;
```

```
        var head, t: term;
            body: argbuf;
            n: integer;
935         minus: boolean;
        begin
            if isgoal then
                head := NULL
            else begin
940             head := ParseTerm;
                CheckAtom(head);
                Eat(ARROW)
            end;

            n := 0;
945         if token ≠ DOT then begin
                while true do begin
                    n := n + 1; minus := false;
                    if token = NEGATE then
                        begin Eat(NEGATE); minus := true end;
950                 t := ParseTerm; CheckAtom(t);
                    if minus then body[n] := MakeNode(notsym, t, NULL)
                    else body[n] := t;
                    if token ≠ COMMA then goto done;
                    Eat(COMMA)
955             end
            end;
        done:
            Eat(DOT);

            if errflag then ParseClause := NULL
960         else ParseClause := MakeClause(nvars, head, body, n)
        end;

        { ReadClause – read a clause from infile }
        function ReadClause: clause;
            var c: clause;
965     begin
            repeat
                hp := hmark; nvars := 0; errflag := false;
                if interacting then
                    begin writeln; write('# :- '); flush_out end;
970             Scan;
                if token = EOFTOK then c := NULL
                else c := ParseClause(interacting)
            until (¬ errflag) ∨ (token = EOFTOK);
            ReadClause := c
975     end;
```

C.15 Trail

{ The trail stack records assignments made to variables, so that they can be undone on backtracking. It is a linked list of nodes with a *t_kind* of *UNDO* allocated from the global stack. The variables for which bindings are actually kept in the trail are the 'critical' ones that will not be destroyed on backtracking. }

```
980   type trail = pointer;
```
{ Nodes on the trail share the *t_tag* and *t_shift* fields of other nodes on the global stack, plus: }
```
      define(x_reset, mem[$1 + 2])          { variable to reset }
      define(x_next, mem[$1 + 3])           { next trail entry }
985   define(TRAIL_SIZE, 4)

      var trhead: trail;                     { start of the trail }
```
{ *critical* – test if a variable will survive backtracking }
```
      define(critical, (($1 < choice) ∨ ($1 ≥ f_glotop(choice))))
```
{ *Save* – add a variable to the trail if it is critical }
```
990   procedure Save(v: term);
        var p: trail;
      begin
        if critical(v) then begin
          p := GloAlloc(UNDO, TRAIL_SIZE);
995       x_reset(p) := v; x_next(p) := trhead; trhead := p
        end
      end;
```

{ *Restore* – undo bindings back to previous state }
```
      procedure Restore;
1000    var v: term;
      begin
        while (trhead ≠ f_trail(choice)) do begin
          v := x_reset(trhead);
          if v ≠ NULL then t_val(v) := NULL;
1005      trhead := x_next(trhead)
        end
      end;
```

{ *Commit* – blank out trail entries not needed after cut }
```
      procedure Commit;
1010    var p: trail;
      begin
        p := trhead;
        while (p ≠ NULL) ∧ (p < f_glotop(choice)) do begin
          if (x_reset(p) ≠ NULL) ∧ ¬ critical(x_reset(p)) then
1015        x_reset(p) := NULL;
          p := x_next(p)
        end
      end;
```

C.16   Unification

1020
{ The unification algorithm is the naive one that is traditional in Prolog implementations. Tradition is also followed in omitting the 'occur check'.

Nodes of type *CELL* may only point to terms that are independent of any frame: i.e., they may not point to terms in the heap that may contain *REF* nodes. So there is a function *GloCopy* that copies out enough of a term onto the global stack so that any cell can point to it. No copy is needed if the term is already on the global stack, or if it
1025
is a simple term that cannot contain any *REF*'s. }

```
{ GloCopy – copy a term onto the global stack }
function GloCopy(t: term; e: frame): term;
    var tt: term; i, n: integer;
begin
    t := Deref(t, e);
    if is_glob(t) then
        GloCopy := t
    else begin
        case t_kind(t) of
        FUNC:
            begin
                n := s_arity(t_func(t));
                if is_heap(t) ∧ (n = 0) then GloCopy := t
                else begin
                    tt := GloAlloc(FUNC, TERM_SIZE + n);
                    t_func(tt) := t_func(t);
                    for i := 1 to n do
                        t_arg(tt, i) := GloCopy(t_arg(t, i), e);
                    GloCopy := tt
                end
            end;
        CELL:
            begin
                tt := GloAlloc(CELL, TERM_SIZE);
                t_val(tt) := NULL;
                Save(t); t_val(t) := tt;
                GloCopy := tt
            end;
        INT, CHRCTR:
            GloCopy := t
        default
            bad_tag('GloCopy', t_kind(t))
        end
    end
end;
```

{ When two variables are made to 'share', there is a choice of which variable is made to point to the other. The code takes care to obey some rules about what may point to what: (1) Nothing on the global stack may point to anything on the local stack; (2) Nothing on the local stack may point to anything nearer the top of the local stack. Both these rules are necessary, since the top part of the local stack may be reclaimed without warning. There is another rule that makes for better performance: (3) Avoid pointers from items nearer the bottom of the global stack to items nearer the top.

The tricky *lifetime* macro implements these rules by computing a numerical measure of the lifetime of an object, defined so that anything on the local stack is shorter-lived than anything on the global stack, and within each stack items near the top are shorter-lived than items near the bottom. }

{ *lifetime* – measure of potential lifetime }
define(*lifetime*, ($1 * (2 * ord(is_glob($1)) − 1)))

{ *Share* – bind two variables together }
procedure *Share*(*v1*, *v2*: *term*);
begin
    if *lifetime*(*v1*) ≤ *lifetime*(*v2*) **then**
        begin *Save*(*v1*); *t_val*(*v1*) := *v2* **end**
    else
        begin *Save*(*v2*); *t_val*(*v2*) := *v1* **end**
end;

{ *Unify* – find and apply unifier for two terms }
function *Unify*(*t1*: *term*; *e1*: *frame*; *t2*: *term*; *e2*: *frame*): *boolean*;
    var *i*: *integer*; *match*: *boolean*;
begin
    t1 := *Deref*(*t1*, *e1*); *t2* := *Deref*(*t2*, *e2*);
    if *t1* = *t2* **then**   { Includes unifying a var with itself }
        Unify := *true*
    else if (*t_kind*(*t1*) = CELL) ∧ (*t_kind*(*t2*) = CELL) **then**
        begin *Share*(*t1*, *t2*); *Unify* := *true* **end**
    else if *t_kind*(*t1*) = CELL **then**
        begin *Save*(*t1*); *t_val*(*t1*) := *GloCopy*(*t2*, *e2*); *Unify* := *true* **end**
    else if *t_kind*(*t2*) = CELL **then**
        begin *Save*(*t2*); *t_val*(*t2*) := *GloCopy*(*t1*, *e1*); *Unify* := *true* **end**
    else if *t_kind*(*t1*) ≠ *t_kind*(*t2*) **then**
        Unify := *false*
    else begin
        case *t_kind*(*t1*) **of**
        FUNC:
            if (*t_func*(*t1*) ≠ *t_func*(*t2*)) **then**
                Unify := *false*
            else begin
                i := 1; *match* := *true*;
                while *match* ∧ (*i* ≤ *s_arity*(*t_func*(*t1*))) **do begin**
                    match := *Unify*(*t_arg*(*t1*, *i*), *e1*, *t_arg*(*t2*, *i*), *e2*);
                    incr(*i*)
                end;
                Unify := *match*
            end;

```
1110       INT:
                 Unify := (t_ival(t1) = t_ival(t2));
           CHRCTR:
                 Unify := (t_cval(t1) = t_cval(t2))
           default
1115             bad_tag('Unify', t_kind(t1))
           end
       end
   end;
```

{ *Key* – unification key of a term }

```
1120  function Key fwd((t: term; e: frame): integer);
          var t0: term;
      begin
```
          { The argument t must be a direct pointer to a compound term.
            The value returned is $key(t)$: if $t1$ and $t2$ are unifiable,
```
1125        then key(t1) = 0 or key(t2) = 0 or key(t1) = key(t2). }

          if t = NULL then panic('Key');
          if t_kind(t) ≠ FUNC then bad_tag('Key1', t_kind(t));

          if s_arity(t_func(t)) = 0 then
             Key := 0
1130      else begin
             t0 := Deref(t_arg(t, 1), e);
             case t_kind(t0) of
               FUNC: Key := t_func(t0);
               INT: Key := t_ival(t0) + 1;
1135           CHRCTR: Key := t_cval(t0) + 1;
               REF, CELL: Key := 0
             default
                 bad_tag('Key2', t_kind(t0))
             end
1140      end
      end;
```

{ *Search* – find the first clause that might match }

```
      function Search(t: term; e: frame; p: clause): clause;
          var k: integer;
1145  begin
          k := Key(t, e);
          if k ≠ 0 then
             while (p ≠ NULL) ∧ (c_key(p) ≠ 0) ∧ (c_key(p) ≠ k) do
                 p := c_next(p);
1150      Search := p
      end;
```

C.17 Interpreter

{ The main control of the interpreter uses a depth-first search procedure with an explicit
stack of activation records. It includes the tail-recursion optimization and an indexing
scheme that uses the hash codes computed by *Key*. }

```
1155   var ok: boolean;                              { whether execution succeeded }

       define(debug_point, if dflag then begin write($1, ' : ');
               PrintTerm($2, $3, MAXPRIO); writeln end)

       { PushFrame – create a new local stack frame }
       procedure PushFrame(nvars: integer; retry: clause);
1160      var f: frame; i: integer;
       begin
          f := LocAlloc(frame_size(nvars));
          f_goal(f) := current; f_parent(f) := goalframe;
          f_retry(f) := retry; f_choice(f) := choice;
1165      f_glotop(f) := gsp; f_trail(f) := trhead;
          f_nvars(f) := nvars;
          for i := 1 to nvars do begin
             t_tag(f_local(f, i)) := make_tag(CELL, TERM_SIZE);
             t_val(f_local(f, i)) := NULL
1170      end;
          goalframe := f;
          if retry ≠ NULL then choice := goalframe
       end;
```

{ Tail recursion can be used only under rather stringent conditions: the goal literal must
1175   be the last one in the body of the calling clause, both the calling clause and the called
clause must be determinate, and the calling clause must not be the original goal (lest
the answer variables be lost). The macro *tro_test(p)* checks that these conditions are
satisfied, where *p* is the untried part of the procedure for the current goal literal. }

```
       { tro_test – test if a resolution step can use TRO }
1180   define(tro_test, (g_first(g_rest(current)) = NULL) ∧ (choice < goalframe)
             ∧ ($1 = NULL) ∧ (goalframe ≠ base))
```

{ If the *tro_test* macro returns true, then it is safe to discard the calling frame in a resolution step before solving the subgoals in the newly-created frame. *TroStep* implements
this manoeuvre: read it after you understand the normal case covered by *Step*. }

1185   Because the calling frame is to be discarded, it is important that no pointers from the
new frame to the calling frame are created during unification. *TroStep* uses the trick of
swapping the two frames so that *Unify* will make pointers go the right way. The idea is
simple, but the details are made complicated by the need to adjust internal pointers in
the relocated frame. }

```
1190   { TroStep – perform a resolution step with tail-recursion }
       procedure TroStep;
          var temp: frame; oldsize, newsize, i: integer;
       begin
          if dflag then writeln(' (TRO) ');
1195      oldsize := frame_size(f_nvars(goalframe));    { size of old frame }
          newsize := frame_size(c_nvars(proc));    { size of new frame }
          temp := LocAlloc(newsize);
          temp := goalframe + newsize;            { copy old frame here }

          { Copy the old frame: in reverse order in case of overlap }
1200      for i := oldsize − 1 downto 0 do mem[temp + i] := mem[goalframe + i];
```

```
      { Adjust internal pointers in the copy }
      for i := 1 to f_nvars(goalframe) do begin
         if (t_kind(f_local(temp, i)) = CELL)
              ∧ (t_val(f_local(temp, i)) ≠ NULL)
1205          ∧ (goalframe ≤ t_val(f_local(temp, i)))
              ∧ (t_val(f_local(temp, i)) < goalframe + oldsize) then
            t_val(f_local(temp, i)) := t_val(f_local(temp, i)) + newsize
      end;

      { Overwrite the old frame with the new one }
1210  f_nvars(goalframe) := c_nvars(proc);
      for i := 1 to f_nvars(goalframe) do begin
         t_tag(f_local(goalframe, i)) := make_tag(CELL, TERM_SIZE);
         t_val(f_local(goalframe, i)) := NULL
      end;

1215  { Perform the resolution step }
      ok := Unify(call, temp, c_head(proc), goalframe);
      current := c_rhs(proc);
      lsp := temp − 1
   end;
```

1220   { The *Step* procedure carries out a single resolution step. Built-in relations are treated
as a special case; so are resolution steps that can use the tail-recursion optimization.
Otherwise, we allocate a frame for the first clause for the current goal literal, unify the
clause head with the literal, and adopt the clause body as the new goal. The step can
fail (and *Step* returns *false*) if there are no clauses to try, or if the first clause fails to
1225   match. }

```
   { Step – perform a resolution step }
   procedure Step;
      var retry: clause;
   begin
1230  if s_action(t_func(call)) ≠ 0 then
         ok := DoBuiltin(s_action(t_func(call)))
      else if proc = NULL then
         ok := false
      else begin
1235     retry := Search(call, goalframe, c_next(proc));
         if tro_test(retry) then
            TroStep
         else begin
            PushFrame(c_nvars(proc), retry);
1240        ok := Unify(call, f_parent(goalframe), c_head(proc), goalframe);
            current := c_rhs(proc);
         end
      end
   end;
```

1245   { The *Unwind* procedure returns from completed clauses until it finds one where there is
still work to do, or it finds that the original goal is completed. At this point, completed
frames are discarded if they cannot take part in future backtracking. }

```
       { Unwind – return from completed clauses }
       procedure Unwind;
1250   begin
         while (g_first(current) = NULL) ∧ (goalframe ≠ base) do begin
           debug_point('Exit', g_first(f_goal(goalframe)), f_parent(goalframe));
           current := g_rest(f_goal(goalframe));
           if goalframe > choice then lsp := goalframe − 1;
1255       goalframe := f_parent(goalframe)
         end
       end;
```

{ The *Backtrack* procedure undoes all the work that has been done since the last non-deterministic choice (indicated by the *choice* register). The trail shows what assignments
1260   must be undone, and the stacks are returned to the state they were in when the choice was made. The *proc* register is set from the *f_retry* field of the *choice* frame: this is the list of clauses for that goal that remain to be tried }

```
       { Backtrack – roll back to the last choice-point }
       procedure Backtrack;
1265   begin
         Restore;
         current := f_goal(choice); goalframe := f_parent(choice);
         call := Deref(g_first(current), goalframe);
         proc := f_retry(choice); gsp := f_glotop(choice);
1270     lsp := choice − 1; choice := f_choice(choice);
         debug_point('Redo', call, goalframe);
       end;
```

{ *Resume* is called with *ok = true* when the interpreter starts to execute a goal; it either returns with *ok = true* when the goal succeeds, or returns with *ok = false* when it
1275   has completely failed. After *Resume* has returned *true*, it can be called again with *ok = false* to find another solution; in this case, the first action is to backtrack to the most recent choice-point. }

```
       { Resume – continue execution }
       procedure Resume;
1280     label exit;
       begin
         while run do begin
           if ok then begin
             if g_first(current) = NULL then return;
1285         call := Deref(g_first(current), goalframe);
             debug_point('Call', call, goalframe);
             if (s_proc(t_func(call)) = NULL)
                   ∧ (s_action(t_func(call)) = 0) then begin
               exec_error('call to undefined relation ');
1290           WriteString(s_name(t_func(call)));
               return
             end;
             proc := Search(call, goalframe, s_proc(t_func(call)))
           end
1295       else begin
             if choice ≤ base then return;
```

```
              Backtrack
           end;
           Step;
1300       if ok then Unwind;
           if gsp − lsp ≤ GCLOW then Collect
         end;
    exit:
    end;

1305 { Execute − solve a goal by SLD-resolution }
     procedure Execute(g: clause);
        label exit;
     begin
        lsp := hp; gsp := MEMSIZE + 1;
1310    current := NULL; goalframe := NULL; choice := NULL; trhead := NULL;
        PushFrame(c_nvars(g), NULL);
        choice := goalframe; base := goalframe; current := c_rhs(g);
        run := true; ok := true;
        repeat
1315       Resume;
           if ¬ run then return;
           if ¬ ok then
              begin writeln; write('no'); return end;
           ok := ShowAnswer(base)
1320    until ok;
        writeln; write('yes');
     exit:
     end;
```

C.18   Built-in relations

{ Each built-in relation is a parameterless boolean-valued function: it finds its arguments
1325   from the call in *call*, carries out whatever side-effect is desired, and returns *true* exactly
if the call succeeds.

Two routines help in defining built-in relations: *GetArgs* dereferences the argument of
the literal *call* and puts them in the global array *av*; and *NewInt* makes a new integer
node on the global stack. }

```
1330 var
        av: argbuf;                        { GetArgs puts arguments here }
        callbody: pointer;                 { dummy clause body used by call/1 }

     { GetArgs − set up av array }
     procedure GetArgs;
1335    var i: integer;
     begin
        for i := 1 to s_arity(t_func(call)) do
           av[i] := Deref(t_arg(call, i), goalframe)
     end;
```

```
1340   { A couple of macros that abbreviate accesses to the av array: }
       define(a_kind, (t_kind(av[$1]) = $2))
       define(a_ival, t_ival(av[$1]))

       function NewInt(n: integer): term;
           var t: term;
1345   begin
           t := GloAlloc(INT, TERM_SIZE);
           t_ival(t) := n;
           NewInt := t
       end;

1350   { DoCut – built-in relation !/0 }
       function DoCut: boolean;
       begin
           choice := f_choice(goalframe);
           lsp := goalframe + frame_size(f_nvars(goalframe)) − 1;
1355       Commit;
           current := g_rest(current);
           DoCut := true
       end;

       { DoCall – built-in relation call/1 }
1360   function DoCall: boolean;
       begin
           GetArgs;
           if ¬ a_kind(1, FUNC) then begin
               exec_error('bad argument to call/1');
1365           DoCall := false
           end
           else begin
               PushFrame(1, NULL);
               t_val(f_local(goalframe, 1)) :=
1370               GloCopy(av[1], f_parent(goalframe));
               current := callbody;
               DoCall := true
           end
       end;

1375   { DoNot – built-in relation ¬ /1 }
       function DoNot: boolean;
           var savebase: frame;
       begin
           GetArgs;
1380       if ¬ a_kind(1, FUNC) then begin
               exec_error('bad argument to call/1');
               DoNot := false
           end
           else begin
1385           PushFrame(1, NULL);
               savebase := base; base := goalframe; choice := goalframe;
               t_val(f_local(goalframe, 1)) :=
                   GloCopy(av[1], f_parent(goalframe));
```

```
            current := callbody; ok := true;
1390        Resume;
            choice := f_choice(base); goalframe := f_parent(base);
            if ¬ ok then begin
               current := g_rest(f_goal(base));
               DoNot := true
1395        end
            else begin
               Commit;
               DoNot := false
            end;
1400        lsp := base − 1; base := savebase
         end
      end;
```

{ Procedures *DoPlus* and *DoTimes* implement the *plus*/3 and *times*/3 relations: they both involve a case analysis of which arguments are known, followed by a call to *Unify*
1405 to unify the remaining argument with the result. The *times*/3 relation fails on divide-by-zero, even in the case $times(X, 0, 0)$, which actually has infinitely many solutions. }

```
      { DoPlus − built-in relation plus/3 }
      function DoPlus: boolean;
         var result: boolean;
1410  begin
         GetArgs;
         result := false;
         if a_kind(1, INT) ∧ a_kind(2, INT) then
            result := Unify(av[3], goalframe, NewInt(a_ival(1) + a_ival(2)), NULL)
1415     else if a_kind(1, INT) ∧ a_kind(3, INT) then begin
            if a_ival(1) ≤ a_ival(3) then
               result := Unify(av[2], goalframe,
                              NewInt(a_ival(3) − a_ival(1)), NULL)
         end
1420     else if a_kind(2, INT) ∧ a_kind(3, INT) then begin
            if a_ival(2) ≤ a_ival(3) then
               result := Unify(av[1], goalframe, NewInt(a_ival(3) − a_ival(2)), NULL)
         end
         else
1425        exec_error('plus/3 needs at least two integers');
         current := g_rest(current);
         DoPlus := result
      end;

      { DoTimes − built-in relation times/3 }
1430  function DoTimes: boolean;
         var result: boolean;
      begin
         GetArgs;
         result := false;
1435     if a_kind(1, INT) ∧ a_kind(2, INT) then
            result := Unify(av[3], goalframe,
                           NewInt(t_ival(av[1]) ∗ t_ival(av[2])), NULL)
```

```
              else if a_kind(1, INT) ∧ a_kind(3, INT) then begin
                 if a_ival(1) ≠ 0 then
1440                 if a_ival(3) mod a_ival(1) = 0 then
                        result := Unify(av[2], goalframe,
                                          NewInt(a_ival(3) div a_ival(1)), NULL)
              end
              else if a_kind(2, INT) ∧ a_kind(3, INT) then begin
1445             if a_ival(2) ≠ 0 then
                    if a_ival(3) mod a_ival(2) = 0 then
                        result := Unify(av[1], goalframe,
                                          NewInt(a_ival(3) div a_ival(2)), NULL)
              end
1450          else
                 exec_error('times/3 needs at least two integers');
              current := g_rest(current);
              DoTimes := result
           end;

1455    { DoEqual – built-in relation = /2 }
        function DoEqual: boolean;
        begin
           GetArgs;
           current := g_rest(current);
1460       DoEqual := Unify(av[1], goalframe, av[2], goalframe)
        end;

        { DoInteger – built-in relation integer/1 }
        function DoInteger: boolean;
        begin
1465       GetArgs;
           current := g_rest(current);
           DoInteger := a_kind(1, INT)
        end;

        { DoChar – built-in relation char/1 }
1470    function DoChar: boolean;
        begin
           GetArgs;
           current := g_rest(current);
           DoChar := a_kind(1, CHRCTR)
1475    end;

        { DoBuiltin – switch for built-in relations }
        function DoBuiltin fwd((action: integer): boolean);
        begin
           case action of
1480       CUT: DoBuiltin := DoCut;
           CALL: DoBuiltin := DoCall;
           PLUS: DoBuiltin := DoPlus;
           TIMES: DoBuiltin := DoTimes;
           ISINT: DoBuiltin := DoInteger;
1485       ISCHAR: DoBuiltin := DoChar;
           NAFF: DoBuiltin := DoNot;
```

```
        EQUALITY: DoBuiltin := DoEqual;
        FAIL: DoBuiltin := false
      default
1490        bad_tag('DoBuiltin', action)
      end
    end;
```

C.19 Garbage collection

{ Finally, here is the garbage collector, which reclaims space in the global stack that is no longer accessible. It must work well with the stack-like expansion and contraction of
1495 the stack, so it is a compacting collector that does not alter the order in memory of the accessible nodes.

The garbage collector operates in four phases: (1) Find and mark all accessible storage. (2) Compute the new positions of the marked items after the global stack is compacted. (3) Adjust all pointers to marked items. (4) Compact the global stack and move it
1500 to the top of *mem*. That may seem complicated, and it is; the garbage collector must know about all the run-time data structures, and is that one piece of the system that cuts across every abstraction boundary.

Because of the relocation, *Collect* should only be called at 'quiet' times, when the only pointers into the global stack are from interpreter registers and the local stack. An
1505 example of a 'non-quiet' time is in the middle of unification, when many recursive copies of the unification procedure are keeping pointers to bits of term structure. To avoid the need to collect garbage at such times, the main control of the interpreter calls *Collect* before each resolution step if the space left is less than *GCLOW*. If space runs out in the subsequent resolution step, execution is abandoned without much grace. This
1510 plan works because the amount of space consumed in a resolution step is bounded by the maximum size of a program clause; this size is not checked, though. }

```
    var shift: integer;                    { amount global stack will shift }

      { Visit – recursively mark a term and all its sub-terms }
    procedure Visit(t: term);
1515    label exit;
        var i, n: integer;
      begin
        { We reduce the depth of recursion when marking long lists by
            treating the last argument of a function iteratively, making
1520        recursive calls only for the other arguments. }
        while t ≠ NULL do begin
          if ¬ is_glob(t) ∨ marked(t) then return;
          add_mark(t);
          case t_kind(t) of
1525      FUNC:
              begin
                n := s_arity(t_func(t));
                if n = 0 then return;
                for i := 1 to n − 1 do Visit(t_arg(t, i));
1530            t := t_arg(t, n)
              end;
```

```
                CELL:
                    t := t_val(t);
                INT, CHRCTR:
1535                return
                default
                    bad_tag('Visit', t_kind(t))
                end
            end;
1540  exit:
      end;

      { MarkStack – mark from each frame on the local stack }
      procedure MarkStack;
          var f: frame; i: integer;
1545  begin
          f := hp + 1;
          while f ≤ lsp do begin
              for i := 1 to f_nvars(f) do
                  if t_kind(f_local(f, i)) = CELL then
1550                  Visit(t_val(f_local(f, i)));
              f := f + frame_size(f_nvars(f))
          end
      end;

      { CullTrail – delete an initial segment of unwanted trail }
1555  procedure CullTrail(var p: trail);
          label exit;
      begin
          while p ≠ NULL do begin
              if x_reset(p) ≠ NULL then
1560              if ¬ is_glob(x_reset(p)) ∨ marked(x_reset(p)) then
                      return;
              p := x_next(p)
          end;
      exit:
1565  end;

      { MarkTrail – remove dead trail nodes, mark the rest. }
      procedure MarkTrail;
          var p: trail;
      begin
1570      CullTrail(trhead); p := trhead;
          while p ≠ NULL do
              begin add_mark(p); CullTrail(x_next(p)); p := x_next(p) end
      end;

      { Relocate – compute shifts }
1575  procedure Relocate;
          var p: pointer; step: integer;
      begin
          shift := 0; p := gsp;
          while p ≤ MEMSIZE do begin
1580          step := t_size(p); t_shift(p) := shift;
```

```
            if ¬ marked(p) then
                shift := shift + step;
            p := p + step
        end
1585  end;

        { AdjustPointer – update a pointer }
        procedure AdjustPointer(var p: term);
        begin
        if (p ≠ NULL) ∧ is_glob(p) then begin
1590        if ¬ marked(p) then
                panic('adjusting pointer to unmarked block');
            p := p + shift − t_shift(p)
        end
        end;

1595  { AdjustStack – adjust pointers in local stack }
        procedure AdjustStack;
            var f: frame; i: integer; q: pointer;
            label found, found2;
        begin
1600    f := hp + 1;
        while f ≤ lsp do begin
            q := f_glotop(f);
            while q ≤ MEMSIZE do begin
                if marked(q) then goto found;
1605            q := q + t_size(q)
            end;
        found:
            if q ≤ MEMSIZE then AdjustPointer(q);
            f_glotop(f) := q;

1610        q := f_trail(f);
            while q ≠ NULL do begin
                if marked(q) then goto found2;
                q := x_next(q)
            end;
1615    found2:
            AdjustPointer(q);
            f_trail(f) := q;

            for i := 1 to f_nvars(f) do
                if t_kind(f_local(f, i)) = CELL then
1620                AdjustPointer(t_val(f_local(f, i)));
            f := f + frame_size(f_nvars(f));
        end
        end;

        { AdjustInternal – update internal pointers }
1625  procedure AdjustInternal;
            var p, i: integer;
        begin
        p := gsp;
```

```
          while p ≤ MEMSIZE do begin
1630        if marked(p) then begin
              case t_kind(p) of
                FUNC:
                  for i := 1 to s_arity(t_func(p)) do
                    AdjustPointer(t_arg(p, i));
1635            CELL:
                  AdjustPointer(t_val(p));
                UNDO:
                  begin
                    AdjustPointer(x_reset(p));
1640                AdjustPointer(x_next(p))
                  end;
                INT, CHRCTR:
                  skip
                default
1645              bad_tag('Adjust', t_kind(p))
              end
            end;
            p := p + t_size(p)
          end
1650    end;

      { Compact – compact marked blocks and un-mark }
      procedure Compact;
        var p, q, step, i: integer;
      begin
1655    p := gsp; q := gsp;
        while p ≤ MEMSIZE do begin
          step := t_size(p);
          if marked(p) then begin rem_mark(p);
            for i := 0 to step − 1 do mem[q + i] := mem[p + i];
1660        q := q + step
          end;
          p := p + step
        end;
        gsp := gsp + shift;
1665    for i := MEMSIZE downto gsp do mem[i] := mem[i − shift];
      end;

      { Collect – collect garbage }
      procedure Collect;
      begin
1670    write('[gc'); flush_out;

        { Phase 1: marking }
        Visit(call); MarkStack; MarkTrail;

        { Phase 2: compute new locations }
        Relocate;

1675    { Phase 3: adjust pointers }
        AdjustPointer(call); AdjustPointer(trhead);
```

```
          AdjustStack; AdjustInternal;

          { Phase 4: compact }
          Compact;
1680      write(']'); flush_out;
          if gsp − lsp ≤ GCHIGH then exec_error('out of memory space')
       end;
```

C.20 Main program

```
          { Initialize – initialize everything }
          procedure Initialize;
1685      var i: integer; p: term;
       begin
          dflag := false; errcount := 0;
          pbchar := ENDFILE; charptr := 0;
          hp := 0; InitSymbols;

1690      { Set up the refnode array }
          for i := 1 to MAXARITY do begin
             p := HeapAlloc(TERM_SIZE);
             t_tag(p) := make_tag(REF, TERM_SIZE);
             t_index(p) := i; refnode[i] := p
1695      end;

          { The dummy clause call(P) :− P is used by call/1. }
          callbody := HeapAlloc(2);
          g_first(callbody) := MakeRef(1);
          g_first(g_rest(callbody)) := NULL
1700   end;

          { ReadFile – read and process clauses from an open file }
          procedure ReadFile;
          var c: clause;
       begin
1705      lineno := 1;
          repeat
             hmark := hp;
             c := ReadClause;
             if c ≠ NULL then begin
1710            if dflag then PrintClause(c);
                if c_head(c) ≠ NULL then
                   AddClause(c)
                else begin
                   if interacting then
1715                  begin pbchar := ENDFILE; readln end;
                   Execute(c);
                   writeln;
                   hp := hmark
                end
1720      end
```

```
        until c = NULL
    end;

    ifdef (turbo, {$I pplib.inc})

        { ReadProgram – read files listed on command line }
1725 procedure ReadProgram;
        var i0, i: integer;
            arg: tempstring;
    begin
        i0 := 1;
1730    if argc > 1 then begin
            argv(1, arg);
            if (arg[1] = '-') ∧ (arg[2] = 'd')
                ∧ (arg[3] = ENDSTR) then begin
                dflag := true;
1735            incr(i0)
            end
        end;
        for i := i0 to argc − 1 do begin
            argv(i, arg);
1740        filename := SaveString(arg);
            if ¬ openin(infile, arg) then begin
                write('Can''t read '); WriteString(filename); writeln;
                abort
            end;
1745        write('Reading '); WriteString(filename); writeln;
            ReadFile;
            closein(infile);
            if errcount > 0 then abort
        end
1750 end;

    begin                                    { main program }
        writeln('Welcome to picoProlog');
        Initialize;
        interacting := false; ReadProgram;
1755    interacting := true; lineno := 1; ReadFile;
        writeln;
    end_of_pp:
    end.
```

Cross-reference listing

Index